HIDE-AND-SEEK

By the author:

Non-Fiction

HIDE-AND-SEEK

Fiction

THE HOSPITAL WAR

SUMMER DOCTOR

THE DYNASTY

JUNIPER ISLAND

THE BOY CAME BACK

HIDE-AND-SEEK

The Effect of Mind, Body, and Emotion
on Personality and Behavior
in Ourselves and Others

CHARLES H. KNICKERBOCKER, M.D.

1967
DOUBLEDAY & COMPANY, INC., GARDEN CITY, NEW YORK

To my wife

for all the obvious reasons, and others.

C.H.K.

CONTENTS

Part One—OTHERS

Part Two—OURSELVES

Part One

OTHERS

1

Faces that We Meet

"You're It!" the children cry as they play the game of hide-and-seek.

One child hides his eyes, counts to a hundred as the other children hide from him, and then he looks for them, but cautiously. If he spots another child behind a tree, it is not enough for him to call the name; he must get back to home base first, or else he will be "It" all afternoon.

Such elements of mutual deception and evasion, of hiding and seeking and running home again, which we see in the childhood game of hide-and-seek, are often present in adult relationships as we pursue happiness in various individual ways and search for maturity into a troubled world.

Said T. S. Eliot in *The Love Song of J. Alfred Prufrock*, "There will be time to prepare a face to meet the faces that you meet." This statement of the poet is hopeful, wistful, and defensive. In another sense, it is also hopeless, for we do not seem to have sufficient time. We try to fix our faces up to face the world. We know that the faces around us have been fixed up for our benefit. We seek truth in all of our relationships, but yet we are afraid of truth. When we hide our eyes to avoid unpleasant truth, we block ourselves from communication with others and we sometimes seem to be out of touch with ourselves.

Our patterns of adjustment, balance, and imbalance depend upon our individual personality. Our behavior is the result of dynamic interplay of forces from mind, body, and emotion which in turn are modified by our inheritance, our family background, our education, our experience, our relative sanity, our relative maturity, and the circumstances of the moment. If our behavior strikes other people as reasonable, logical, and appropriate, they consider us normal. If our behavior seems unreasonable, illogical, or inappropriate, they consider us abnormal. Such behavior patterns, and especially those considered abnormal, are the subject of this book. We are concerned with motivation. Why do people act that way toward us? Why do we act the way we do?

Fundamental knowledge of the forces shaping personality, of the factors concerned with behavior and motivation, is at present primitive. Advances in the pure sciences and in technology during recent years have been rapid, but advances in such fields as psychology and psychiatry have been slow. We often do not know why people act the way they do, and we often do not understand ourselves. And yet, there is a growing body of knowledge which can cast light on motivation and behavior in others and ourselves. Some of this information comes from the pure sciences and technologies; some from the much less pure science of biology; some from the experience of physicians and other counselors working with sick people. To this can be added material from the work and thinking of people in such unrelated areas as the creative arts, religion, philosophy, ethics, and theoretical psychiatry.

This book attempts to gather material from these various sources into a comprehensible pattern representing present knowledge of some facets of human personality, motivation, and behavior. I am borrowing rather heavily from many other people for this purpose. I am also using a considerable body of material from my own personal and professional experience.

I think it advisable to present my credentials for such an ambitious project. I have been a physician in private practice for eighteen years. This book basically concerns psychiatry and psychology, but I am an expert in neither field. Professionally, I specialize in diseases of the heart and lungs. I had a course in psychiatry in medical school and I have been reading in the field ever since; many patients who consult me in the office are presenting psychiatric problems masked as physical disease, and many of my patients with physical disease have psychiatric complications; it is therefore necessary for me, and for any practicing physician, to act like a psychiatrist from time to time, though I am not a psychiatrist and often do not know what I am doing in this field.

I have great respect for psychiatrists as individuals and as practicing physicians. They do fine work under trying and difficult conditions. I have rather less respect for psychiatry as a science, and for certain schools of psychiatric thought I have no respect at all. I find some of the psychiatric literature fascinating and helpful; a good deal of it, however, makes no sense to me and strikes me as convoluted, involuted, perverted, and obscure. I think that Sigmund Freud was a genius and a great man. I think that many who follow the trails he blazed are as muddled and confused as the patients they are trying to treat. I think that much of the artificial theorization falling under the general heading of Freudianism is ingenious and clever but has no practical application to the problems of the ordinary man. I think that Carl Jung was a great physician and that some of his conclusions are more important and valuable than those of Freud. I think that psychiatrists often get so involved in the emotional lives of their patients that they neglect and forget some of the pertinent available knowledge from clinical non-psychiatric medicine. I have seen psychiatrists forget the body as they concentrate on the mind and the emotions. I have also seen non-psychiatric physicians forget the mind and the emotions as they concentrate on physical disease. I think that the patient is a unity who cannot be subdivided by specialty.

In psychology, I have no credentials at all. I have never even had an introductory course in the subject. The ignorant tend to be suspicious of the learned, and I am suspicious of formal psychology as a science. Theoretical psychologists are prone to interpolate laboratory findings on the experimental animal, findings and measurements on the human volunteer, statistics, subjective interview material, and intellectual theorization too literally and too simply. Clinical psychologists often seem to lack sufficient training in medicine and the pure sciences. I am inclined to think that psychology at present is more of an art than a science. I think it should be the art of observation of the behavior of ordinary people in their customary environment. I am inclined to think that poets, dramatists, artists, and novelists have a deeper understanding of certain aspects of psychology than professional psychologists.

I do not pretend to understand psychology and psychiatry better than the experts. The more I try to work in such fields, the less I seem to know. However, taking a somewhat different perspective than such experts, using some of the material from their fields while rejecting some of it, adding material from other fields that they often do not consider, and reinforcing this with personal and professional experiences of my own, I have come up with an approach which is being presented here. I hope it may be of interest to the intelligent general reader. Perhaps it may be of help to him. We all seek better understanding of other people and ourselves.

The first part of the book considers other people: the faces that we meet. Everybody is an individual, different from every other individual, but people tend to fall into certain recognizable personality patterns: some are happy, some are sad, some remote, some hostile, some rigid, some muddled, some confused. We will tackle the project first on the basis of these and other personality groups. For this portion of the study, I make frequent use of the case history technique.

Some of the cases presented here are famous people, identified by name. Most have been given imaginary names and their stories somewhat changed to conceal the identity of the actual persons described. Many have been patients of mine. Some I have read about. Others have been described to me by people I have known. All are true stories about real people.

The second half of the book attempts to use information gathered from our study of others applied to the problems of the self.

Human personality, behavior, and motivation is mysterious, but there are certain aspects of the human equation amenable to logic, common sense, and practical understanding, even in our present state of ignorance. Let us take a look at these together.

2

The Smart Ones

Abraham (Case 1)

Abraham was smart. His superior intelligence was noted at an early age. He learned to walk and talk early, and he had somehow acquired the art of reading before he went to school. His father taught him chess when Abraham was five, and within a year he was beating his father, an average player, regularly. He beat several better adult players in the neighborhood with equal ease. Abraham might have become a child prodigy chess champion, but he seemed to lack a real interest in the game, despite his skill, and he seldom played it after childhood.

In school, Abraham had excellent grades and always led his class. He got along with the other children well enough, but he had no close friends. He did not like sports or games, and he preferred his own company to that of his classmates. He continued this pattern in high school, leading his class but not joining in any social activities of his group. His chief interest was mechanical; he loved to tinker with engines, and he spent a lot of his free time in local garages; he acquired the reputation of being the best amateur mechanic in town.

Abraham won a scholarship to a world-famous Institute of Technology. At the college level, again he led his class, and again he had no friends. His teachers were aware that they were dealing with genius, and they attempted to interest him in research. Despite unusually high levels of mechanical and mathematical aptitudes, however, Abraham lacked ambition; he mastered material presented to him immediately, but he did not strike out into new pathways on his own.

On the strength of a brilliant college record, Abraham was offered an excellent job in the mechanical engineering department of a large industrial corporation. He handled the technical aspects of his job in a superior fashion, but the work didn't seem to interest him. He quit the job in six months.

He married an intelligent, lively, well-adjusted girl, one of the only people with whom Abraham had ever been able to communicate. She was aware of his unusual intellectual gifts, and also of his social deficiencies and lack of material ambition. She tried to widen his social horizon and increase his ambition, without great success, but the marriage was a happy one, in the early years. Several children followed, all intelligent and gifted.

Abraham's career was progressing in a downward direction. He passed through a succession of jobs of progressively lesser requirements and salary, but he quit each job after a few months. After several such episodes of brief employment, he stopped looking for work altogether, and his wife was compelled to become the family breadwinner. Abraham stayed home with the children. He outfitted a cellar workshop for himself and puttered around there a good deal of the time. His wife expected that he might come up with a brilliant invention some day.

Instead, however, Abraham packed a bag and left home one afternoon without warning, and he did not return. In succeeding years, he sent his wife small sums of money now and then, and an occasional letter, but she never saw him again. Abraham led a gypsy life, roaming from town to town, finding temporary employment as a garage mechanic. He was always recognized as a good employee, but an unapproachable and antisocial person. Abraham never stayed in one location very long. Within a few weeks or months, he hit the road again, traveling alone.

Abraham's gift of high intelligence did not seem to bring him happiness. Brains alone are not enough; man has a social need. Abraham's solitary nature suggests emotional disturbance, perhaps a schizophrenia. His intelligence was not enough to overcome it; his high intelligence may, in fact, have contributed to his social disorder. Society places a premium on brains, rewarding the intelligent with scholarships, educational opportunity, employment advantages. But the high IQ does not necessarily bring happiness, and, in fact, may bring definite problems in adjustment.

The average man, with average intelligence, tends to fear and suspect the person gifted with intelligence higher than his own. The intelligent man is aware of suspicion and resentment around him. Perhaps Abraham noticed the expression on the face of one of the good adult chess players whom he had beaten when he was seven years old, and for this reason, perhaps, he did not play the game very much. Abraham did not wish to go through life feared and resented by the people around him. In school, he certainly noted the suspicion and resentment of children who worked harder to get worse grades than he; sensitive to their resentment, he did not play with them after school. At work, assignments that were difficult to others came easily to him, and other men resented it. The work itself, too easy for him, quickly became monotonous and boring. Abraham felt more comfortable alone. He felt more comfortable with engines than with people, for engines work according to predictable and understandable laws, and engines do not talk back. High raw intelligence, ordinarily considered a gift, was a handicap to Abraham; he could not learn to live with it and with people at the same time; and the only way that Abraham could live in any comfort was alone, where the resentment and suspicion of less intelligent people would not bother him.

Bert (Case 2)

Bert, also, was smart. He led his class in school and was particularly gifted in the language arts. He wanted to be a poet.

Unlike Abraham, Bert was not a loner. Bert had a strong social need and, except when he was reading or writing, felt uncomfortable alone. His literary gift was genuine; several of his poems were accepted and published in national magazines while he was still in high school. This gave him real distinction in his social set, but Bert wanted more than distinction. He wanted to be popular. He needed understanding and affection from male friends, and, from women, love.

Bert was liked, for he had a generous and impulsive and warm-hearted nature, but he was not as popular as he wished. The leading scholar in the class and published poet was not accorded the same respect and affection as the captain of the football team. Bert seemed to feel that he would be more appreciated if he drew attention to himself. He became, therefore, a little wild, unconventional, flamboyant, something of a show-off. He did draw attention to himself and with it a certain admiration from his peers, for the young admire defiance of authority. Yet, Bert's unconventional and colorful speech and attitude sometimes made his classmates nervous. They sensed that Bert was overdoing the act and pushing a little bit too hard. He was sort of a genius but sort of an odd-ball too, they decided.

Bert got into a prestige college easily with a scholarship. The collegiate atmosphere was good soil for unconventional flamboyance. He got good grades but he also managed to get himself expelled for a rather serious disciplinary infraction.

"A poet doesn't need a college education," Bert informed his parents.

Bert's parents were disappointed by his failure to conform, but they realized that creative talent is often associated with non-conformity. They didn't want him to live the Bohemian life in Greenwich Village, but they couldn't stop him, since he had passed his twenty-first birthday.

Bert grew a beard and learned to play the guitar. He did not often wash. He sought the society of other unwashed guitar-playing types, similar free spirits who did understand him. He and his free friends placed high value on creative expression of individuality, low value on the inhibiting conventional standards of society against which they raised singing voices in protest. They expected to live life fully and to the hilt, enjoying all available gratification, and not expecting to live beyond the age of thirty, for living death begins at thirty, if not some time before.

Bert was able to sell occasional small pieces to national publications, but such sales were irregular; they did not advance his reputation or his bank account; it was often necessary for him to wash dishes to earn enough money to eat. He enjoyed the fuller life, conducting free experiments with heterosexual promiscuity and with homosexuality, with alcohol, marijuana, heroin, and LSD. Immediate gratification was at hand, but permanent satisfaction appeared to be lacking. Social protest, as many Bohemians discover, requires a strong constitution, and Bert began to show signs of physical illness, which began to rob him of the energy necessary for unconventionality. His thirtieth birthday was now approaching with alarming speed, and so he attempted suicide unsuccessfully. A period of extensive hospitalization was required. After his eventual recovery, Bert went home again.

He lived with his parents after that. They were moderately wealthy, and Bert never had to seek employment. He did not marry. He puttered in the garden, grew orchids as a hobby, was director of several charitable institutions. He continued to write, but he never again submitted any of his poems, and never again achieved publication.

Together with high raw intelligence, Bert showed considerable emotional and social immaturity. High intelligence and high emotional maturity show no direct correlation. Bert seemed to have a need for popularity somewhat greater than average, for which his intelligence and literary gift was more handicap than asset. He compensated for intelligence in a way that seems unintelligent. His personality pattern was self-destructive. Search for immediate gratification led to lack of gratification on the longer term. Pathways of freedom led him into confinement. The Greenwich Village atmosphere, far from enabling him to become a successful poet, blocked him from this goal. Self-destructive activity is an unfortunately common human pattern, and we will encounter it in our present study again and again.

Carol (Case 3)

Carol was a plain girl, retiring and shy. An excellent student, she spent a great deal of her time doing homework, and she was regarded as a grind. She graduated from a distinguished woman's college with high honors, and started working on her Ph.D.

Carol had always been inclined to be afraid of boys, of men, and she had never dated very much. In her first year of graduate school, however, she met a man with whom she fell in love. She married him, stopping her formal education short of her degree to do so. She became a housewife, devoting her time to cooking, cleaning, and sewing, and rearing the children who began to appear in rapid succession.

Carol's husband was a good man, solid, dependable, and considerate. He brought home good wages as a master carpenter. He had no formal education beyond the high school level. Carol thought no worse of him for this. A man's value is not measured by his degree of formal education.

Carol thought of herself as an average housewife. She did not seem to regret her lack of a graduate degree. What good is a graduate degree to a housewife? In fact, she considered herself lucky. The educated spinster in academic and professional circles is often a frustrated cold unhappy person. Carol was surrounded by people who loved her, needed her, cherished her.

The years passed. The children grew up, departed, married.

Carol became a grandmother several times. Her relationship with her husband remained warm. He was a good provider and he loved her. There were certain things on an intellectual level he could not share with her. He preferred bowling and hunting and fishing to reading; television was better than the theater or ballet. He never was an easy conversationalist. A practical man, he had little interest in the world of ideas.

There was much less for Carol to do in her house after her own children left it. She read a good deal. She belonged to a literary club, a public affairs club, and she did some volunteer work at the local hospital. She thought of getting a part-time job, or even of continuing her education, but her husband did not seem to approve of this. Also Carol got sick. She visited doctors regularly two or three times a month. Her illnesses did not appear to be serious or dangerous, but they did not seem to be amenable to cure. Her husband sometimes said, in joke, that she enjoyed poor health.

Carol was caught in the trap which seems to be much too common: the trap of the woman with a mind. What can a woman do with intelligence? Do men love women smarter than themselves? Are bright women without love happy? Does it take any brains to breed and rear children and to keep a home? If a woman is plain and intelligent, should she turn down a man who loves her just because he lacks a college degree? Would she ever have another chance?

The intelligent woman often feels it necessary to conceal her intelligence in order to achieve the proper female role. This brings her compromise, but it may also bring her emptiness, especially in later life when the children leave the home. It is sometimes possible for the woman successfully to run a home, rear the children, and conduct a career simultaneously. This double duty is too much for many women. Later on, when the children go, many women successfully return to higher education and a career. Those who do not and who cannot fill a void left by grown and departed children may find that emptiness expresses itself in physical symptoms. Every doctor's office is full of older female patients of this kind.

We have observed three people of superior intelligence whose intelligence appears to have been a handicap in adjustment. Is this necessarily the case? It is probably necessary for most persons with superior intelligence to compromise their intelligence to a certain degree in order to fulfill the social need. The occasional dedicated and tough-minded genius may be able to dismiss the suspicion and resentment of people with less intelligence than he, displaying his gifts in an arrogant and high-handed manner, in which case he is likely to command more respect than affection. Some persons have a lesser social need than others. The genius may retreat to an ivory tower, where other people will not bother him, or he may select the academic groves where society is composed of people as intelligent as he. Even in the campus atmosphere, however, he may be lonely, for other intelligent people will have different gifts and special interests. Loneliness is a problem for the person with high intelligence. Genius is apt to be a solitary condition.

It is relevant to note that many successful people, the prosperous, the famous, are not men of intellectual genius, and may often be of quite average intelligence. In studying the famous men of genius, we see that a great many of them show patterns of severe social maladjustment despite great achievement. On the other side of the fence, many people seem to compromise their gift to meet the social need. A study made of a group of Quiz Kids, child prodigies, indicated that most of them, in later life, made very good social adjustments but few of them made outstanding accomplishments which might have been expected from their native raw intelligence.

Does this represent human waste? Yes. Does a society which fears and resents individual intelligence force itself toward mediocrity while shooting for the lowest common denominator? Yes. Is society, by fearing intelligence, showing a sort of immaturity? Yes. It ought to be possible for the individual with superior intellect to utilize his gift and still attain a successful social adjustment. This is possible, fortunately, and it does happen, occasionally. It is difficult. However, should not the more intelligent be required to handle more difficult problems? It would appear that raw brains are not enough. Something else is required.

Albert (Case 4)

He was a German Jewish boy, a shy, gentle, sensitive person. He was warm-hearted and generous, and people liked him. He was also smart, very bright indeed, especially in mathematics. He became a theoretical mathematician, highly original, distinctively creative.

With the advent of Hitler, Albert left Germany and came to America. His adjustment into the American community was immediately successful. He was a popular person in his neighborhood. His work continued with equal success. His basic achievement, expressed in a simple formula, was so fundamental and important that it changed the shape and the future of the entire human race.

Albert shunned publicity and remained a shy and modest man. He could not avoid becoming a celebrity. But despite the frightening nature of his ability and accomplishment, he was a much beloved man.

It was generally believed that only two or three men alive could understand what Albert was talking about in the field of higher mathematics, but little girls used to go to him for help in doing their arithmetic. His life was long and rich and full and satisfying. His name, of course, was Albert Einstein.

3

The Slow Ones

Although it may seem surprising to think of superior intelligence as a handicap, low intelligence obviously presents a problem. Mastery of the machines and gadgets of everyday life requires some intelligence, and illiteracy today is as disabling as blindness. Although there is a continuing need for broom pushers and hod carriers, much work once done by the unskilled laborer is now done by the machine. The uneducated, and especially the man whose intelligence is too low for education, falls farther and farther to the rear.

At the bottom level of mental deficiency, the individual is helpless, and custodial care in an institution is the only answer. At the upper level of mental deficiency, meaning intelligence only somewhat lower than average, social adjustment is relatively good, and no problem is noted, by society or by the individual. In a welfare state, particular care is devoted to the individual with lesser education and intelligence; the state takes care of its slow citizens fondly, as if aware that they constitute its chief support. In such fields as public entertainment, it sometimes seems as if the intended audience was those of limited intelligence. This may constitute a long-run problem to our culture and civilization, but it does not present individual problems in the community.

Between the top and bottom, there is a level of retarded intelligence which presents problems in adjustment. These people are usually unaware of their problem, lacking the intelligence to understand it, and they are unable to provide any solutions for themselves, given the basic nature of the difficulty. They are strongly dependent on those who care for them and make the decisions on their behalf, which primarily means parents of the retarded child.

At this point I wish to voice a personal prejudice. I am opposed to the use of the term "exceptional child" in this connection. Retarded persons are exceptional if the word is taken to mean that they are different. But I think a euphuism which defines by suggesting its opposite is intellectually dishonest and sometimes dangerous. In this connection, it is necessary for the parents of the retarded person to recognize and accept the fact before they will seek proper professional advice and guidance. It may be more comforting to consider the child "exceptional" but help can be obtained only when the fact is clearly faced that the child is mentally retarded. It is healthier to call him so.

Donald (Case 5)

Donald was born normal; his physical and mental development was normal for the first few years. At the age of five, he developed a sudden severe acute illness with high fever and convulsions. Donald was treated at home by a country doctor without the advantages of hospital diagnostic and therapeutic techniques. The diagnosis in Donald's case can only be guessed in retrospect, but presumably he had meningitis. He did not recover fully. He was left with minor physical disabilities and more importantly, his further mental development was retarded. He retained the mind of a five-year-old child.

Donald's parents tried to send him to school, but it was immediately apparent that he was inadequately equipped for formal education. Special tutoring in the home for the disabled was available; this was briefly tried, without success. Donald's parents considered institutionalization but decided against this step. He was a docile and affectionate child, their only child, and they could not bear the thought of separation. Therefore Donald stayed at home.

Donald's care became almost a full-time job to the parents, the mother especially. She often said with pride that she had never spent a single night outside of her own home since the day Donald was first taken ill. During his waking hours, Donald was under the direct observation of one parent or the other, usually the mother; she could not bear to leave him with a baby-sitter or even an understanding friend or relative. The social life of Donald's parents was, by necessity, extremely limited. Donald had no contact with children his own age; in fact, his only contact other than his mother and his father was the doctor who made occasional visits.

As adolescent and young adult, Donald retained the mentality and manner of an affectionate five-year-old. As he grew older, his disposition became more erratic and he showed occasional moments of ill-temper and irascibility. These moments came whenever there was slight variation from rigidly established daily routines. He sometimes showed manifestations of jealousy of the father whenever the mother showed undue affection toward the father in Donald's presence.

Some thirty-five years after Donald's original illness, Donald's father died suddenly of coronary thrombosis. Donald scarcely seemed to notice the absence of the paternal parent in the home.

Five years later, Donald's mother developed cancer. She refused surgery on the grounds that Donald could not be deprived of her care and attention during her hospitalization. As Donald's mother grew weaker, it became obvious that outside help would be required. A kindly in-law entered the scene. This good woman visited the house daily at first, doing the cooking and the household chores; later, she moved into the house, leaving her own home and family to do so. Kind as she was, the in-law could not handle Donald very well; his temper tantrums became more frequent.

When, finally, the mother died, the problem of Donald became an emergency. It was necessary to commit him to a state hospital, where he passed the few remaining years of his life, and where he remained a problem to the authorities. He had to be kept on the closed ward, under restraint and heavy sedation, with feedings administered by tube.

Elaine (Case 6)

Elaine was born retarded. She had one of the congenital conditions showing both physical and mental abnormality. The attending physician recognized the condition on the first day of life. Although doctors dread breaking such tragic news to a new mother and father, the physician did not shirk this obligation. The parents accepted the bad news with great maturity.

Elaine lived at home for the first few years of her life. Few institutions, either public or private, have nursery facilities for the very young. When Elaine reached school age, the difficult decision had to be made: institutionalize her or keep her at home. The advice of specialists was sought. It was decided to admit Elaine into a good private boarding school for the retarded child. Elaine's father was a successful businessman and the cost was not a serious problem. After the expected initial adjustment period, Elaine grew to like the school. She got along well with the other children and the staff. Her parents and her several brothers and sisters visited her at school frequently, and she came home for holidays and for a summer vacation.

Elaine's basic intelligence was permanently limited by her disease; she was, however, within the limits, teachable. Learning processes were slow and arduous, but she was given patient, intensive, skillful, and dedicated training. She learned to dress herself, feed herself, and to take care of her own personal hygiene. Eventually she learned to read, slowly, and write, slowly, and to do simple arithmetic. She even learned a skill, becoming adept at needlework.

When Elaine reached the age of twenty-one, it was no longer possible to keep her in the school, for that institution had a maximum age limit. Another decision arose: whether to transfer her to an institution for adults or to send her home. Because of her good progress and because of the good home environment, the decision was made to send her home.

There she lived quite happily, making a good adjustment both within the home and in the community outside. She even contributed to her own support, bringing in small sums of money as a dressmaker. After the death of her parents, Elaine moved in with one of her married sisters, where again she had a good adjustment. A gentle and affectionate person (as so many retarded people are), she was loved by children and completely accepted on her own terms by adults that she encountered.

I do not know the results of IQ and other psychological testing on Elaine, and such testing was never done in Donald's case, but it is reasonable to suppose that Donald and Elaine were roughly equivalent in terms of raw intelligence. In both cases, the mental disability was permanent. But the end result in terms of teaching, training, and social adjustment were at opposite poles in these two cases.

Several factors weighted the odds heavily in favor of Elaine. She had the advantage of excellent specialized care, and Donald did not. Her father could afford private care, and Donald's could not. Elaine's parents knew that she was retarded from birth; Donald was normal for the first five years, and it was therefore much more difficult for his parents to accept the fact of his mental disability. There were other children in Elaine's family; Donald had the privilege and burden of being his mother's sole concern.

It is unfortunate the economic factors often make such a difference in the outcome of these cases. Private care is very expensive, beyond the means of many families. Public care is often miraculously good, considering the overwhelming obstacles; workers in the field are skillful and dedicated, overworked and underpaid; but the public case load is far too heavy and the public resources far too few. In an affluent welfare state, increasingly substantial amounts of public money will be addressed to this problem on both research and clinical levels, and miracles will occur in increasing numbers, but the problem is a staggering one.

As previously indicated, in the upper levels of mental retardation, adjustment difficulty is minimal, and at the bottom levels, institutional custodial care is mandatory. It is in the middle where the parents must make the difficult and often cruel choice: whether to keep the child at home or put him into an institution. Finances and available facilities will often determine the choice.

When good care is available, and financially feasible, and when the child is potentially teachable, I feel that the choice for institutionalization is the proper one. Many families make the other choice and keep the child at home and do an extraordinarily good job with it. They invest much tenderness and love in the retarded child and they find (as do professionals in the field) that such an investment is rewarded by great tenderness and love in return from the retarded child. A crippled mind does not necessarily mean a crippled emotional structure, and the great majority of retarded persons can and do give love to those who take care of them. The choice of home care has a number of dangers, however.

Teaching of a retarded child is difficult, requiring much training and the proper temperament, which few parents possess. The retarded child at home does not learn and advance anything near as well as the child in the proper school. Retarded children also have a social need. At home, they are often shut up in the attic and have little contact with others outside of the home; retarded persons tend to make normal children and adults nervous and they themselves are nervous in the presence of strangers who do not understand. At a special school, the child has the company of others of his kind and of adults who do know and understand. Keeping a retarded child in the home, also, tends to have a crippling effect on the father and the mother, limiting their social life, as clearly shown in Donald's case. In general, persons with mental deficiency are inclined to be frail and weak physically. Many die young. Today, however, thanks to the antibiotics, many retarded persons live to a geriatric age. If they live at home, they may outlive their parents. When a retarded person has been cared for exclusively by a devoted parent until his middle years, loss of that parent is very apt to precipitate an emergency as seen in Donald's case. Such bereaved retarded persons may become dangerous to themselves and others and become a difficult public problem for the rest of their lives.

It is encouraging what excellent adjustments can be made by retarded persons, given the proper training. It is discouraging how often economic and social factors prevent such persons from receiving the specialized care necessary to produce the good result. Occasionally, it is surprising to see one of these people make a good adjustment without any training at all.

Fred (Case 7)

Fred had mental retardation from birth of approximately the same degree as that of Donald and Elaine. He had no physical disability.

Fred came from a large family of limited means. The family was too large and the means too limited for the parents to pay much individual attention to any particular child. The children were thrown into life, sink or swim, and some turned out well, some turned out badly. Some were smart and some were stupid, and Fred, obviously, was the stupidest. He was so stupid that there was no point in expecting him to go to school, a matter on which the parents, the parole officers, and the teachers agreed. Fred wasn't a bad boy; in fact, he was a good boy; he did not get into trouble with the law; perhaps he was too stupid for delinquency; he was certainly too stupid for school.

The rule of life in Fred's home was that when you stopped

going to school you got a job, unless you were in jail, or, if female, married. Fred began getting odd jobs early when others of his age were in school. Though stupid, he was good-natured, and most people liked him. The jobs he got were simple, because he couldn't handle anything else. Specifically, he swept out the store for several merchants in town. He continued such janitor work in adult life. He was a good janitor; he liked being a janitor; he worked long hours for multiple employers and they were pleased with him.

Today, in fact, Fred is one of the most valued workers in town. There are a number of small stores with marginal profits whose owners cannot afford to pay a janitor very much; the state had a minimum wage law of $1.25 an hour, and some small storekeepers could not afford a janitor at these wages. But Fred was exempt from the minimum wage because he was illiterate, and he was happy to work at 50¢ an hour. More prosperous stores, which could afford the standard wage, can't find janitors. In an affluent society with universal education, who wants to be a janitor? Well, Fred does. The better stores pay Fred $1.25 an hour or even $1.50. Fred doesn't care how much they pay him. He would probably work for nothing, for he likes to work. But people pay him as much as they can afford, because he's steady and reliable and cheerful, and they would be ashamed to take advantage of him.

Fred may not be the richest man in town, but he's far from the poorest. He has never been on relief. He owns his own little house, and he even owns a television set. Fred loves television, and he watches it a great deal of the time, when he isn't working.

4

The Happy Ones

No single psychological factor is "pure." By this I mean that no such factor operates independently; each is modified by other factors; human behavior is governed by the simultaneous operation of multiple variables.

Intelligence which differs from average in either direction, high or low, is perhaps the most "pure" of the psychological factors, and this is why we started at that point, working from the relatively known and obvious in the direction of the unknown. Raw intelligence can be measured objectively. I don't put as much faith in the IQ or other tests measuring intelligence as do many experts in the testing field. Such a measurement is not quite scientific or exact, but it certainly can give reliable estimations. The average man can assess intelligence with no great difficulty. Meeting a stranger, one can take a pretty shrewd guess as to the degree of his intelligence after speaking with him for a few minutes. This is one of the first things we do notice on meeting a new face. However, while fairly "pure" and relatively obvious, the degree of raw intelligence, high or low, does not determine maturity or adjustment. Emotional factors enter in to determine the balance. From this point forward, in considering psychology, we will be dealing almost entirely with the emotions, rather than the intellect. Emotions are not "pure" in any way.

Sound objective measurements of the emotions are lacking. We have difficulty defining them; emotions are complex, devious, and serpentine. We recognize emotional factors in ourselves and the people that we meet all the time; we are always under their direct or indirect influence. The subtle and complex nature of the emotions, their subjective and unmeasurable quality, is what makes human psychology difficult to discuss or study or understand. If we try to set down some simple general principles, we oversimplify the problem, and the human is not simple. If we try to take into account all the subtle variables, we get entangled in our language and soon we make no sense. We may invent ingenious theories and attempt to confirm and reinforce the theory with clinical observation, but then we build the house on sand; we are tempted to bend and distort the observations to fit the theory; this is a basic criticism of Freudian thinking as a whole. We attempt objective research on animals, because we can subject the experimental animal to conditions we could never impose on a human volunteer, but simple animal behavior does not necessarily apply to the human. When we set up human experiments, we impose artificial conditions and laboratory psychology is not necessarily identical with the psychological reactions of the man in the street. We can attempt to get psychological information by testing. But what good criteria do we have as guidelines for the test? We can attempt to get information by interview, but what witness is reliable on the subject of his own emotions? Our best information still would seem to be the reactions of people as we observe them under ordinary conditions. This is an art, the art of observation, and not a science. Artistic opinion is subjective, personal, biased by prejudice and taste; so, however, is human psychology.

While confessing our inability to deal with the subject as a science and announcing our intention to deal with it as art, we must nevertheless make use of some quasi-scientific definitions and concepts if we are to have any base for communication and hope to make any sense at all.

Let us make certain postulates about emotions. We postulate, first, that the emotions are separate and distinct from the intellect or intelligence. Although intelligence may modify and control and influence emotional reaction to a certain extent, the emotions operate on a different level, divorced from the intellect. On the one hand, we think, and on the other hand, we feel, and the two are different.

We must also postulate the existence of the subconscious mind. This concept is impossible to prove and it may even be difficult to defend, but it seems to ring true, and most of us do accept the validity of the concept. We think of the iceberg: ten percent showing above the ocean, the great mass of it lying under water. We have a thin surface area of conscious thinking and perception. We have a big subsurface area, where we do not think, where we can perceive only dimly, but where we feel; here the mass of our emotions is at play: love, hate, fear, rage, sorrow, joy, jealousy, and so forth. Jets of emotion come spurting to the surface, play around for a while, and then sink again into the depths. We have only superficial insight. Certain conditions bring us deeper insight: just before and just after sleep, in dreams, under the influence of sedating, intoxicating, or hallucinatory drugs, in the act of creation, in enjoyment of the arts, under highly stressful circumstances, perhaps during psychotherapy or psychoanalysis. We never have complete insight of the subconscious mind. It is postulated that our basic adjustive balance, or lack of balance, is largely dependent upon emotions at the subconscious level.

We must now set down two definitions from psychiatry. Terminology has always been a problem in psychiatry; schools of classification and definition come and go. The two terms I am about to offer were taught me many years ago; they have been widely and generally used throughout the years; although some experts deny the validity of these concepts, they are accepted by most experts, and most non-psychiatrists accept them and use them too. I refer to *neurosis* and *psychosis*. The terms are not easy to define. As a matter of fact, some thinking that went into the writing of this book has caused me to revise my definitions and to fit a slightly different meaning to words I have been using without thought for years. But despite problems in definition, the manifestations of the two conditions are readily recognized by the trained observer in most cases, and the words are helpful in discussing patterns of human behavior.

We should first note that psychosis and neurosis are not mutually exclusive. They are not opposites like black and white, or complements like red and blue. They are disorders of a different system. Neurosis and psychosis can occur in the same patient, consecutively or together; this fact has not always been appreciated by the specialist and failure to recognize it has led to error in management and therapy.

Psychosis is a disorder of the thinking process. Raw intelligence is not necessarily disturbed, although it may often be, but psychosis can occur in a brilliant person. The psychotic is, however, irrational. The characteristic manifestation of psychosis is a disorientation as to person or time or place or "reality." Psychosis implies insanity. The psychotic is the lunatic, the madman; he is crazy.

The psychotic acts as if he had physical disease of the brain. In fact, he does. Until recently such a statement could not be made, for physical brain disease could not be demonstrated in some conditions called psychotic because of the typical disorientation. In some psychoses, brain disease or damage has always been quite obvious. Today, laboratory evidence suggests that all conditions showing the characteristic psychotic disturbance of thinking do have physical or physiological brain disease. The exact nature of the brain disease is not always clear, but the evidence does now seem sufficient to implicate brain disease in psychosis.

Neurosis is classically defined as unresolved emotional conflict at the subconscious level, expressed in physical symptoms, but without physical disease of the brain or other parts of the body. Diseases of the kind called psychosomatic are seen in association with neurosis, but these are felt to be secondary manifestations of the basic emotional conflict, the result and not the cause of the trouble. The actions and reactions of the neurotic may seem illogical; he may not seem to think rationally; the severe neurotic may be more confused than the mild psychotic; but fundamentally the neurotic is sane. He has normal orientation. His characteristic pattern is that of self-defeating or self-blocking behavior, presumably due to unresolved emotional conflict.

We recognize psychosis by abnormal behavior. There are no absolute guidelines for normality of behavior. Behavior will differ according to the individual and the circumstances, and we make allowances accordingly. When an individual acts in a manner strikingly outside of the limits of average and expected, we recognize that he is acting abnormally. Our personal standards of evaluation will depend on our own personality and adjustment to a considerable extent, but strikingly abnormal behavior is obvious to most of us, even if we ourselves happen to be psychotic or neurotic.

The behavior of the neurotic, though self-defeating and self-blocking, may not appear to be abnormal on superficial examination. The abnormality of the neurotic person expresses itself through symptoms: he feels badly. His condition is identified by absence of organic physical disease of sufficient degree to cause the symptoms and by the presence of evidence suggesting subconscious emotional conflicts.

Abnormal behavior is seen in persons neither psychotic nor neurotic. Some non-psychotic non-neurotic individuals act very strangely indeed. They may have a personality disturbance. They may have unusual social adjustments for reasons other than brain disease or subconscious emotional conflict. We will note examples of such personality or social maladjustments later in the book.

We now turn our attention to happy people. We are considering happiness of an abnormal or inappropriate degree.

Can happiness be abnormal? Is not happiness the hallmark of balance, adjustment, and maturity? To a considerable extent, yes, of course, but total happiness is neither appropriate nor normal. We possess knowledge of sorrow, pain, disease, war, poverty, injustice, and suffering throughout the world; unblemished personal happiness in light of this knowledge would be selfish and inappropriate. Each of us also has foreknowledge of his own inevitable death; no matter how religious or resigned we may be, this foreknowledge must carry at least a trace of sorrow. Relative happiness in relatively happy times is normal of course. Failure to enjoy happiness is pathological. But happiness in unhappy situations or excessive happiness at any time is inappropriate and is an abnormal adjustment to the stress of life.

Sam (Case 8)

Sam is in "show biz." He is not a star or a celebrity, and his name would not be recognized by the average newspaper reader, but he is known in the trade as a steady, dedicated, and successful professional. In a business noted for its ups and downs, Sam's career has remained on a high plateau, from before World War I down to the present day. His income has averaged a hundred and fifty thousand dollars a year. He has succeeded in almost all aspects of the trade: as actor, writer, director, and producer of plays, movies, and television shows. His specialty is light comedy; he produces entertainment rather than art and his products are ephemeral, but he has been consistent in pleasing the public's taste.

Many theatrical personalities come from broken homes, but Sam had a happy childhood with warm strong attachments to both father and mother. In a business noted for recurrent marriage and divorce, Sam has maintained a marriage with his first and only wife for more than half a century.

Despite this record of adjustment and success, the last twenty years of Sam's life have been anything but placid. Trouble began in the form of a mild depression when he was around fifty years old. This was associated with one of his few professional failures, and it came at a time of depressing national crisis, so Sam was inclined to attribute his mood to environmental circumstances. The depression did not last long. He soon felt well, in fact somewhat too well; he entered a phase of excitement, overactivity, and euphoria. This passed and again he was depressed. He continued to work, concealing his depression, but he felt miserable, considered suicide, and in fact made a couple of abortive suicidal attempts. The mood swung again. Again he became elated, overactive, and excited. He worked all day and played all night. He was immersed in multiple ambitious projects; he placed hundreds of long distance telephone calls; he traveled extensively by plane, often chartering private planes when commercial schedules did not suit his whim. He was living life to the hilt, enjoying every moment, getting along on two or three hours of sleep each night. He showed such an overdrive of energy that few people could keep up with him.

During Sam's two mild periods of depression, his family and friends apparently had not noticed anything unusual about him. During his second period of overactivity, they became aware that he was not well. He considered himself a dynamo of energy, a fountainhead of creativity, a bubbling tireless good fellow of exuberant charm and expansive good spirits. His energy was undeniable, but not all of his ideas were good, and some were positively bad. Sam seemed to have lost his facility for timing, judgment, and taste. His charm was too expansive, his spirits overwhelming. In short, he began to look and act like a maniac.

The phase passed and again was replaced by depression. For the next few years, he passed through alternating periods of depression and of mania, with relatively brief normal periods between. With this emotional pattern, it was inevitable that Sam would come to the attention of psychiatrists. He consulted several. None of them had any difficulty recognizing the pattern, for it is fairly common, but none of them were able to help him at first. When depressed, Sam sought advice because he felt badly but rejected treatment because he felt hopeless and lacked interest in the future. In elated periods, he consulted psychiatrists only on the insistence of family and associates, but then he felt so well that he did not wish treatment of any kind.

Finally, he had a manic period of greater length and severity. He began making serious business mistakes and his social patterns became erratic and dangerous. Mixed in with excessive and exuberant good spirits were hints of irascibility and violence. He fought with friends, disrupted parties with embarrassing incidents, engaged in fisticuffs with strangers in bars. Always a devoted family man, he quarreled with his wife and left her, starting a chain of brief lurid promiscuous affairs with women of a lower social order. He also began tangling with the law, accumulating a fairly imposing record of brief imprisonments for disorderly conduct, vagrancy, assault, and drunken driving. Finally, he was involuntarily committed to a good psychiatric institution. There he received appropriate treatment. He developed insight into his condition.

He has lived with the condition on reasonable terms ever since. He continues to have recurrent depression and recurrent mania alternatively with normal periods between. He knows that each abnormal phase will be followed, sooner or later, by abnormality in the opposite direction. He recognizes that both types of abnormality are dangerous, to himself and to others. He is able to detect the early symptoms of either phase before they are apparent to others, and whenever he notes premonitory symptoms he immediately signs himself into a private institution where he stays until the phase is passed. On average, he spends two or three weeks at a time in the institution two or three times a year. When not in the institution, Sam is an altogether sane and well-adjusted man. Despite the interruptions and although he is now well into the geriatric age group, his professional career remains as active and successful as ever.

Sam is a classic example of the common and serious psychosis called manic-depressive disease. This is a true psychosis according to our postulated definitions earlier in the chapter.

Manic-depressive disease, as the name implies, has two

phases: the upward swing of mania, the downward swing of depression, both part of the same disease. The pattern of the two phases is highly variable. The mood swings may be all manic or mostly manic; they may be all depression or mostly depression; they may be mixed unpredictably, or they may alternate. Some patients have a great many periods of crisis. Some patients have only a few breakdowns, and in some the disease may be manifested by one attack in a lifetime, which may be either mania or depression. Characteristic of the condition is a normal period between the mood swings in either direction; also characteristic is psychotic disorientation during the crisis. The disease is one of middle and later adult life in a person, usually a social active outgoing person, who has previously shown excellent adjustment.

Since mania and depression are so different—opposite, in fact—one might wonder why the two phases are considered part of one disease. Would it not be more logical to consider this two contrastingly opposite diseases? Opposite disorders, however, would not be likely to crop up in the same individual, and the majority of manic-depressives do show both phases. It is more in accord with clinical observation to consider this condition an exaggeration of normal mood swing, manifested by abnormal swings in either direction or both.

Let us take note of a phenomenon which operates in many areas of biological function. Assume two opposite and opposing forces, and presume that there is a middle area between the two poles where equilibrium and a state of balance exists. In biology, this will seldom be a fixed stable point, for life is a variable and dynamic process, but there will be a range of fluctuation between the poles. Now presume that there is a swing beyond the normal range, too far in the direction of one pole; this represents imbalance or disease. Often one of the body's many corrective factors will come into play, pulling toward the opposite pole, back into the range of health. The correcting force may pull too hard, overcorrecting, causing imbalance in the opposite direction. Thus is set up a pendulum to-and-fro motion, an exaggeration of the normal pendulum, producing alternating periods of imbalance in opposite directions with a phase of normality between. Manic-depressive disease is obviously this sort of cyclic or periodic disease. There are a number of purely physical disorders showing the same sort of excessive pendulum swing.

This brings us to a consideration of what have been called biological clocks. This is not to be confused with the pendulum motion of periodic disease; we're talking about something else now. I am not sure that biological clock is a very good name for the phenomenon. The process defined by the phrase essentially is a long quiescent period interrupted by shorter bursts of activity. Such activity involves the whole body, a chain of physiological reactions basically triggered by nervous excitation in the brain. These bursts occur in a regular and predictable pattern; this pattern in turn often occurs in the same phasic rhythm as certain environmental forces: rising and setting of sun and moon, earth rotation, seasons, tides, and so forth. At first glance, these rhythmic bursts of activity seem to be in response to the specific environmental rhythms, but the interesting thing about the biological clock is that it continues to function internally even when the external stimuli have been removed.

For example, a fish may rise or fall in the ocean in a cyclic pattern related to night and day or to the tides. Take the fish out of the ocean, put him in a laboratory tank where there are no tides, in a dark room where night and day cannot be distinguished, and the fish will continue to rise and fall on his usual pattern. In other words, something is built into the organism of the fish controlling his phasic activity even when he is separated from the external force which appears to be causing it. The laboratory rat shows bursts of muscular activity according to definite predictable cyclic patterns. You can blind the rat; you can remove his various endocrine glands; you can put him to sleep with drugs or alcohol; but none of these will stop the pattern of his bursts of activity. The only way to stop this pattern is to freeze the rat down to the point where spontaneous breathing and heart beat stop.

There has been much recent interest in the phenomenon of the biological clock. Very complex ones have been studied in such fields as ecology and marine biology; some have been identified in the human, and probably there are others as yet unnoticed. It seems likely that manic-depressive disease is a disorder of a biological clock.

The clock mechanism apparently operates in the brain, in the primitive part of the brain stem called the hypothalamus. The hypothalamus is apparently the area of the brain where subconscious emotional reaction occurs. Brain tissue activity, here and elsewhere in the brain, is manifested by a combination of electrical and chemical changes. Apparently in manic-depressive disease there is an imbalance of chemical and electrical forces, producing disturbance of the emotions as they express themselves in moods.

At the moment, we are concerned only with the manic phase of manic-depressive disease, representing a type of inappropriate abnormal happiness. We will discuss the other phase, the depression, in the next chapter.

This book will not discuss details of treatment of psychiatric disease, a technical subject we will leave to the experts, but we will from time to time consider some generalities of treatment principles. Treatment of the manic phase of manic-depressive disease is guided by the basic nature of the disease: in time, the mood will pass. The manic patient feels very well, euphoric and happy, and therefore does not request treatment. He is usually brought to treatment involuntarily, committed because of the wake of social catastrophe behind him. Being psychotic, he lacks insight, often resenting the implication that he is sick. He regards himself as a prisoner, rather than a patient.

During the manic phase, the patient is not amenable to psychotherapy; he cannot talk or listen rationally. Between mood swings, he is normal, accessible to reason, and at such interim periods a great deal of insight can be communicated to him, but he is often not available for psychotherapy at such times because of the fact that he is normal then.

One would like to calm the patient down, in order to handle him more easily, while waiting for the mood to pass. Sedatives are valuable to some extent. The manic person before commitment usually treats himself with sedatives, often barbiturates, most often alcohol. One form of alcoholism—and only one—is a manic individual treating himself; this sort of person is the spree drinker who, between sprees, does not care for alcohol at all. More specific than sedatives or alcohol is the newer family of drugs called tranquilizers, which, when properly used, may be very helpful. Hydrotherapy, soothing baths, is useful in the acute phase. Occupational therapy may help. These measures are adjunctive. They relieve the violent symptoms of mania. They do not cure the mania, which will in time cure itself, and they do not prevent the mania. We do not know how to prevent a manic crisis. We can treat and shorten a depressive crisis a good deal better than a manic one, as will be discussed later on. We can reassure the patient and his relatives that it will pass away. The patient may be very difficult and very dangerous until it does, however. The manic patient may feel euphoric, expansive, and simply wonderful, bubbling with charm and good spirits, but violence is in him, just below the surface, as anybody encountering a manic patient instinctively knows and fears. In the Biblical sense of the word, these people are possessed.

Harry (Case 9)

Of the many people like Harry I have known, I chose him as an example here because he was a psychiatrist, and therefore had valuable insights into his own condition.

Harry was a dynamic, enthusiastic person who worked and played sixteen or eighteen hours every day, needing little sleep, enjoying every minute of his activities. He often said, "I was born with my thermostat turned up high."

He applied the same overdrive to his profession, his hobby, and his sport. Professionally, he saw more patients than most psychiatrists can manage. He worked long days and also he didn't believe in the fifty-minute hour, often keeping therapeutic interviews brief. Because of his own dynamic personality, he attracted dynamic people as patients: executives, celebrities, people from the theatrical and publishing worlds. Incidentally, Harry was one of several psychiatrists consulted by Sam, the manic-depressive of our last case history. Harry had a particular gift in establishing rapport with the hyperactive and disturbed. "They think of me as one of their own," he said.

For his hobby, Harry was a writer. He had a genuine literary gift, received favorable critical attention, and some of his pieces have been anthologized. His literary work was perhaps more noted for quantity than quality; his output was enormous; he published book after book after book.

For his sport, he was a swimmer. This didn't mean a few idle splashes in the YMCA pool. Harry went down to the harbor and set off to sea like a freighter, swimming several miles out and several miles back.

Harry knew his energies were excessive. He had much in common with the manic phase of manic-depressive disease, but his mood was constant, without relaxation or depression, and he was not psychotic. He sometimes wondered if there was a physical cause, for certain glandular disturbances such as hyperthyroidism cause excessive energy, but his metabolism rate was normal or low. There is a technical name for Harry's sort of personality, and he knew it: hypomania.

Harry had undergone psychoanalysis in the course of his training, but this program did not change his mood. From time to time he consulted psychiatrist associates, but they had nothing to offer. He tried various sedatives and tranquilizers without much success. The most useful drug to him was alcohol. He was a moderately heavy drinker; however, he never seemed drunk and nobody considered him alcoholic. Harry was professionally in-

terested in alcoholism and treated a good many alcoholics in
his practice. He evolved the unusual technique of treating alcoholics by conducting the therapeutic interview over drinks in
bars and cocktail lounges. Most therapists would consider this
technique foolish and explosively dangerous, but Harry got away
with it. He did not share the common view of most workers
in the field that alcoholism can be controlled but not cured
and that the controlled alcoholic should never dare to take a
single drink. Harry believed that alcoholics can be cured and
learn to drink safely in social moderation. Some of his results
seemed to justify the point of view.

Harry carried with him an air of expansive good humor, charm,
and euphoria. He enjoyed life, and yet he knew that there was
something wrong with him.

"If you enjoy yourself all the time, why would you want to
be otherwise?" I once asked him.

"Because I know my energy and good-humor is pathological,"
he said.

"What difference should that make?"

"I am an incomplete man," he said. "I like people, but I
am too restless. I can never take the time to turn an acquaintance into a friend. I am happily married; I am fond of my
wife, and never wanted any other woman, but I am incapable
of love. I enjoy medicine, but I can't feel deeply enough to
have true sympathy. I am immune to sorrow or grief. I keep
myself too busy to think. Can a man be complete who can't
make a friend, feel tragedy, love a woman, or meditate?"

Harry's condition, hypomania, is defined in the dictionary
as mania of a moderate degree. In clinical usage, however,
there is a different connotation. Mania implies the disorientation of psychosis. The hypomaniac is sane and rational.

There are few hypomanic psychiatrists, for the specialty
requires patience and reflection. There are many hypomanic
doctors; most of them are surgeons. The classic example of
hypomania is the driving successful executive who has been
so well and often described in fiction and non-fiction studies.

They are successful and often rich; they have great energy; they seem to be afraid of solitude and of their own company.

These people are not psychotic. They are not neurotic. There is a similar neurosis where the neurotic keeps himself excessively busy in material pursuits to compensate for personal insecurity and inadequacy, but the hypomaniac does not block himself from achieving a life goal. Self-blocking is implicit in the definition of neurosis. The hypomaniac, on the contrary, succeeds in achieving his goal. This may be considered a personality disorder. Does it have a physical cause? One might speculate that the mid-point in the biological clock system of mood is too far over in the direction of excitability; I suspect that there is an excess irritability of nervous and muscle tissue to stimuli. The thermostat, as Harry said, is turned up too high.

Hypomaniacs are the happiest of men. And yet they have a vague feeling of incompleteness akin to unhappiness. Satchel Paige, the great Negro pitcher whose philosophy hummed even louder than his fast ball, said, "Don't look over your shoulder; you might see something gaining on you." Budd Schulberg also phrased it aptly: "What makes Sammy run?"

Irene (Case 10)

This is a silly case, and we won't spend much time with it, for Irene was a silly girl, and this was her problem. She was a giggler. Irene giggled at her own jokes, at other people's jokes. She giggled at serious remarks. She giggled at completely inappropriate occasions, such as at her father's funeral. Irene was a pretty girl, intelligent, nice, but nobody liked her, because she giggled.

Giggling is a charming girlish trait and, as such, is charming, in girls, under the proper circumstances. It may be carried to the point of irritation in certain shy and insecure people as a defensive mannerism. Carried still further, such as the

act of giggling at a funeral, the mannerism becomes pathological. In the case of Irene, giggling was a sign of a psychosis,
hebephrenia, sometimes considered a disease of its own,
usually considered a type of schizophrenia. We will discuss
a more advanced case of hebephrenia later. Irene is mentioned here as another example of inappropriate happiness
as an indication of psychosis.

Jack (Case 11)

Jack was a joker. He liked his jokes broad, coarse, and dirty.
Most especially, he liked practical jokes. He wasn't silly and
didn't giggle; he wasn't manic or hypomanic, having no excessive
drives, and being, in fact, quite lazy. He seemed like a very
pleasant, cheerful, friendly fellow at first glance. But life was a
joke to him, and he treated everything as a joke. He was unaware
of pain, grief, sorrow, or tragedy, and when such things came
near, in his own life or that of others, Jack made a joke of it.
His sense of humor was inappropriate, and people who knew
him did not like him very well.

Jack is difficult to classify. He is not psychotic or neurotic.
Perhaps he is a mild variant of the psychopathic personality,
which we will be discussing in detail later. Humor is a great
stabilizer; an appropriate sense of humor is one of the hall-
marks of maturity; the humorless person usually has an adjustment problem of some type. But humor may be inappropriate.

The psychology of humor fascinated Freud and many who
have studied it since. There is laughter which expresses the
pure joy of life. Very often the wisecrack or the joke approaches dangerous ground, subject matter close to that
which shocks us, offends us, or frightens us. Our brief initial
reaction to the joke is a gasp of shock, offense, or fear;
then we see that this is only a joke, that we are not really
threatened by the subject; out of our relief, we laugh. Such

laughter is a good release, serving as a safety valve to our repressions and our fears, a healthy antidote to neurosis. It is not healthy to take oneself too seriously. The brave man and the wise man, both, are able to laugh. He still will fear that which threatens him, but when he can laugh his defenses and adjustments have been fortified. We also laugh at the ridiculous and the incongruous. Man is inclined to be a pompous and arrogant ass; the best antidote to pomposity and arrogance is laughter.

But laughter may be ridicule, a mask for hatred and sadism, and this laughter isn't healthy. This is a hidden sword. The line between the ridiculous and ridicule is subtle. The joker who oversteps the line consistently is a cruel sadistic person. We recognize that it is the joker, and not the subject of his joke, who threatens us. And this, we rightly feel, is not funny at all.

Karl (Case 12)

Karl was an old man when I met him as a young man. We do not see the problem represented by his case today, which is fortunate.

Karl played around in his youth, which is not unusual, and he was carelessly unwise, which is apt to be a tendency of the young. He developed a sore on his penis. This did not hurt him or bother him in any way, so he did not seek treatment for it, and in a few weeks, it went away. Two months later, he developed a faint skin rash. This also went away without treatment.

Karl settled down as he grew older, which is normal. For the next thirty years, he was a quiet steady conservative dependable hard-working shoemaker.

Then, abruptly, his personality changed. He became happy, expansive, euphoric, and insane. He believed himself to be the King of Persia, surrounded by harems and rubies and race horses and complex international plots. He was committed to a state hospital where he lived for the rest of his life and where I had the opportunity to examine him. He was a very happy man. Why shouldn't the King of Persia be happy?

Serological tests of Karl's blood and spinal fluid were positive in a specific way. He had paresis, one type of advanced syphilis involving the brain. Euphoria is a characteristic symptom of paresis.

This, obviously, is a psychosis. In this psychosis, identification of the physical disease is obvious. Physical destruction of brain tissue by the spirochete causing syphilis can readily be demonstrated under the microscope. Once such damage has occurred it cannot be repaired by treatment. We see advanced syphilis only very rarely today; serological blood testing is done widely, for marriage licenses, in pregnant women, for entry into the armed services, on routine hospital admissions, and the like, and syphilis rarely eludes detection long enough to reach the advanced stages. Discovered in the early stages, it can be cured with penicillin before organic brain damage has been done. The medical student of today may never see a case of paresis. When I was in medical school, every psychiatric institution lodged a case or two.

In this book, we will mention rare conditions only rarely, to prove specific points. We mention Karl and his paresis to show a psychosis where the physical disease of brain is obvious and evident and to show a condition where complete and blissful happiness is obviously the result of serious disease.

5

The Gloomy Ones

Louise (Case 13)

Louise was a cheerful person, optimistic, attractive, intelligent, busy, a good wife and mother, a useful member of her community. Her family and friends always considered her very well adjusted.

In her mid-forties, Louise noticed some irregularities in her menstrual periods, and she correctly came to the conclusion that she was entering the "change of life." There were associated symptoms of fatigue, backache, and hot flashes, and, from time to time, she found herself depressed. Her reading and conversation with other women led her to believe that these symptoms were not in any way unusual, and she resolved to ignore them in the reasonable expectation that they would go away.

The symptoms grew worse, especially fatigue and depression, and Louise consulted her family physician. The doctor did the usual examinations and tests, reassured her as to the absence of malignancy, and agreed with her own diagnosis of a menopausal syndrome. He prescribed mild sedatives, tranquilizers, and estrogenic hormones. The sedatives and tranquilizers seemed to make her worse; the estrogens relieved the hot flashes but nothing else.

Louise became more gloomy and depressed. She lost interest in the various activities, hobbies, and social pursuits which previously had kept her busy, and she seemed to lose interest in her husband and the children. Previously a meticulous housekeeper, she grew careless and her home was always "in a mess." Previously a well-groomed woman, she now began to look sloppy and disheveled. She ate poorly and lost weight. She slept poorly and got up in the morning more tired than when she had gone to bed. Formerly fond of gay brightly colored dresses, she now chose drab dull clothing. She seldom smiled. A gray veil seemed to have fallen over her personality. She was gloomy and morbid. She thought of death frequently, and she spoke of suicide.

Louise visited her family doctor again. He recognized the personality change as soon as she walked into the office. He understood the problem, a depression state, which is not uncommon. He recognized potential danger, and considered referring Louise to a psychiatrist, but decided to defer this step in the hope that simpler measures would be effective. Although she acted depressed, she complained of inner tension, so he increased the dose of tranquilizer. She complained of insomnia, so he prescribed barbiturates for sleep.

Louise took the new prescriptions to the corner pharmacy and had them filled. At bedtime that night, she swallowed all the capsules from both vials. In the morning, her husband could not rouse her. He phoned the doctor; the doctor called an ambulance; Louise was rushed to the hospital. Her stomach was pumped out and supportive measures applied. She was semicomatose for a couple of days, but then recovered physically. She remained emotionally depressed. She was transferred to a private institution under the care of a good psychiatrist. In a few weeks, Louise came home. She was fully recovered. The depression did not recur. She became again cheerful, active, busy, optimistic, and well-adjusted, and so remained for the rest of her life.

There are several types of pathological depression. The external manifestations of depression are much the same, no matter what the type. Louise presents most of the features of a typical depression state. She was somewhat disoriented and psychotic at the height of the attack and it was felt that she had manic-depressive disease. In her case, there were no manic episodes, and she had only this single attack with no recurrences.

We have discussed the manic phase of this complex and common cyclic disease. Depression seems to be more common in this condition than mania. Depression does not carry the implication of social catastrophe, but it is more dangerous to the individual patient because of the risk of suicide. Typically, the manic phase is seen in men, the depressed phase in women, though both occur in either sex. We have noted the highly variable pattern of the condition in the individual case and the tendency to onset in later life. The manic phase is often seen in a hyperactive, busy, social sort of person, and so is the depressed phase; accordingly, the manic phase seems to be an exaggeration of the normal personality while the depressed phase seems like a personality reversal. In both phases, the patient is psychotic, disoriented, inaccessible to logic and reason.

The manic person feels well, excessively exuberant, and therefore does not seek treatment for his symptoms; he comes to the attention of the therapist involuntarily on account of his socially disruptive conduct. His mania being cyclic, the chief object of therapy is to hold him, calmly and quietly and safe from social consequences, until the mood passes in the natural course of the disease. The depressed person feels badly and seeks treatment for symptoms which are often referable to a physical complaint. A more active treatment approach is therefore desirable, because of the intensity of the patient's complaints. Furthermore, a risk of suicide is real and present, and the patient may be able to kill himself even under institutional conditions. As in the manic phase, the depressed phase of manic-depressive disease will pass, but a permissive treatment program is not justified.

The depressed patient acts unengaged with the concerns of the world, but feels a distressing inner anxiety, of which he complains. Because of the complaints of anxiety, seen so often as symptoms of neurosis, well-meaning physicians are inclined to treat the symptoms of anxiety, rather than those of depression, with sedatives and tranquilizers, which are so often helpful in relieving neurotic anxiety. In depression, the neurotic as well as the psychotic kind, sedatives and tranquilizers make the symptoms worse; furthermore, giving a depressed patient such drugs is giving him a means of possible suicide. This mistake, which was made in the case of Louise, is made far too often.

The initial approach to treatment of depression was made on an arbitrary basis following a clinical observation: namely, that a depressed patient will often snap out of the depression when faced with a shock or a stressful situation, a fact which is true of the neurotic but not the psychotic depressions. An attempt was made to produce shock artificially as a treatment technique. Metrazol and other drugs which produce nervous tissue excitation resulting in convulsions were tried: so was insulin, the life-saving hormone of the diabetic, which in excess doses causes a shock-like reaction; and electroshock was tried, induction of convulsions, coma, and shock with electrical current. Electroshock proved the most useful; it was the mainstay of treatment of depression for many years, and still has a valuable place today. It works equally well with neurotic and psychotic depressions.

First tried didactically and continued because of practical success, electroshock was used for many years with no scientific explanation of its efficacy. Recently, some clues have been uncovered. The evidence is incomplete and fragmentary, but we can now state a possible reason for the effectiveness of electroshock in treatment of depression which may also be related to causative factors in manic-depressive disease.

The evidence comes from new research into the phenomenon of sleep. There is a certain stage of sleep, occurring naturally in a periodic fashion, where there is a sharp increase in bodily movements of the sleeper. Among many other manifestations of this phase of sleep is a rapid movement of the eyes and it has been called REM sleep, the initials standing for rapid eye movement. There are also typical brain wave patterns, as recorded on the electroencephalogram, during REM sleep. REM sleep is apparently responsible for giving us the refreshing and healthful effect we associate with sound sleep. You can artificially interrupt the REM period of sleep without waking the subject up. The animal or human deprived of REM sleep shows the same harmful results as if the subject had been deprived of sleep altogether: fatigue, tension, irritability, reduction of reaction time, and eventually, if deprivation of REM sleep is long continued, actual insanity or psychosis. Interestingly, REM sleep appears to be the time when most dreaming occurs. This gives a physical basis for the Freudian impression that dreaming is necessary for sound emotional health. When an animal or normal human is deprived of REM sleep for a certain length of time and then subsequently permitted to sleep undisturbed, there will be a greater than normal proportion of REM sleep; in other words, he is able to compensate or "catch up" for lost REM sleep.

An animal deprived of REM sleep is abnormally sensitive to electric current, a smaller amount of electricity being required to send the animal into convulsions or shock. Such an animal, first deprived of REM sleep and then given electroshock, does not compensate with additional REM sleep later when left undisturbed. In other words, it seems as if the shock served instead of the REM sleep, discharging excess energy in the brain. A human depressed patient after electroshock similarly needs less REM sleep: the electricity, perhaps, has discharged his stored up energy. Here is a theoretical reason for the effectiveness of electroshock in depression. Here too, it will be seen, is a close parallel to the phenomenon of the so-called biological clock. We have said that manic-depressive disease seems to be a disturbance of a biological clock. The normal person alternates bursts of activity with periods of quiescence. In depression, these bursts seem to be dampened; electricity seems to release it. In mania, the bursts are excessive. Both the mania and the depression are periodic, thanks to an inner clock.

The Russians have been interested in electroshock and have developed a milder form, called electrosleep, produced by an instrument called the Electroson. They have been using this technique, not only in depression, but for insomnia, as a possible means of anesthesia, and for a whole variety of diseases, psychotic, neurotic, and psychosomatic. Americans have tended to be skeptical of electrosleep, for Russian scientific literature is vague and non-specific, according to our standards, and brief American experience with machines like the Electroson has been relatively unsatisfactory. It may be that the Russians are getting good results from the Electroson through suggestion, rather than physiological effects. In America, clinical therapeutic interest in depression is swinging away from electroshock, in the direction of drug therapy, but as any space expert knows Russian science cannot be dismissed. There is much we do not understand about cyclic electric patterns in the human brain, and this area may bring us much vital information in the future.

The interested reader is referred to a fascinating book called *Sleep* by Luce and Segal, where present knowledge of REM sleep and many other aspects of the dark third of our lives is explored in rich and fascinating detail.

Today, electroshock in this country is being replaced by drug therapy. Another fascinating new frontier in biomedical research is in the field of brain neurophysiology, out of which new drugs for treatment of depression have evolved. Work on drugs in depression followed work on drugs in schizophrenia, and we will discuss the subject in more detail in connection with schizophrenia. Here, discussing a complex matter in an elementary way, we may say that there is a family of organic chemicals in the brain which appear to be concerned with storage, release, and transferral of nervous energy. These chemicals are amines. Together with the amines, there is found in brain tissue an enzyme called monoamine oxidase, which destroys the amines. Following research on the amines in other connections, it was postulated that when the activity of this enzyme is too great (or the supply of amines too little), a dampening of nervous excitation may occur, such as in a depression. A group of drugs was then developed which inhibits the effects of the enzyme. These drugs, used in depression, are helpful and, in fact, often work in a dramatic and specific way. They are called MAO inhibitors (the initials standing for monoamine oxidase) or, the popular term, "psychic energizers." These drugs are more specific than such older drugs as caffeine, and the amphetamine derivatives such as Benzedrine, which increase wakefulness and tension and are inclined to make a depressed person anxious and more uncomfortable than ever. The psychic energizers appear to work directly to overcome depression. Here, starting with laboratory theory and confirmed by treatment results, is further evidence that manic-depressive disease represents organic disturbance of brain tissue function. Such clues of the chemical nature of the disturbance do not in any way conflict with the evidence of electrical disturbance; electrical and chemical phenomena co-exist and work together in producing the normal reactions of nervous tissue and both would tend to be disturbed in brain disease.

There are other sorts of psychotic depression than the depressed phase of manic-depressive disease, two in particular. There is the fairly rare so-called post-partum depression, seen in the new mother shortly after childbirth. This is almost undoubtedly because of some imbalance of female sex hormones, the exact nature of which has not been identified. Another kind of psychotic depression, fairly common, is seen in elderly senile people with arteriosclerosis of the blood vessels of the brain. In arteriosclerosis, depression tends to be progressive and permanent; there is no cyclic tendency toward recovery; response to therapy is inclined to be poor.

There are also depressions which are neurotic, showing the same manifestations as psychotic depressions except that the patient retains a sane rational mind. A neurotic depression may represent an inappropriate length or depth of depression in response to some environment circumstance—illness, employment, or financial problems, death in the family —which normally causes depression. This has been called "reactive" depression. There are also neurotic depressions which are not reactive and are not associated with an obvious external cause.

It is, obviously, normal to be depressed from time to time, life being full of tragedy, reversal, and frustration. The person who does not become depressed in the face of depressing circumstances shows psychological disturbance of another type. It is also normal to have periods of depression without external cause. Everybody gets up on the "wrong side of the bed" from time to time. There are weekly depressions which we call "blue Monday"; women have monthly depression days; most persons in cold climates are depressed in February and in hot climates in August. These phasic depressions again suggest to us the phenomenon called the biological clock. This suggests that neurotic depressions, like psychotic depressions, may represent disturbance of a biological clock. Even the reactive depression, where a person overreacts to a depressing situation, may be related to this phenomenon. All kinds of depression may be of similar causation; we have noted that manifestations of depression are the same, no matter what the cause, and such treatments as electroshock and psychic energizers work in neurotic as well as psychotic depressions. What is the difference, then? Why do we draw a line between psychosis and neurosis in depression? The line is simply that of sanity: whether the depressed patient is rational or disoriented. Perhaps the physiological brain disturbance is primary in the psychotic, whereas in the neurotic it may be secondary to emotional conflict. We can only speculate.

Given a depressing circumstance, how much depression is

appropriate? Of course this varies according to individual and circumstance. In the frequent example of a death in the family, experience gives us rough guidelines. In this instance, we know that depression of three to six months is appropriate and depression up to a year not inappropriate. Deep depression lasting longer than a year after death in the family is inappropriate and pathological. Life, after all, is for the living, and we cannot waste it grieving for the dead.

Depression is a disabling and destructive condition. The patient loses his pleasure and fun in life, much of his ability to work and play, his capacity to love and be loved, even his ability to perform the routine chores and tasks of daily life. Depression is an emotional paralysis, fully as disabling as physical paralysis. Depression may be accompanied with physical symptoms, especially those of chronic fatigue, and a depressed patient often presents himself to his physician with this complaint. Since fatigue and depression are often the first symptoms of many chronic physical diseases, the physician must first do examinations and tests to rule out such disease. Not infrequently a physical abnormality may be found and it is tempting to both patient and physician to attribute the depression to some minor physical abnormality, rather than the other way around. Both physician and patient would prefer to find a physical cause than a psychiatric cause for a given symptom. Diagnostic error of this kind, common and understandable, tends to fix the depression and make the symptoms permanent.

In depression states, whether neurotic or psychotic, there is always the risk of suicide. Not all depressed people try to commit suicide, and not all suicides are the result of a depression state, but depression must be regarded as a potentially fatal condition. Few other psychiatric diseases threaten the life of the patient, and depression might be called the fatal psychiatric disease. Since suicide is one of the leading causes of death, since many suicides are patients in depression, since many forms of depression respond well to treatment, it is fair to say that suicide is a leading preventable cause of death.

The exact frequency of suicide is impossible to measure, since there is an associated social stigma, and many suicides are attributed to more natural causes on death certificates. A number of so-called accidents are suicides. I recall a case in which a man was killed in a single-vehicle automobile crash, a true accident; one year later, on the anniversary of her husband's death, at the same spot on the same road, at exactly the same time of night, his widow died in a single-vehicle automobile crash. This is too much for sheer coincidence.

Some apparent suicides are really accidents. Occasionally, one hears of persons hanging or strangling themselves under bizarre circumstances suggesting sexual perversion of a masochistic type; in this instance, the victim probably did not intend to kill himself, only to satisfy the perversion. A good deal more common is the dramatic type of "false suicide" put on as an "act" to frighten or influence a parent or a lover; sometimes the act may be too effective and the victim may kill himself by accident when his true aim was to live and enjoy a neurotic victory.

There is a type of suicide in the twilight zone between true suicide and accident, usually associated with sleeping pills in combination with alcohol. The victim, wishing sleep and groggy from sedation already taken, apparently loses the ability to count and accidentally takes too many pills. In these cases, one often feels that there must have been at least a subconscious suicidal influence at play. This sort of half-accident, half-suicide, has been seen a number of times in celebrities from the world of "show biz."

Most suicides are seen in people with pathological depression. Is it necessarily abnormal to kill oneself? Is there justification for the emotionally stable person to commit suicide? One thinks of the patient with the progressive fatal disease; on the surface, it appears logical for such a person to end his own suffering. However, the great majority of people under terminal conditions continue to cling to the breath of life, and suicide is not the average expected behavior even in this dire situation. One also thinks of the person caught in a hopeless life situation: the captured spy taking his cyanide pill, the prisoner hanging himself in his cell, the caught embezzler leaping from his office window. Again, however, most persons in a hopeless situation do not give up hope, continuing to dream of parole, pardon, or escape. Some suicides seem to have a positive rather than a destructive motivation: the victim giving his life to a cause, in order to become a hero or martyr, and thereby further the cause. Despite these various exceptions, most suicides are the result of a depression state; many depressions are curable; and many suicides, therefore, represent preventable death.

The concept of suicide as a preventable death is not accepted by many otherwise excellent physicians. I know a number of fine doctors who adopt a fatalistic attitude toward the problem of suicide, feeling that there is no way to keep a person determined to destroy himself from succeeding in his act. However, in view of the frequent association of suicide with depression and of the excellent results of treatment of depression in many cases, I consider that fatalism toward this problem is not a bit more justified than a fatalistic nihilistic attitude toward, for example, acute appendicitis.

An unwarranted casual attitude toward the risk of suicide is often seen in friends and relatives of the patient. This attitude is best summed up in the platitude, "Those who talk of suicide do not commit suicide." The exact contrary happens to be the case. People who speak of suicide are exactly those who try it. If one notes that a friend or relative, depressed, is speaking of suicide, one faces an emergency problem of the same order as acute appendicitis. Prompt treatment may be expected to cure; neglect may produce preventable death. Psychiatrists are well aware of the serious nature of this problem, and they consider depression with suicidal tendencies as one of the few real emergencies in psychiatric practice.

In recent years, it has been recognized that the potential suicide has often been giving a valuable clue in advance, the so-called "cry for help." This cry may be vague and non-specific, like that of a lost child, but it is very real. Too often it is met with the reply, "You'll be all right. Snap out of it!" The depressed patient, however, cannot snap out of it alone; he needs professional help in a hurry, and he must be watched carefully until such help can be obtained.

Recognition of the cry for help has led to the formation of agencies in many large cities, with a twenty-four-hour telephone coverage, manned by experts trained to answer the call of the potential suicide. Such agencies save many lives. Many more lives could be saved if the medical profession and the general public could learn to regard the problem with less fatalism or a less casual attitude. It is depressing to think of depression; depressed people are depressing companions; but depressed people are sick people, and good treatment is available. In many cases, this sickness can be cured.

6

The Muddled Ones

As this chapter heading implies, we are now considering delirium or confusion. This means disorientation and therefore, by our previous definitions, psychosis.

Confused delirious persons are obviously "out of touch." There is no problem recognizing them as insane. Though serious neurotics often show confusion and a muddying of intellect, one can pierce the muddy waters and, at bottom, touch the rational mind. Conversation with a psychotically confused person is a weird and unearthly sensation. Ordinary words are used, which should have an ordinary meaning, but the psychotic person uses them and interprets them with private meanings of his own. No true communication is obtained. You find yourself trying to adapt your words to his comprehension levels, and trying to interpret his words as if they were a foreign tongue; soon, you are not making any more sense than he is. You may begin to doubt your own state of sanity.

Since true communication with language cannot be obtained with a psychotic patient, it is my feeling that psychotherapy should not be attempted on psychotics. This may sound like a perfectly obvious statement, but it has not always been obvious to the specialists. The professional literature is full of references to lengthy psychotherapy applied to the psychotic; psychoanalysts seem particularly prone to this practice. Such therapy, in my experience, uniformly fails, unless the psychosis passes off spontaneously in the natural course of the disease, which can happen in psychosis. I am inclined to think that the therapist who attempts talking-listening therapeutic techniques on a patient who can neither talk nor listen rationally is more than a bit muddled himself. I have been present on a few occasions when a muddled therapist was trying to talk or listen to a muddled patient; the resulting conversation, truly, is out of this world!

Since by our definitions the psychotic is insane and the neurotic retains his basic sanity, it is natural to think that psychosis is more serious, permanent, and less curable than neurosis. Psychosis has serious implications, of course, and involves serious brain disturbance or disease, but the psychotic is by no means hopeless; his condition is by no means permanent; he may often be cured. We have seen that the manic phase of manic-depressive disease, a psychosis, is temporary, passing away spontaneously. The depressed phase of this psychosis is also temporary and, as we have seen, is in many cases very responsive to specific therapy. We will soon note other psychoses where the outlook and response to treatment is even more favorable. By the same token, the neurotic, though sane, may be very resistant to treatment; his condition may be very disabling and permanent. Psychiatrists may prefer to manage certain types of psychosis than certain neuroses and results of management may well be better.

I do not imply that psychosis is necessarily temporary, curable, or benign. All brain disease has serious implications. In the psychotic, his outlook and his response to treatment depend upon the nature of his basic brain disease. If the brain disease is temporary or curable, so is the psychosis and if the brain disease is progressive and resistant the psychosis will be too. The neurotic is usually, though not invariably, able to get along fairly well in society. The psychotic usually, though not invariably, can't get along in society at all. This chapter considers acute psychosis with delirium; the acutely psychotic delirious person is totally disabled for ordinary life. Everybody knows that he is crazy; the strait jacket and involuntary confinement are called for without delay; the delirious acute psychotic is not permitted to wander around loose very long.

Max (Case 14)

I had several things in common with Max, although I never met him. He became a doctor. He attended the same medical school as I and was a member of the same medical fraternity there, but he graduated the year before I entered. The older brothers remembered one incident from Max's medical school career quite vividly. Others also remembered it; the incident was mentioned more than once in our lectures on psychiatry, and one faculty psychiatrist put this case in one of his books.

Max was intelligent; you have to be fairly intelligent to get into medical school. He was conscientious; you have to be fairly conscientious to stay in medical school. Like all medical students, he feared the examinations and he crammed for them. On this occasion, he overdid his preparations.

Max burned the midnight oil for a week. He studied almost all of every night, sacrificing sleep; he had no exercise or recreation; he smoked too many cigarettes, drank too many cups of coffee, and perhaps he also took Benzedrine to keep awake.

It was four o'clock in the morning, and all the brothers were asleep, except Max, still burning his midnight oil. Suddenly he screamed, took up his book, and threw it into the corner. He ran to the window and opened it, leaned out, and yelled into the dark and sleeping alley, "Stop shining those lights in my eyes!" He then ran all over the fraternity house, shouting the same remark.

His fraternity brothers woke up. They tried to quiet him, but Max was irrational, confused, and delirious. Several of the brothers managed to subdue him by force—it took several of them to do it—and they dragged him down to student health. The physician on call there hastily summoned an ambulance with attendants and a strait jacket. Max was rushed to a nearby psychiatric institution and committed. They sedated him and restrained him and gave him soothing baths. Finally, he went to sleep.

Max slept steadily for almost two consecutive days. He woke up rational and normal. He was kept under observation for a few more days, to be sure that he was sane, and then released. He took his deferred examinations, did well on them, and graduated.

I don't know if Max ever had another similar acute psychotic episode. Perhaps he did, or perhaps he learned his lesson. One lesson to be learned: the best way to prepare for examinations, or any other day of crisis, is to get a good night's sleep.

Max is a typical example of the effects of sleep deprivation, a phenomenon which has been studied in the laboratory intensively in recent years. Loss of sleep, and especially loss of that phase of sleep called REM sleep, will characteristically produce psychotic manifestations in a normal volunteer after a certain length of time. Some are more susceptible to REM sleep loss than others; the particular type of psychotic expression will vary from one individual to another; but the seed of psychosis lies in us all. Sleep loss and stress can bring it out.

Ned (Case 15)

Ned was a soldier, an infantryman in one of the several shooting wars of the last half century. Ned was a good soldier, endowed with normal endurance, courage, and discipline. He had shown no previous signs of emotional instability or psychosis.

Ned went into combat with his unit and, with them, was caught in one of the horrible situations characteristic of infantry warfare. The unit was pinned down for days and nights at a time. Casualties were heavy. Ned endured these highly stressful conditions for nearly a week, but then he reached his end point. Suddenly he screamed, threw away his rifle, jumped out of his foxhole, and ran to the rear echelon. He somehow avoided being hit, managed to break through the enemy encirclement, and continued running through friendly territory. He ran to the point of physical exhaustion and then collapsed in a ditch. He was found there, weeping, shuddering, delirious, and psychotic.

Ned is a typical example of a condition seen in soldiers since the first day of battle: the acute psychosis of the foot soldier caught under battle conditions too long. In World War I, the condition was called "shell shock." In World War II, and subsequently, it has been known as "combat fatigue."

The management of this condition is different, and considerably more successful, now, than in World War I. Then the patient was evacuated and taken to psychiatric installations far from the combat zone. The patient was hospitalized under intensive therapy for long periods of time. Treatment was with psychotherapy, with sedation and restraint, and with such techniques known as "truth serum" and "twilight sleep," both being forms of suggestion given to the heavily sedated patient. The results of treatment were, in general, poor. Many patients were evacuated and institutionalized in this country for years; a few of them still may be seen as permanent asylum residents. Most of them had to be discharged from the service for psychiatric reasons, and many have been psychological cripples ever since.

Ned, fighting in more modern times, was given better treatment. He was taken to the rear, but not far, to a rest and recreation center as near as possible to the front. He was not hospitalized. He was given a brief counseling interview. Sleeping pills were offered him, but he didn't want them. What he wanted was a hot shower, clean clothes, hot food, letters from home, a dry bed, and the chance to be left alone. These things were available in the rest and recreation center, which was its purpose.

The acute psychosis with its confusion and delirium disappeared overnight. Ned was nervous for two or three days, but soon he was wondering about his buddies at the front. By the end of the week, he wanted to go back. He requested return to his unit. The request was granted. Ned saw a good deal more combat before the end of the war, but he had no further attacks of combat fatigue, and no further psychiatric difficulty either in service or upon return to civilian life.

The acute psychosis of the combat soldier is obviously the same sort of disorder that we saw in Max, the medical student burning his midnight oil. It is due in part to loss of REM sleep, which produces the physiological disturbance of brain function causing the psychosis. In combat fatigue, additional factors of maximum strain are added.

In World War I and earlier days, the self-limited nature of this condition was not recognized. After restoration of REM sleep and a few days in a safe environment, the acute psychosis disappears. In the overtreated patient of World War I, however, acute psychosis was replaced by chronic neurosis. The soldier, confined and restrained, developed severe guilt: he had deserted and run under fire, while his buddies, under the same fire, bravely stood their ground, and would continue to stand until they were killed, wounded, or relieved. They were the brave ones. He was a coward. Such guilt feelings easily set up emotional conflict, causing neurosis. The psychosis was brief; the neurosis, however, was severe, resistant to therapy, and often permanent.

Return of the patient to his outfit as soon as the psychosis has passed prevents the neurosis. The soldier's pride and self-confidence is restored; he is still a good soldier, fit and worthy of the confidence of his buddies, and he will fight bravely and well again.

Some soldiers develop combat fatigue earlier than others under the same degree of stress. These people perhaps have a somewhat greater degree of emotional instability. But any soldier has an end point; all will develop psychosis if maximum stress is continued for a sufficient length of time.

The degree of stress alone is not the important factor. Any adjusted human, even without benefit of military training, morale, and discipline, can endure maximum stress for brief periods of time. A long period of lesser stress is more damaging than a brief one of greater degree. In April of 1966, an official Pentagon release stated that, in the entire American participation in the Vietnam conflict to that date, there had been only ten cases of combat fatigue in American troops. This sounds extraordinary in view of the fact that more than three thousand soldiers had been killed in action in that theater in this period of time. In some of the battles of World War I, casualties from shell shock exceeded the number killed in battle. Stressful situations in Vietnam have been no less stressful than in any other war. The difference is due to a different kind of warfare. Long battles were not seen in Vietnam; this was hit-and-run warfare; combat contact was limited to a few minutes or hours, and soldiers were not pinned down for days and weeks at a time. This clearly illustrates the importance of the time factor in production of this type of acute psychosis.

Oliver (Case 16)

Oliver was a middle-aged certified public accountant, quiet, conscientious, sober, and stable. He developed a bad cold one day, but, being conscientious, he went to work just the same. He coughed and sneezed, felt hot and feverish, but he did his job. Oliver's cold grew worse for each of the next three days. On the fourth day, he suddenly left his account books, took off his green eyeshade and, removing his clothes, went singing and dancing all over the office, stark naked.

This behavior did not go unnoticed. Oliver was promptly restrained. It took force to restrain him, for he was violent, confused, and irrational. Was Oliver drunk? There was no smell of liquor to his breath. Perhaps the years of adding and subtracting figures had made him flip his lid, for surely he was crazy.

Oliver promptly found himself in a mental hospital. There he was examined. Fortunately it was by a psychiatrist who remembered something about medicine, who was aware that the body can influence the mind, just as the mind influences the body. Not all psychiatrists do remember physical disease. Touching Oliver, this one discovered that the patient's skin was hot and dry. A thermometer was obtained. Oliver had a fever in excess of 105°. Medical consultation was requested, and it was discovered that Oliver had lobar pneumonia.

Treated with penicillin, he quickly recovered from the pneumonia. At the same time, he recovered from his psychosis. He became again, and remained, a quiet and stable certified public accountant. Oliver never again removed all his clothing in a public place.

Pauline (Case 17)

Pauline was a strict and autocratic grandmother, pillar of church and community, Victorian by principle, something of a self-appointed censor in regard to community morals.

She had been bothered for many years by vague indigestion: X rays and tests had shown this to be of a functional nature, unassociated with physical disease. Her physician, an ancient and venerable practitioner, had prescribed Triple Bromides, an ancient and venerable elixir for functional disease of many kinds. Pauline had used this prescription regularly for years. In addition she took a proprietary over-the-counter preparation, widely advertised, which consists of bromides in an effervescent tablet.

In late middle life, a personality change came slowly over Pauline. Her mind remained keen. Her grasp on reality and her orientation seemed as strong as ever except in one respect: she, long a guardian of moral propriety, developed an alarming fondness for dirty jokes and she started using language that would make a sailor blush. Her vocabulary, perhaps appropriate in the madam of a bordello, was obviously inappropriate for

Pauline. When she told an especially gamy anecdote to the minister at a church tea, she was taken, quietly but firmly, to a psychiatrist.

The psychiatrist personally was not offended by her jokes. In fact, he rather enjoyed them. But in Pauline they seemed to represent signs of an early psychosis. He persuaded her to enter his private sanatorium.

In the sanatorium, with no specific therapy, she gradually improved. Apparently she had some sort of self-limited psychosis. The psychiatrist was a man of inquiring mind and he kept looking for a physical cause for her emotional disease. He discovered that Pauline had been ingesting bromides regularly for many years, in the elixir prescribed by her physician and in the proprietary she had purchased over-the-counter. At the sanatorium she had received no bromides.

Bromides are a mild sedative which, in small doses, are useful and safe. This is a cumulative drug, however, which piles up in the system when usage is prolonged, and when drug levels get too high, toxicity results. A characteristic manifestation of bromide toxicity is psychosis.

Other mild safer sedatives were substituted for bromides in the future. In future, Pauline's language would not have made any sailor blush.

George (Case 18)

George was a jazz composer, an exceptionally brilliant and original one. Many of his popular songs have become incorporated into the American heritage and his few classical compositions won him a unique place in musical history.

George was an intense and active man, the sort of man who might be prone to emotional disturbance, but for most of his life he was very sane. He moved in the fast circles of Broadway and Hollywood where neurosis is an accepted fact of life. Many of his friends were in analysis. Therefore, when, in early middle life, George developed periods of confusion and memory loss, it was natural for him to consult an analyst. The man he chose, though well trained in psychoanalysis, was not a physician and had no medical training. The analyst presumed that George's troubles were emotional and George entered analysis.

Shortly thereafter, George developed blinding headaches. He then sought medical advice. Neurological study showed abnormality; George was subjected to surgery; a brain tumor was discovered; George died immediately after surgery.

George's last name was Gershwin.

Quentin (Case 19)

Quentin was a retired railroad employee. He adjusted well to retirement, keeping busy with many hobbies and recreations, enjoying a reasonable pension.

Television came into Quentin's area for the first time, and he got himself a television set. He enjoyed television and watched it by the hour. His reaction to the entertainment on the little screen was not, however, normal. Quentin seemed to believe that he was watching, not electronic images, but real little people living in a box whom he was watching through a window. This might have been dismissed as an old man's harmless fancy, but it was not harmless. The little people began to dominate his life. He tried to feed them through the back of the set and became disturbed when they would not eat. He tried to talk to them and became angry when they would not reply. Finally he smashed the glass in an attempt to let them out. His behavior in other respects became disoriented and irrational, and it was necessary to commit him to the state mental hospital where he passed the last few years of his life.

Television may be responsible for certain problems in contemporary life but it cannot be made the villain for Quentin's breakdown. He had arteriosclerosis of the blood vessels of the brain. Without television, Quentin would have shown the first manifestation of psychosis in some other way.

Psychosis may be caused, directly or indirectly, by physical disease of almost any kind. It is seen in association with infection, such as the pneumonia in Oliver's case; there may be direct disease of brain, as in the case of George Gershwin and of Quentin; it may be due to a toxic substance or poison of almost any kind, as in the case of Pauline. It is difficult to think of any physical disturbance which, at times, is not associated with psychosis.

The outlook of psychosis depends upon the outlook of the physical disease and whether or not permanent brain injury has been sustained. If the disease is curable or self-limited and permanent brain damage has not occurred, the psychosis will be temporary.

In the management of psychosis, a physical examination is mandatory. The possibility of a curable physical disease causing the psychosis must be explored. For this reason, I feel that psychiatric diagnosis should only be attempted by a physician. Workers in the field without medical training— the clinical psychologist, the non-medical analyst—may be well qualified to do psychological testing and to treat psychiatric disease, but they are insufficiently trained for diagnosis. This sort of non-medical worker may miss the brain tumor or the pneumonia or the bromide intoxication. In the case of George Gershwin it is not possible to say whether accurate diagnosis at an earlier stage would have led to successful surgery and saved his life, but this is at least a possibility. Gershwin was only thirty-eight years old at the time of his death, apparently just approaching full development of a highly original and creative talent, and his loss, if indeed it was theoretically preventable, was a tragedy.

Why does one patient with pneumonia go psychotic while most pneumonia patients do not? We can only speculate, but presumably some of us are closer to the threshold for psychosis than others. Why does one psychotic patient remove his clothes, another tell dirty jokes, still another see real little people in his television set? Again we only speculate, but perhaps each of us has specific areas of potential emotional conflict, similar to those which cause neurosis, where a psychosis will be expressed when the brain is sufficiently diseased. In other words, perhaps, the expression of psychosis and the cause of neurosis lie in the same general plot of ground. There are experts who maintain that there is no difference between neurosis and psychosis. Such people make no distinction between sanity and insanity and would classify us all on a scale of relative insanity, I suppose. To me, the line between sanity and insanity is quite real and clear, and I have come to believe that insanity implies physical or physiological disease of the brain. Could neurosis also be the reflection of physiological disease of brain? Will we in time abandon the concept of subconscious emotional conflict? Perhaps. I'm inclined to think that there is physiological brain disturbance in neurosis, but that it is secondary, and that the emotional conflict is primary and real. I think that the expression of psychosis in a given individual is dictated by the weakest area of his emotional balance, and therefore psychosis and neurosis, while disorders of different systems, are correlated. Body, mind, and emotion interplay; the human is a unity.

7

The Remote Ones

There are two common serious and important psychoses, with characteristic psychotic disorientation and irrationality during acute phases, in which no clear evidence of associated physical brain disease had been discovered until quite recently. The exact nature of the brain disturbance has not yet been clarified, but recent laboratory evidence has given us valuable clues. One of these two conditions is manic-depressive disease, both phases of which we have discussed. The other is schizophrenia, the subject of this chapter.

The depressed phase of manic-depressive psychosis may be considered potentially fatal, because of the inherent risk of suicide. The manic phase produces a wake of social catastrophe. Schizophrenia does not carry appreciable risk of suicide; although in one type of schizophrenia, violence is a real and present danger, the majority of schizophrenics do not disturb their fellow man. Schizophrenia is, however, the great disabler among psychoses. We have noted that manic-depressive disease is cyclic, with a return to normality following a crisis in either direction to be expected in the natural course of the disease. Not so with schizophrenia: this is a chronic disease and the natural course is apt to be permanent disability or increasing deterioration. Manic-depressive disease is a condition of middle or later life. Schizophrenia, typically, is a disease of the young, with onset in early adult life, adolescence, and, not infrequently, in children. Given the early onset and the chronic nature of the disease, schizophrenia may seriously disable the useful life of the individual for many decades.

I was taught in medical school that ten percent of the population will be, at one time or another, patients in an institution for the insane; I doubt if the figure is any less today and it may well be greater. I was taught that between a quarter and a third of the patients in mental institutions are permanent residents who will not be returned to society. This figure is improved today, thanks to newer therapy techniques, but perhaps one percent of our total population are permanent asylum residents who remain confined for the rest of their lives. Approximately half of these are schizophrenics. Schizophrenia constitutes from fifteen to twenty percent of first admissions to public mental hospitals. This constitutes a formidable amount of disability, and makes schizophrenia by far the most important and serious psychosis.

The condition was first recognized as a disease entity about a hundred years ago and was first called "dementia praecox." This term was used for fifty years and still crops up today. It does not seem like a valid term. It means early or precocious dementia; while the condition, in common with psychosis in general, is characterized by dementia, and while it does have an early onset, "dementia praecox" would imply that mental deterioration is a normal consequence of aging, which is not necessarily the case, and that schizophrenia is a process of precocious mental aging, which again is not the case.

In 1911, the word "schizophrenia" was introduced and has become the generally accepted diagnostic term. Schizophrenia means, literally, "splitting of the mind." While something of this general nature does occur, schizophrenia isn't a very accurate diagnostic label either. There is apt to be confusion with personality splitting, a different sort of disorder, quite rare and fascinating, where two or more different and distinct personalities occur alternatively in the same individual. Personality splitting, because of its interesting manifestations, has received a lot of attention in the literature, both professional and lay, but we will not discuss it here because of the rarity of the condition. One case in particular has been studied at length, the case made famous by the book called *Three Faces of Eve*. As an incidental note, I once met Eve in one of her personalities during one of her many stays in a mental institution. Although personality splitting has certain features in common with schizophrenia, it is usually considered a disease of its own.

A feasible way to attack our consideration of schizophrenia would be through introduction of the terms "introvert" and "extravert." These words were coined by the great Swiss psychiatrist Jung—and I use Jung's original spelling of "extravert" rather than the more common modern spelling "extrovert." The validity of these terms has been accepted, and they have entered common parlance. We recognize the extravert as the doer, energetic and sociable, who concerns himself with deeds and people and the externals of environment. The introvert is the thinker: shy, contemplative, and reserved.

Jung originally hoped to classify personality on the basis of inwardness and outwardness and he subdivided extraverts and introverts into four types of each, a total of eight classes. However, such a classification is arbitrary and complex, and has not been generally accepted. There are many other personality facets. If we accept that some people tend to be more extraverted and some more introverted, the concept is useful and we need not carry it any further.

As a generality, manic-depressive disease is seen in extraverted people. Schizophrenia is seen in introverts. If you take the typical picture of the introvert—the absent-minded professor, the ivory tower philosopher, the confused bewildered shy teen-ager, the artistic recluse—and magnify the manifestations to a pathological degree, you have drawn the portrait of a schizophrenic.

Robert (Case 20)

Robert was a shy, brilliant, preoccupied college student, who placed high scholastically and low in social adaptability. He came to the attention of the university authorities in his junior year when his grades, previously excellent, dropped to flunking levels. He seldom came to class, and, when he did, he slept. He did not often speak when spoken to, and his replies were shallow, flat, and inappropriate. He seemed to retreat into himself, losing contact with the outside environment. He was preoccupied, remote, apathetic, inactive. His classmates considered him "way out," "far off on Cloud 9."

Brought to the attention of the student health physician, then to a psychiatrist attached to the university, and finally committed to a public mental institution, he remained a permanent resident of that institution. In the asylum he remained to himself. He was docile and easy to manage; he showed no hallucinations, delusions, or violent tendencies; but he did not speak or mingle or mix. He lived alone, completely inside himself, completely out of touch with anything beyond himself.

Susan (Case 21)

Susan was a high school girl, shy, retiring, and rather silly. She was a giggler. Although she laughed frequently, her laughter was inappropriate and she did not really seem to have a sense of humor. She became moody, seclusive, preoccupied, irritable, careless. Her schoolwork became completely inadequate, and she had to be withdrawn from school. She began to have delusions and hallucinations, at times feeling that she was the Virgin Mary about to be visited by the Angel Gabriel, at other times convinced that her family was trying to poison her. Her speech became incoherent; she was given to dramatic posturing and gestures, often accompanied by laughter. She regressed toward childhood in her toilet training, wetting and soiling her bed, and she ate in a ravenous animal fashion, like a pig at a trough, despite her conviction that the food was poisoned. She too had to be committed to a public institution and became a permanent resident. She was silly, childish, remote, inaccessible, resistive, and difficult to manage. A great deal of the time, she laughed.

Tony (Case 22)

Tony, a service station attendant, worked for a couple of years following graduation from high school. He seemed well adjusted and showed no evidence of psychiatric difficulty. He then married his high school sweetheart. Immediately after the honeymoon, Tony suffered an alarming personality change. He became suspicious and hostile, developing hallucinations and delusions; he believed that a group of conspirators from the planet Mars was out to get him; he described them as little green men with powerful radar antennae directed against him; they were trying to destroy him with radio waves. He got so excited, noisy, disturbed, confused, and violent that he had to be committed to the asylum in a strait jacket.

In the asylum, Tony went into a curious state of semi-coma. He lay motionless and would not respond to questions or directions or painful stimuli. His limbs assumed strange rigid postures. If you placed one of his extremities in a bizarre elevated position, which a normal person could not hold for more than a few minutes, the extremity would remain in that position for hours at a time. He would not eat and had to be fed with a tube. He would not speak. He was incontinent of urine and feces. This state was a permanent condition.

These cases—Robert, Susan, Tony—show three common patterns of schizophrenia. Robert may be said to have simple schizophrenia, characterized by remoteness, showing a pathological degree of introversion without other typical schizophrenic manifestations. This pathological introversion is characteristic and diagnostic of schizophrenia.

Susan had a specific type of schizophrenia called hebephrenia, sometimes considered a disease of its own, but usually thought of as a schizophrenic variant. Hebephrenia, literally, means youthfulness of mind; it is characterized by retrogression of mind, emotions, and habits toward childhood and infancy. Typically, the hebephrenic patient shows a pathological and inappropriate silliness. We have discussed a milder case of hebephrenia earlier, Irene, the giggler, in Chapter 4.

Tony shows a characteristic schizophrenic manifestation not infrequently seen, the bizarre trance-like state which is called catatonia.

There is another very frequent symptom of schizophrenia, the so-called paranoid reaction, which implies pathological suspicion and inappropriate feelings of persecution often associated with delusions and hallucinations. Susan and Tony showed some paranoid symptoms, although Robert did not. Paranoid reactions are seen in other conditions than schizophrenia but commonly are seen in this disease. We will discuss the paranoid reaction in more detail in the next chapter.

No man is an island, said John Donne. The schizophrenic patient acts as if he were trying to become an island. He withdraws into himself, abandoning contact with others and the exterior environment. His emotions become flat and inappropriate. He is apt to substitute abstract intellectualization for emotional rapport with other people. His major difficulty appears to lie in contact and communication with others. He may not attempt to communicate and may resist attempts to communicate with him. When he does try communication, his thought patterns are illogical, irrational, disturbed, confused.

The schizophrenic often acts as if he had little or no interest or concern in the world about him. He fails to show the expected emotional reaction to exterior events. It often appears that his emotions are dampened, superficial, or even lacking. However, when he does attempt communication, he reveals a rich vivid emotional inner life of fantasy which is in marked contrast to the barren poverty of his exterior relationships. The speech of a schizophrenic attempting to communicate is garbled, lacking in logic and consistency; it has been called a "word salad." When he writes down his thoughts—many schizophrenics have potential gifts in language arts and many would rather write than speak—the writing is very much like that of the fictional technique called the "stream of consciousness." Such books as *Ulysses* and *Finnegan's Wake* by James Joyce closely resemble writing by schizophrenic patients. Similarly, when they draw—and many schizophrenic patients have potential artistic gifts—the drawing is like that called surrealistic, resembling work by such artists as Salvadore Dali. Books by Joyce and paintings by Dali cannot be dismissed as the products of a schizophrenic mind because of a central core of cohesion and because of the positive communications to others achieved by such books and paintings, but stream of consciousness and surrealism are very close to schizophrenic expressions.

The delusions, hallucinations, and fantasies of the schizophrenic often have an obvious sexual coloration. The schizophrenic often breaks down in adolescence or early adult life coincident with or soon after the first direct confrontation with the phenomenon of sex. Sex is an intense interior experience to the individual; it is also an intense exterior experience related to another person. The schizophrenic's instinctive approach is inward and not outward; his instinctive sexual expression is onanistic; it might be fair to say that schizophrenia is an onanistic sort of disease.

People with full-blown schizophrenia are not seen on the streets; the profound nature of the disturbance makes them unable to take care of themselves, and custodial care in an institution is required. For this reason, the average person seldom meets the schizophrenic, although schizophrenics are relatively common. On the other hand, since institutions are full of schizophrenics, the therapists attached to institutions see a great deal of the condition; fully half of their patients may be schizophrenic. Because of the enormous volume of case material, schizophrenia has been studied in greater detail than any other psychiatric condition, and conclusions drawn from study of the schizophrenic dominate the professional psychiatric literature. The expert is rather apt to build his theories of emotional disease and health from observation of the schizophrenic. Since the expert is talking about a condition he sees frequently, which the average citizen sees rarely, perhaps it is no wonder that the theories and conclusions of the expert sound very strange indeed to the rest of us.

• Most of the life of the schizophrenic is interior thinking and fantasy; much of it involves use of symbolism; much of it concerns sex. Accordingly, such concepts as the Oedipus complex, castration fears, penis envy, phallic symbols, and the other trappings of the dynamic school of thought often seem applicable to the schizophrenic; however, they seem inapplicable to other types of psychosis and neurosis and to the emotional life of the man on the street. It is for this reason, I believe, that the mythology of Freudianism is so attractive to specialists seeing much schizophrenia, and so fantastic, artificial, and inappropriate to the rest of us. It might be reasonable to point out that much psychiatric professional literature is based on the bizarre weird communications from bizarre weird patients whose disorder is in the area of communication. It is not valid to presume that all people think as schizophrenics think; the dynamic mythology is not appropriate when applied to neurotic and to normal emotional expression.

We have noted a mild form of mania in persons not psychotic called hypomania. We have noted that hypomaniacs are frequently busy, happy, and successful people.

Let us now take note of the personality which resembles schizophrenia but in which there is no psychosis. This has been called the schizoid type of personality. Like the hypo-maniac, the schizoid person retains his rationality and is sane. Hypomaniacs, we have noted, are the doers. Schizoids are the thinkers. Schizoids tend to be highly intelligent and highly artistic but not highly social, not very productive, and not very successful. They withdraw into academic groves or ivory towers or into the solitary haunts of the recluse. Here, they may produce, in small quantity, work of high quality or distinction. The work is apt to be in such fields as philosophy, theoretical mathematics, theology (of the mystical rather than the pastoral type), scientific research (theoretical, not applied), or the more private of the art forms where the creator works alone. These people have little interest in material success and are poor busi-nessmen. They may become famous or successful or both because of the high quality of their work, but they handle fame and fortune poorly. In general, schizoids do not make good teachers, good friends, or good mates.

We have noted that many schizophrenic patients are long term or permanent residents of mental institutions. We have also noted that schizophrenia has been more intensively studied than any psychiatric condition. These facts, added together, equal an obvious conclusion: schizophrenics react to treatment poorly. If psychoanalysis or psychotherapy of the so-called dynamic school ever had the opportunity to prove itself, it should be in schizophrenia, but in schizo-phrenia this type of treatment fails. The reason for the failure should be obvious: talking and listening are not ap-propriate when at least one of the two parties cannot talk or listen rationally. It is surprising that many experts still are unable to accept this rather obvious conclusion.

Today, many schizophrenics, once permanent asylum resi-dents, are being returned to society. The better results today are due to drugs, the relatively new family of drugs called tranquilizers.

In small doses, tranquilizers are useful in calming anxiety

in neurotics. For good results in schizophrenia, much higher doses are required, doses too high to be tolerated by the average neurotic. This suggests a specific effect of the drug in schizophrenia.

Discovery of the tranquilizer family of drugs came about in a devious and indirect fashion. In India, for many thousands of years, an herbal root had been used by primitive peoples with good results in certain conditions. Investigation of this folk remedy proved it to have a sound pharmacological basis, which is often the case when folk medicines are studied. Primarily, the drug was found to be useful in lowering blood pressure in hypertension; imported to this country, various derivatives of the Indian snake root have proved to be an important drug, perhaps the basic drug, in present treatment of hypertension. Indian snake root drugs apparently lower blood pressure partly by slowing pulse rate and partly by inducing a mood of tranquilization. Study of the tranquilizing effects led to discovery of other different chemicals producing the same tranquilizing effect.

The effect of tranquilization is not fully understood but appears to be related to certain chemicals, especially an amine called serotonin, another amine called norepinephrine (which has an action partly opposite and partly similar to the hormone commonly called adrenaline), and an enzyme called monoamine oxidase. We have mentioned these amines without naming them and have mentioned the enzyme by name in connection with drugs useful in depression, stating that the enzyme destroys the amines, and that psychic energizers (MAO inhibitors) seem to work in overcoming depression by inhibiting the action of the enzyme. The development of the drugs for depression came after the investigation of the drugs we are now talking about, the tranquilizers.

Serotonin, norepinephrine, and monoamine oxidase are found naturally throughout the body. They are in high concentration in the primitive part of the brain stem called the hypothalamus. We have noted that the hypothalamus appears to be the seat of emotional reaction, also the probable location of the mechanism causing the biological clock phenomenon. One might say that the hypothalamus was the happy hunting ground of the id, so to speak.

In the hypothalamus, presumably, a complex metabolic reaction involving serotonin, norepinephrine, and monoamine oxidase (and no doubt other substances as well) influences emotional reaction. When this reaction gets out of balance, psychiatric disorder results. We have seen how the same system is involved in depression. We note now that it is apparently implicated in schizophrenia. One group of the tranquilizer family of drugs blocks the action of norepinephrine. Another family of tranquilizers stimulates serotonin effect. Presumably this is why they work. And presumably a disturbance in the reaction of the amines—excess norepinephrine action, or decreased serotonin action—is part of the physical brain disease in schizophrenia. Clinicians have always had a tendency to consider schizophrenia and manic-depressive disease as psychoses of a somewhat similar nature. Laboratory evidence has tended to confirm this impression and it has also led to useful specific drugs to treat both the depression of manic-depressive disease and schizophrenia.

The hallucinatory family of drugs, especially LSD, apparently causes interference of the same amine-enzyme balance in the hypothalamus. The toxic psychosis so often caused by LSD acts very much like an artificially induced schizophrenia. We will discuss hallucinatory drugs later in another connection.

Recent research suggests that a vitamin—nicotinamide or Vitamin B3—and its derivatives may be of value in treating some schizophrenics resistant to tranquilizers. A Canadian worker in the field, who is both a psychiatrist and a biochemist (a combination of specialties which would have sounded very strange a few years ago but which sounds most appropriate today), believes that nicotinamide and derivatives are important in the epinephrine-norepinephrine system of the body, tied in with this same biochemical reaction we have been discussing. He believes that disturbance of this reaction produces hallucinations, anxiety, catatonia, and disturbed levels of consciousness: the symptoms seen in schizophrenia. We know of two diseases where nicotinamide deficiency produces trouble: pellagra (a dietary deficiency disease) and alcoholism (where there is also a dietary disturbance). Hallucinations with psychosis are part of the pellagra picture. A hallucinatory psychosis is also seen in certain phases of chronic alcoholism. So many clues of information from the laboratories of the biochemists begin to interlock and increase our understanding of psychosis.

It would now begin to seem that Jung's conception of introvert and extravert has a biochemical basis. We see schizophrenia in introverts and manic-depressive disease in extraverts, and we have also seen similar biochemical disturbances which may be related to the cause of these psychoses.

In light of the newer biochemical clues, it seems even less likely that talking-listening therapy techniques would be of value in psychoses like schizophrenia and manic-depressive disease. The thought of trying to influence a biochemical reaction by talking to it, or listening to it, reminds one of King Canute talking to the tides.

8

The Dangerous Ones

The days of the snakepit, fortunately, have gone. We do not cast lunatics into dungeons because we are afraid of them; now, we realize they are sick; we try to understand the sickness and treat it if we can. However, a superstition, a vague fear or dread of contact with emotionally disturbed persons, is hard to shake. We have an instinctive feeling of danger when we meet such people.

In the vast majority of cases, disturbed people, even raving lunatics, are not dangerous to deal with, especially if you understand the problem and have experience handling sick people. The most delirious person will sense kindness and react to it, just as he may sense fear and strike out against it. Patience, gentleness, understanding, self-confidence, and quiet firmness of command will enable one to deal with violently disturbed people just as these same qualities will produce success in any situation.

It would not be fair, however, to say that disturbed persons are never dangerous. Is there any human being, disturbed or sane, who is not potentially dangerous under certain circumstances? In delirious psychotics, violence and danger is quite obvious on the surface. Obvious danger can usually be controlled because one is prepared for it. Quiet danger, hidden danger, masked danger catches us unawares and therefore is more dangerous than the violence which loudly shouts its name.

This chapter will concern certain types of disturbance which are dangerous because the danger is not obvious. These people do not seem disturbed; the acts of aggression and violence erupt suddenly, without warning, like a snake which strikes without a rattle. This sort of danger can be met only when the personality disturbance is recognized as carrying latent violence.

Victor (Case 23)

Victor was a war veteran. He brought home with him a trophy, a revolver once belonging to an enemy officer; proud of this weapon, he often carried it around with him.

Victor was quiet to begin with. After discharge from service, he was quieter than ever: remote and seclusive, definitely a "loner." He was known to have had a rough time in combat, and people made allowances.

He was a rather suspicious person. From time to time, he spoke as if he had some secret knowledge. Perhaps he was an agent or a spy, engaged in some secret mission for the government; he spoke as if this might be the case. He had been heard to remark that he had to be careful, that certain people and organizations were out to get him; he gave this as his reason for carrying a gun.

One day, Victor was seated in a barbershop, having a haircut. Suddenly, for no good reason, he pulled his revolver out from under the sheet; without provocation or warning, he shot the barber; he shot the barber and customer in the other chair; he shot two waiting customers, and, with the final bullet, shot himself. The shooting was over in twenty seconds. The score: three dead, including Victor, two seriously wounded, one slightly wounded. His motivation for this burst of homicidal insanity was not known and must remain a matter of speculation. It was known that Victor was a good shot.

Although insanity was not suspected prior to Victor's death and therefore exploration of Victor's disturbances could not be made, it may be presumed with reasonable accuracy that Victor was schizophrenic. His remoteness and pathological suspicions give this clue. Certainly he was paranoid. Paranoid manifestations may be seen in any psychosis, or in neurosis, but are particularly characteristic of the schizophrenic.

Once again, we must make an excursion into semantics. The word paranoid means "like paranoia." Paranoia, literally, means outside of or beyond the mind. The term is used to refer to a specific condition, probably a psychosis, perhaps a personality disorder, which is fascinating and rare. True paranoia implies that the patient has a system of interlocking ideas which are divorced from what the rest of us consider reality. This system is based on a single premise which we consider to be unrealistic and false, but all the interlocking ideas based on the premise are perfectly logical and rational if the original premise happened to be true. The true paranoiac is often not suspicious, often not dangerous, often able to make good social adjustments, and he is normal in every way except for his delusional system. He may think that he is Napoleon, and, if you could grant the fact that he was Napoleon, all his adjustments and ideas are perfectly consistent for Napoleon. He may think that he is in contact with the spirit world, or that he has the gift of prophecy. A fascinating example of true paranoia was General George S. Patton, Jr. Patton was a military genius, obviously successful in his profession and considered sane. However, Patton believed—completely and thoroughly believed—that he had been alive since the beginning of history, that he had always been a soldier, and that he personally had participated in many famous historical battles. His recollections of his previous lives were unearthly. Sometimes conducting modern battles at the scene of an ancient battle, Patton seemed to know the terrain from *déjà vu,* although in this life he had never been there before. He often won modern battles by applying strategy which had been used (and which he believed he himself had used) in ancient battles.

Paranoid reactions, distinguished from the rare true paranoia, are fairly common. There is a delusional system—interlocking ideas based on a false premise but logical if the premise were true. In addition, in the paranoid reaction, there is a feeling of persecution and pathological suspicion. The true paranoiac may feel somewhat persecuted and somewhat suspicious of the world because nobody else seems to accept the delusion which he himself knows to be true; but his usual reaction is that of a smug superiority on account of the secret knowledge he alone possesses. The paranoid patient, on the other hand, has an element of fear and aggression; the elements of his delusion threaten, rather than help, him, and he strikes out against the delusion in an irrational and dangerous way. The true paranoiac glories in the secret knowledge that he has fought in all the battles of history and uses this knowledge to win a present battle. The paranoid patient, under observation of the radar apparatus of the little green men from Mars, may strike out against an innocent passer-by whom he thinks is a green man from Mars. A good many of the illogical acts of violence we read about are acts of paranoid people striking back against their delusional systems. The paranoid reaction, particularly common in schizophrenia, is particularly dangerous in schizophrenia, because the schizophrenic is characteristically remote and inaccessible; he does not communicate his delusions, suspicions, and feelings of persecutions in a way that others recognize as dangerous; when he strikes out against his delusions, the act may be completely unexpected, out of the clear blue sky. A paranoid schizophrenic is one of the most dangerous of all human beings, and his danger is often completely unrecognized.

Incidentally, symptoms of persecution and suspicion are

not pathological if the persecution is real and the suspicion justified. I vividly remember a little old lady who consulted me, complaining that, in the house where she was employed as cook, there were gangsters planning murders, running narcotic rings, and organizing jewel robberies. She had taken her suspicions to the police, but they had laughed at her. I took her suspicions as a paranoid reaction, and I was afraid she might commit an act of illogical violence against her employer. I attempted to steer her into the hands of a psychiatrist, without result. Her employment was temporary, for one summer only, and after she left the job she had no further feelings of persecution and suspicion. Some years later, to my chagrin, I discovered that my patient's suspicions happened to be true. Her employer that summer was the beautiful and notorious Virginia Hill, mistress to the underworld, friend of the subsequently murdered Buggsy Siegel, key witness in the Kefauver crime investigations of 1951, who after a lurid life finally committed suicide in March of 1966.

William (Case 24)

William was an average red-blooded American boy. Dangerous? Who would think so? He was just a little wild, that's all; no evidence of psychosis, neurosis, or personality disturbance. He drove too fast in an automobile. Doesn't every American boy drive an automobile too fast?

One Saturday night, William went to a dance in the family car. Returning from the dance in the wee hours with a carload of friends, William had an accident. His car struck a utility pole at a high rate of speed. All occupants of the car were killed: seven dead, including William.

This case is by no means unusual. Accidental death upon the highway is, as everybody knows, appallingly high. We kill far more people with the automobile than we ever do in war. Why should William be included in a chapter on dangerous disturbances?

I think there is a sort of person who could fairly be called an automobile murderer. I think he is appallingly common. I think that he is among our most dangerous citizens, that his danger is due to emotional disturbance, and that his disturbance is largely unrecognized.

There has been a great deal written and said recently about the intrinsic mechanical danger of the American automobile. It is true that American manufacturers have put style ahead of safety in the cars they make; it is equally true, as auto manufacturers say in their own defense, that they can't sell safety and that the public will not pay the extra cost of safety devices. Certainly, an occasional car comes off the assembly line mechanically imperfect and unsafe; certainly, entire lines and models will be mechanically defective; one can hardly expect perfection even from uniform products of an assembly line or expect uniform perfection of every design from every engineer. It is my own opinion, however, that the American automobile is safe when it is safely used. Accidents are caused by driver or owner error, sometimes by neglect of maintenance and periodic mechanical check-ups, usually by mistakes of the man behind the wheel.

A careful investigation was made in William's accident. Post-mortem blood alcohol determinations revealed that William was sober. Alcohol and auto accidents have a high degree of correlation, according to some studies very high. Some safety-minded persons have concluded that stringent control and punishment of the drinking driver is the best attack on the problem of highway death. I don't agree. We will discuss alcoholism later in more detail, but in general I think that alcohol brings out manifestations of an inner disturbance already present but does not itself cause the disturbance. I do not think that the moderate social drinker, after a couple of cocktails or a few beers, is dangerous behind the wheel. If such a man has had too many, he knows it, and he drives very slowly and very carefully. He may nick a fender in a parking lot or miss his own garage door, but he is rarely involved in a serious accident. In fact, there is some evidence to suggest that small quantities of alcohol improve a driver's ability, especially the sort of driver who is tense and nervous at the wheel; the relaxing effect of small alcohol consumption on such a driver improves his performance.

One major highway danger is the chronic alcoholic behind the wheel. These are common and it is they who boost the statistical correlation of accidents and high blood alcohols.

The other highway danger of alcohol is in the person we are now discussing, the automobile murderer, who has an emotional disturbance. Alcohol brings out the disturbance but does not cause it. These people, dangerous when sober, are more dangerous when drinking. The safe driver remains safe after his social drink.

William's accident happened on a bright moonlight night. The pavement was bare and dry. Traffic was thin. The accident occurred on a long straightaway. In other words, good night driving conditions prevailed. In my experience, far more driving accidents happen under good conditions than when the conditions are bad. I live in a cold climate where our winters are severe. We don't have our bad accidents during blizzards; we have them when the weather is good. There are many people in my area who must drive in connection with their work, no matter what the weather: doctors, truck drivers, taxi drivers, traveling salesmen, police, firemen, ambulance drivers. These men almost never seem to have a serious accident. It isn't weather or road; it's that man behind the wheel.

In the investigation of William's case, it was learned that he had been spurned by a young woman at the dance. The last hour at the dance, he had been burning mad. He left the dance, infuriated, and he drove away, mad, and he hit the telephone pole because he was still enraged.

The dangerous guy behind that wheel is the aggressive driver, dangerous when sober, more dangerous when drinking because drinking brings out the aggression. More of them are young than old, for two reasons: the young are more apt to be aggressive than the old; and the aggressive driver may not live long enough to grow old.

The automobile is powerful. Slight pressure with the foot brings into play the power of several hundred horses. Many people use the power and speed of the automobile as an outlet for emotional aggression. They drive out of anger and hatred, and they drive to kill. The wonder is not how many accidents we have on the highway, but how few! The next time you drive, look around. See how many instances of aggressive driving you can count. You will see so many that you may be tempted to drive straight home, slowly and carefully, put the car into the garage and let it stay there.

How can we get the automobile murderer off the road? At the moment, we can't. When and if national emotional health improves, automobile accidents will be reduced. As long as emotionally crippled drivers are on the roads in great numbers, no matter what manufacturers do to the cars and no matter what legal blood alcohol level is established by the law, automobile accidents will continue to be a leading cause of death. There is only one thing the sane driver can do about it at the moment: drive defensively. Drive as if every other driver was trying to kill you. Many of them are. When you feel aggressive because of the crushing pressures of life which you cannot overcome, go hit a golf ball, or knock down candlepins in the bowling alley; yell at your wife if you dare to, or otherwise yell at the dog; but stay away from the wheel of the automobile.

Zachary (Case 25)

Zachary was clumsy. Give him a knife, and he would cut himself. Give him a hammer, and the nail he hit would be on his thumb. Ladders and Zachary were incompatible, and fenders didn't last long on his automobile. In high school chemistry, the professor felt he had to exempt Zachary from the lab; he simply caused too many accidents.

After school, Zachary found employment in heavy industry.

There was nothing on his references to indicate that he was accident prone. Eventually, Zachary was transferred to duty behind a desk, but not before he had accidentally tripped the wrong lever and dumped several tons of structural steel on a group of fellow workers, one of whom was killed.

The phenomenon of accident proneness was noticed and named many years ago. It was a fashionable problem for study and discussion for a time, but now is no longer fashionable. Some experts maintain that the syndrome does not exist, but I think it does. I have known a number of such people, and I think they are reasonably common in every environment.

These people are obviously dangerous to themselves, for their accidents cause fractures and lacerations. Interestingly, though, the accident prone person seldom kills himself or produces serious disability to himself. The condition has been considered as a suicide equivalent, but I think it is not, for almost uniformly the self-inflicted injury is not serious in these cases. The accidents, however, often are serious to other people. I think that the accident prone person is dangerous, and therefore he is included in this chapter.

Do accidents "just happen" accidentally as the name implies? Of course. People are overwhelmed by environmental forces beyond their control. People get careless and absent-minded; they attempt things for which they are not prepared or equipped; they take unnecessary chances; they display ignorance. An accident is most apt to happen when the victim is very young (he doesn't know better) or very old (his ability to handle himself isn't as good as it used to be), or drunk (with loss of judgment and reaction time), or sick, or tired, or emotionally disturbed. The average person does not have more than one or two or three major accidents in a lifetime; of course one major accident may terminate the lifetime; however, most people don't have accidents. There is the group of people who have accidents, major and minor, with steady and monotonous regularity. These people aren't infants or elderly or tired or sick or drunk at the time of the accidents; they do seem to be emotionally disturbed. The disturbance, however, is not obvious, and often goes unrecognized, which makes these people more dangerous.

The accident prone person, I have noticed, is often an extravert, but he is also insecure and lacking in self-confidence. This is a paradox, because the extravert is inclined to be secure and confident. This feature of the personality is almost diagnostic. There is a physical characteristic which, to me, is very suggestive; the muscle action of the accident prone person is overreactive, overcorrective, rigid, and jerky. When reaching to grasp an object, they tend first to overreach and then to overcorrect, and it is this jerky muscle action which causes accidents. These people walk with a rapid but erratic gait. Often strong, they are poorly coordinated. I don't know if these people have ever been studied from the point of view of muscle balance and tone, but I suspect a characteristic abnormality would be found. I don't think, however, that the jerky uncoordinated muscle tone is primary; I think it is a manifestation of a psychological disturbance; these people have erratic, jerky, and stumbling personalities. They are nice people, polite people, and they apologize frequently; they have to apologize frequently for the occurrences they cause. They seem to be saying that it is not you they are trying to injure but themselves. They seem to be self-flagellants, masochists, bound to a lifelong campaign of minor self-injury as punishment for an imagined lack of value and worth. This would make the syndrome a neurosis. It is dangerous, because innocent victims do not realize the danger of proximity to a person who is accident prone.

Aaron (Case 26)

Aaron liked fires. Living in a small town where there was a volunteer fire department to supplement the three full-time firemen, he wanted to belong to the volunteers. He was ineligible because he had not yet reached the age of twenty-one. Whenever there was a fire, however, Aaron dropped whatever he was doing and hastened to the scene.

Fires also seemed to like Aaron; they broke out in places where Aaron had just been. In the summer of his seventeenth year, there was an epidemic of fires, some of which might have been set. The fire chief looked for suspects, and Aaron's name was on the list.

One night that summer, the fire chief was patrolling and saw flames flickering around the roof of a large empty house. After placing the alarm through his car radio, he parked and got out. While waiting for the engines to arrive, he made a quick survey of the scene, and he discovered Aaron sitting in the shadows, watching the fire. Aaron was doing something which disgusted the chief but which the chief knew was diagnostic. He arrested Aaron. After the fire had been controlled, Aaron was questioned and he confessed, not only to setting this particular fire, but fourteen other fires in the preceding year and a half.

The average citizen seldom meets an arsonist. Every community has potential arsonists in residence, however, and I believe the arsonist is much more common than is generally recognized. There are many fires, and a surprising number of them are set. Some are set for insurance gain, some for malice or revenge, many out of carelessness, and quite a few by the true arsonist, of whom Aaron is an example.

The true arsonist is neurotic. He has, and this may be surprising, neurosis with sexual manifestations. He sets fires for pleasure, and the pleasure he gets is sexual; he often has an orgasm watching the flames, and he may engage in open masturbation at the scene. For this and other obvious reasons, he operates at night. To the best of my knowledge, he is exclusively male; he is usually unmarried; he is often of the adolescent or early adult age group. Some professional firemen are potential arsonists; I am not trying to suggest that members of the fire department go around setting fires, although this has been known to occur, but some firemen accept the poorly paid job which consists of long monotonous waiting periods punctuated by emergencies of great danger on account of the pleasure they find in flames. There is something compelling about flame: part life and part death, part warmth and part destruction, which engages us psychologically in the area of taboo and transgression which is the similar area to that of sexual conflict and expression.

The arsonist who expresses sexual conflict with flame destroys property. He does not intend to destroy people; selectively, in fact, he chooses structures known to be unoccupied. But fire has a tendency to get out of control. Lives are often lost. I regard the arsonist, rare though he may seem to be, as much more common than is recognized and far more dangerous than he appears to be.

The most dangerous of all personality types, I think, is the type often called psychopath, sometimes called sociopath. Difficult to understand, difficult to explain, often unrecognized, impossible to deal with, impossible to treat, and unfortunately common: the psychopath deserves a chapter of his own.

9

The Odd Ones

Old Bill (Case 27)

Old Bill was a lawyer, graduate of a reputable law school, though he had never practiced and had never taken his bar exams. It was believed that Bill had a small inheritance, for he did no regular work and was without visible means of support. He lived in alleys and flophouses in the slum area of town, a typical wandering homeless man, a bum.

Old Bill became well known to the police force of the city where he lived, although he was booked only once for a minor charge which was dismissed for lack of evidence. But every cop knew that wherever Old Bill happened to be there accidents happened. He was not accident prone; the accidents did not happen to Old Bill. People were never injured in these accidents; the damage was to property. Old Bill seemed to base his life on causing accidents for no apparent purpose except his own entertainment.

One morning, a scaffolding on a building was discovered lying in the street, and Old Bill was inspecting the remains. Another time, a trolley car ran off its tracks, and Old Bill was watching. Once, a partially finished ship in a shipyard accidentally launched itself, floated down the river for a short distance and sank; Old Bill was watching in a rowboat.

Old Bill's most spectacular accomplishment concerned a draw-bridge. One evening, the bridge was raised to permit the passage of a freighter underneath, and suddenly the bridge began to come down on top of the ship. The bridgekeeper frantically pushed all his switches and buttons, but the bridge continued to descend, squarely onto the masts of the ship, snapping them off. As usual there were no injuries, and as usual Old Bill was in the audience.

The bridgekeeper identified Old Bill. For some weeks, Old Bill had been dropping by, chatting with the bridgekeeper, but showing no apparent knowledge of or interest in the mechanism of the drawbridge. The mechanism had been tampered with, an expert job with complete rewiring of the circuits; presumably, Old Bill had done this when the keeper wasn't looking, but there was no evidence to connect him with the job.

Old Bill was a practical joker of advanced degree. The accidents he caused were funny to those not directly involved and were arranged so skillfully and carefully that there was never associated injury. Presumably Old Bill had a grudge against the world and he used his rather considerable intel-ligence and mechanical aptitude expressing his grudge in a manner appealing to his rather special sense of humor. Old Bill is an example of the psychopathic personality.

I read of the case of Old Bill in a book called *Psychiatry in General Practice* by Melvin W. Thorner. I have told the story in my own words, but the facts were taken from Dr. Thorner's book, and I used the same name for the patient, Old Bill. I am using the case for two reasons. First, it is a good story. The image of the descending drawbridge sticks in the mind. And second, I wish to indicate my gratitude to Dr. Thorner's book. He outlines his material according to personality pattern and I have used a somewhat similar method of organization in the first part of this book. Despite its formal textbook title, *Psychiatry in General Practice* is well worth reading; it is crammed with fascinating case histories told in a delightful anecdotal style. Unfortunately, the book has been out of print for many years and I have been informed by the publisher that no second printing or revision is contemplated.

The accidents caused by Old Bill were funny, at least if you weren't the owner or the captain of the ship caught by the drawbridge. In general, the psychopath is not funny. He is a terrible thorn in the side to law-enforcement agencies, policemen, judges, parole officers, wardens, psychiatrists, and social workers, to society in general, and to countless individual innocent victims in particular. The psychopath expresses his disorder by aggressive acts against society, and his conduct brings him into conflict with the law.

The word psychopath or psychopathic personality comes from the nineteenth century and is directly derived from the concepts of Cesare Lombroso, the Italian physician who was the father of modern scientific criminology. It was Lombroso's theory that there is a "criminal man" in whom moral degeneracy is associated with physical stigma. The committing of crimes of violence was felt to be associated with a certain type of personality termed psychopathic, thus combining impulsive homicidal mania with the concept of the criminal man. This theory of the causation of violent crime has now been discarded, but the term psychopath or psychopathic personality has been retained. Lawyers and psychiatrists and criminologists have wrestled with the term ever since, and there is no general agreement on the definition of the psychopath, but the existence of an antisocial amoral type of personality can hardly be doubted. More recently an attempt has been made to introduce the word "sociopath" for psychopath, to get away from the implications of the Lombroso degeneracy, but the word psychopath sticks and I will use it in this connection.

Everybody has trouble defining the psychopath. It is difficult to illustrate the condition with one or two or three simple case histories. Psychopaths have things in common, which makes this a personality pattern, but the lives of the individual psychopath are varied, complex, and different. The psychopath has a characteristic type of immaturity and egocentricity which denies social and moral responsibility. Rules and regulations are necessary in society. We know that they are necessary, and yet we inherently resent them to the extent that they inhibit and prevent us from satisfying our selfish pleasure-seeking desires. The young will normally protest against taboo and will normally experiment with acts of transgression. For the sake of society, we train the young to keep the law. As we age and mature, we ourselves conform. The psychopath does not conform. He continues to act out his rebellion against society. These actions make him criminal and cause innocent victims to suffer at his expense; we therefore resent him and we seek to restrain and punish him. Yet, in a way, we perversely admire him; he expresses the resentment of authority which we often feel and which we might express if we weren't so damn civilized and proper. This combination of resentment and admiration makes the psychopath a figure of paradoxical and special interest. Accordingly, he is a favorite subject of the journalist and novelist, and the reader examines him avidly. To some extent, the psychopath takes pleasure in being a sort of folk hero. He does not know that he is, in actuality, an enemy of society.

Perhaps the most apt description of the psychopath is contained in the phrase "confidence man." The psychopath has plenty of confidence in himself; others take the psychopath into their confidence; and the psychopath uses the confidence of his victims to prey on them. The psychopath lacks a conscience. He lacks responsibility. We automatically assume, on meeting a stranger, that this stranger is an honest and ethical person who understands the rules and regulations as well as we do and who will play the game according to the rules. We trust him. We presume that he will not take advantage of us. Perhaps such an assumption is unwarranted, given the general unreliability of human nature, but without it society couldn't operate at all. Without trust and confidence in people around us, every man would have to fend for himself. The psychopath accepts the trust and confidence we give every stranger and misuses it. Furthermore, he himself does not trust strangers; he seems to assume that everybody else is as selfish and unreliable as himself; accordingly he has an entirely different adjustment to the faces that he meets. He lives and thinks on a completely different set of social standards; probably this is the reason that we have such difficulty defining him, understanding him, or dealing with him.

The psychopath may be a swindler or an embezzler. He may defraud insurance companies or peddle political influence. He may deal in salad oil, vicuña coats, tulip bulbs, watered stocks, salted mines, or underwater real estate. If he's a spy, he's a double agent. If female, she will peddle sex. Since he often breaks the law, he is often seen in jail, but he is not an ordinary criminal; he is an aristocrat of criminals, so recognized by both the underworld and the prison authorities, such as a Willie Sutton or a Birdman of Alcatraz. He may be a medicine man, peddling nostrums or a cancer cure. He may be an impersonator: there is a famous impersonator, currently at large, subject of a popular book, who, at various times, has successfully impersonated a surgeon, a schoolteacher, a military officer, and a Trappist monk. The psychopath may be a historical figure like Rasputin. He may be an appealing person, like Old Bill in Dr. Thorner's book, or Robin Hood, or he may be a disgusting person like the Marquis de Sade or Nero or the "heroes" of a recent best-selling "non-fiction novel." He may be prominent and successful as businessman or statesman or professional. He may be a psychiatrist. I have known several psychopathic physicians, all with big practices, all beloved by their patients, and all dangerously bad doctors who were completely unconcerned with the actual welfare of their patients. I have known at least two psychopaths in the pulpit. We have all heard of them in the theater, in politics, in society, in the "jet set." The catalog is numerous.

What do they have in common? The classic study of the psychopath is the book called *The Mask of Sanity* by Hervey Cleckley, a fascinating book, well worth reading. Dr. Cleckley lists sixteen traits comprising the psychopathic personality. I think it worthwhile to list these traits, as given by Dr. Cleckley, and I'll follow each with my own comment in parenthesis.

(1) Superficial charm and good "intelligence." (Usually psychopaths are charming and socially attractive, and other people tend to like and trust them at first glance. This is in contrast to the schizophrenic, whom the psychopath resembles in some ways, for the schizophrenic is remote, withdrawn, and difficult to like. Psychopaths are often intelligent, sometimes highly intelligent, but this is not necessarily the case, for they are found on all intelligence levels, down to and including that of mental deficiency.)

(2) Absence of delusions or other signs of irrational thinking. (In other words, they are not psychotic.)

(3) Absence of "nervousness." (And also, they are not neurotic.)

(4) Unreliability. (You can't trust them.)

(5) Untruthfulness and insincerity. (Psychopaths are pathological liars; conversely, pathological liars are psychopaths.)

(6) Lack of remorse or shame. (Psychopaths have no conscience; this is perhaps the most distinctive feature of the psychopath.)

(7) Inadequately motivated antisocial behavior. (Which is the typical behavior pattern by which we recognize them.)

(8) Poor judgment and failure to learn by experience. (This is the hallmark of immaturity; psychopaths in their typical way are immature.)

(9) Pathological egocentricity and incapacity for love. (This also implies immaturity and is seen in immature nonpsychopathic personalities.)

(10) General poverty in major affective reactions. (This

means thin shallow "flat" inappropriate and superficial emotional response. This trait, as we have seen, is typical of schizophrenia, and this is the chief way in which the psychopath resembles the schizophrenic.)

(11) Specific loss of insight. (This factor is seen in psychosis and in neurosis. Yet, the psychopath is neither psychotic nor neurotic. His lack of insight is of a unique variety. He neither gives nor receives social trust and responsibility. He acts responsible only to himself. He appears to believe that everybody else is equally selfish and irresponsible. Not only does he fail to display obligation toward others but he fails to comprehend that others wish to show an obligation toward him.)

(12) Unresponsiveness in general interpersonal relations. (A trait of disturbed adjustment of almost any type.)

(13) Fantastic and uninviting behavior with drink and sometimes without. (Many psychopaths drink and are poor drinkers. Here, as in many other areas, drink brings out basic maladjustments. One type of alcoholic—and only one—is the psychopath. But, whereas most alcoholics have a heavy degree of guilt and remorse in their maladjustment, the psychopath has no guilt or remorse.)

(14) Suicide rarely carried out. (They may threaten it, or fake it, but they don't do it.)

(15) Sex life impersonal, trivial, and poorly integrated. (This is another trait of immaturity. One kind of psychopath manifests his antisocial behavior with sexual expression; he is included in the class of sexual criminals or sexual deviants; however, by no means all sexual criminals and deviants are psychopaths; some are psychotic, many neurotic, and many show personality disturbance of a nonpsychopathic nature. Although some psychopaths manifest their disturbance with sexual expression and although many psychopaths have lurid sex lives, the actual sex drive of the psychopath is weak and transient. He takes his sex casually and lightly, without responsibility. The individual sex act means very little to him, and the individual sex partner means nothing at all.)

(16) Failure to follow any life plan. (Again immaturity and again a trait the psychopath shares with many other types of maladjusted people.)

To these sixteen traits listed by Dr. Cleckley, two others could be added. Lack of response to therapy, and permanency of the condition.

No man is an island; we have quoted John Donne before; the psychopath thinks he is an island, though. He is unaware of the necessity of bridges between islands, unaware of the membership of the individual in the human race. The psychopath acts like a subspecies with a membership of one. Is social need and social responsibility part of the whole man? The Marquis de Sade did not think so. The divine Marquis, however, possessed the criteria of the psychopath.

What is the basic disturbance of the psychopath? What causes the condition? What is wrong with these people? No answer has been agreed upon; the experts argue with each other, and many theories have been proposed. Dr. Cleckley, who has studied more psychopaths in greater depth than any other expert I am aware of, regards the condition as a deep and subtle disorder disturbing integration and normal appreciation of experience; the psychopath is limited in his ability to participate seriously in the major aims of life. After twenty-five years of study of the condition, Dr. Cleckley, in the most recent edition of his book, concludes that the cause of the psychopath's disturbance has not been discovered or demonstrated.

We have come a long way from Lombroso. We no longer take skull measurements in order to identify a criminal type. The concept of inborn moral degeneracy runs counter to our present approach to treatment of disease and rehabilitation of the socially unfortunate. But, if the psychopath has physical or physiological disease, it has not been identified and no new clues from the research laboratory lighten our darkness in this regard. The psychopath is absolutely resistant to treatment or rehabilitation of any kind.

The concept of a congenital disorder continues to seem appropriate in the psychopathic personality.

The normal infant is born without social inhibitions or knowledge of taboo. The rules and regulations are taught to him. The infant from birth normally has a strong social need. He is taught the rules and regulations by means of his social need; when he is a good boy, he is praised, petted, and rewarded; when he is a bad boy, he is punished and rejected. Together with development of social inhibitions, the child develops a conscience which directs him into paths of social conformity. As an adult, the man in general is praised and rewarded by society when he keeps the rules, punished and rejected when he breaks them. Together with his social need, man also has an individual need, a need to be an individual. When he learns his lessons too well, when he is too inhibited, when he conforms too closely, the expression of his individuality is crushed, and he becomes maladjusted in another way. During the transition from childhood to adult life, specifically during adolescence, the person weans himself away from dependence on his parents, must let his own conscience reward or punish his behavior, must find and express his own individual identity, must first unlearn and then relearn the rules and regulations, and establishes his own social responsibility or lack of it. Somehow in this complicated process, the psychopath breaks down. To feel resentment against inhibition, convention, and taboo is normal; one must make certain individual expressions to achieve and retain individual identity; but the expressions of individuality must not violate social responsibility toward others if the expression is to be mature. The psychopath learns only half of the lesson. He expresses his individuality; he rejects social responsibility.

It is tempting to think that the psychopath's perpetual state of hostile adolescence is neurotic in its origin, due to unresolved emotional conflicts from childhood trauma, but specifically the psychopath is not neurotic. He does not have symptoms. He does not block himself from goals; rather, he seizes immediate goals immediately; the neurotic in general is overinhibited, but the psychopath has no inhibition at all. It is tempting to think that some chemical or electrical imbalance in the hypothalamus prevents the psychopath from learning more than half of the maturity lesson, but if there is such a disturbance we have not yet uncovered it. It is tempting to think that the psychopath, having been given a hard time by society, lives to revenge himself on society; this sort of motivation is the personality disturbance of the "average" criminal, but the psychopath is not average; you can rehabilitate the criminal who comes from a poor environment with gratifying results, but you can't rehabilitate the psychopath. Furthermore, he often comes from good environments. What have we left? Probably, I should think, the remaining possibility is the congenital defect. Some children are born with a harelip or a clubfoot, some without arms or legs, and the psychopath was born without a social need.

What can you do with the psychopath? This indeed is the question. Dr. Cleckley points out that at the beginning of his study twenty-five years ago he was profoundly impressed with two difficulties which stand in the way of dealing effectively with the psychopath. The same two difficulties exist without change today. First, the psychopath has relative immunity to control by law. Second, he has a lack of response to treatment of any kind.

Since the psychopathic person is not disoriented, irrational, or delirious, it is impossible to hold him in commitment in a psychiatric institution for any length of time. Submitted to psychiatric examination, he fulfills the criteria of sanity and he must be released. When the psychopath breaks the law, he is sentenced according to the law, but he is apt to make a model prisoner and is often given early release for good behavior. Released from asylum or prison, he immediately returns to his customary patterns of antisocial behavior, having learned nothing from his experience.

Psychopaths imprisoned for serious offenses frequently draw public sympathy. Many are good press agents for them-

selves; some study law in prison libraries and work out
ingenious loopholes in their own defense; some write auto-
biographies from prison which are favorably received. It is
difficult not to show sympathy for the psychopath, for he
expresses in action the resentments which we feel against restraint and inhibition. The psychopath is quick to sense our
sympathy on this ground; he misinterprets it; he presumes
that we would act in the same antisocial way if we had a little
more courage; he is not aware that the difference between ourselves and him is not the absence of courage but the presence
of social need. It is tempting for us to treat the psychopath
on his own terms, as if he were the victim of circumstances,
rather than the murderer or swindler or embezzler of victims.
It is a fatal mistake to take the psychopath to your bosom in
sympathy, for surely he will embezzle or swindle or murder
you, in cold blood.

The normal man must belong to the human race. Responsibility and maturity are difficult, expensive, and painful; we
would like to express our individuality and to protest inhibition and conformity; but our social need is equal to our needs
as individual. When we deny our social need, we pay for it
with even greater difficulty, pain, and expense. The psychopath has no social need. He doesn't care. He cares only for
himself. He is therefore a nuisance, an irritant, and a danger.
We don't know what to do about him. If we are wise, we
avoid him whenever possible. It is not always possible. There
is a psychopath in almost any group of faces that we meet.

10

The Rigid Ones

Connie (Case 28)

Her mother died of cancer when Connie was fifteen. Connie knew that her mother was in poor health, had had an operation, and was receiving X-ray treatments, but the word "cancer" had not been mentioned in Connie's presence. Her mother's death caught Connie unprepared.

Connie had a severe emotional reaction, not considered inappropriate. It seemed to Connie that she hadn't been getting along very well with her mother in the final weeks. There had been a few arguments between mother and daughter, concerning the curfew hour, use of automobiles, boyfriends, and the like, which is not abnormal between mother and teen-age daughter. Now that it was too late, Connie bitterly regretted such arguments. Connie's grief was mixed with a considerable component of guilt.

A guilt reaction in the bereaved is often seen. The grieving relative wishes he had shown more love to the deceased in time. Connie added her grief and guilt together to equal a feeling of responsibility for her mother's death, as if her peccadilloes with boys and automobiles had somehow caused her mother's death. This reaction may be seen in a minor degree often enough to

be called normal but if sufficiently deep or prolonged is pathological. Connie was stamped by it for life. The word "cancer"
now registered upon her and came to be the label for her
pathological guilt reaction.

From that moment on, Connie was convinced that she herself had cancer. The suspected site of malignancy varied and, at
one time or another, included every part of her body. She visited
a doctor for a cancer check-up every few weeks from the age of
fifteen onward. The examinations were negative, but Connie
could not accept the physician's reassurances. Her annual medical
bills were high. Connie knew the seven danger signals of cancer
and seven hundred others. Every doctor that she consulted took
her worry seriously, for every doctor is afraid of missing an early
malignancy. Each doctor, in due course of time, became aware
that Connie's preoccupation with cancer was abnormal and ob-
sessional. Just as each doctor began to think of referral to a
psychiatrist, Connie lost faith in the physician and changed doctors. She became a "doctor shopper," wandering from one physician to another, looking for a man smart enough to discover the
truth.

The hero dies but once, the coward a thousand times; Connie
died a thousand cancer deaths. Her fear of cancer became the
dominant factor of her emotional life, blocking her from most of
the normal pursuits and pleasures. Ironically Connie finally did
die of cancer, but her death did not occur until nearly seventy
years after that of her mother.

Donna (Case 29)

Donna slipped and fell on an icy sidewalk and was hospitalized
for reduction of a fractured ankle. There was nothing about this
common sort of accident to suggest emotional imbalance; the possibility of psychiatric disturbance was raised by Donna's husband.
"I'll bet she was trying not to step on one of those damn cracks
again," he said.

The doctor did not understand this remark and he requested
clarification. Donna, it seemed, was superstitious about bad luck

that might be brought on by stepping on a crack between pavement blocks in the sidewalk. She walked head down, examining the pavement, sometimes going to ridiculous extremes to avoid stepping on a crack. On this occasion, the landmarks were partially obscured by ice. Becoming aware that she had stepped on a crack between pavement blocks because she hadn't seen it clearly, she tried to jump away, in the process slipping on the ice, falling, and fracturing the ankle. It was brought to her attention that this was a foolish exercise in lifesmanship. She replied that this was proof, wasn't it? She had stepped on a crack. Look what happened to her then!

In the hospital, other quirks in Donna's personality became apparent. Although a hospital is an antiseptic environment, and this one was particularly clean, Donna constantly complained about the dirt and germs. She had a habit troublesome to busy nurses: she insisted on bathing herself every hour.

Casual inquiry into the patient's home life revealed an obsession with dirt. She spent most of her time cleaning her house, and when she wasn't washing floor or furniture, she was washing herself. She never ate in restaurants because of a fear of germs.

The doctor did not inquire into the details of Donna's sex life, details not pertinent to the treatment of fractured ankles, but she was childless, and he suspected that she was frigid. Her husband stated that Donna had a separate bedroom and that she had not been in his bed, or he in hers, for many years.

Connie and her fear of cancer constitute what is called an obsession. Donna's refusal to step on pavement cracks is an indication of compulsion. The two phenomena frequently occur together, in the so-called obsessive-compulsive state, where they interlock as part of one disturbance. Obsession, literally, means siege; the archaic religious meaning of the word was the state of being besieged or beset by an outside evil influence, especially the Devil. The present clinical implication of the word is a persistent, often disturbing, preoccupation with an idea or emotion, often illogical. Compulsion is the state of being driven, or of the feeling of being driven, to the performance of a certain act, often illogical. Obsession is therefore the motivating force and compulsion is the direction in which the force is pushing and the two are interrelated.

To some extent obsessions are normal. Each of us has certain fixed ideas, pet notions, prejudices, which are not generally accepted as logical or appropriate by everybody else. Similarly, compulsions are to some extent normal, when our behavior turns in channels not generally accepted as logical or appropriate by everybody but consistent with our own prejudices and fixed ideas. When carried to a degree of producing symptoms and blocking the individual from his normal goals, obsession-compulsion is neurosis. Carried still farther, obsession-compulsion approaches psychosis; the individual may be irrational; his actions may be obviously psychotic; he may become paranoid toward those who do not share his obsession or understand his compulsion.

Obsession-compulsion is an extension of normal caution and precaution. It is normal caution to be afraid of cancer, a nasty disease which is the second leading cause of death, and normal precaution to seek medical advice in the face of one of cancer's seven danger signals, but obviously it is not logical or appropriate to spend one's entire life having cancer check-ups. If a crack in the pavement is big enough to catch your heel and make you trip, normal caution tells you to step over it, and normal precaution advises you to look down and watch your step from time to time, but this should not be your sole preoccupation when walking. It is caution to fear germs, precaution to wash your hands, but ridiculous to take a bath twenty times a day.

Obsession-compulsion is closely allied to the area of superstition, our primitive heritage of caution and precaution. Most of us, no matter how civilized or sophisticated, do not by choice walk under a ladder or be third on a match and we tend to be conservative on Friday the 13th. Tribal taboo was originally based on appropriate caution and precaution for the tribe; superstition continues its influence after the caution and precaution has become obsolete. It is still good sense not to walk under a ladder, because somebody might dump a paint bucket on your head. In the Boer War, a match held lighted for three might provide sufficient illumination for an enemy sniper and cause you to be shot; you are not likely to be shot lighting three cigarettes in the average sitting room. Friday the 13th is no more dangerous than any day in any month despite the number of evil things which happened on Fridays and 13th days in our mythology and religious heritage.

Obsessions and compulsions are deeply ingrained parts of our personality; in pathological degree, they are resistant to treatment. They occur more often in suggestible people, and in fact obsession and compulsion result, at least in part, from self-suggestion. Accordingly, suggestive therapy, such as hypnosis, may be effective in relieving obsessions and compulsions that have not become too deeply seated. I am inclined to think that milder forms of obsession-compulsion are one of the few conditions where extended formal psychoanalysis is beneficial. Severe obsession-compulsion is incurable.

We have noted that obsession-compulsion occurs in suggestible people and may be due to self-suggestion or hypnosis. Yet, although these people readily adopt attitudes suggested to them by others or themselves, they are stubborn in holding the positions to which they have been suggested. They may be pushed, but they do not swing back. They are rigid; they lack a flexible give-and-take; they do not make adjustments easily. It is not a paradox to say that a person can be suggestible and rigid at the same time, though it may sound like one. They are not a pendulum on a self-corrective spring; they are inert but movable bodies, chessmen on a board. The obsession and compulsion may be expressed pathologically in rigid susceptible people, or they may have no more obsession and compulsion than the rest of us.

Miss Elsie (Case 30)

Miss Elsie was a maiden lady, proper, prim, and drab. A color-less uninteresting person, she had high moral standards and no apparent sense of humor. She wore plain sensible clothing, ate plain sensible food, did not smoke or drink, did not go to the movies, did not own a television set; she read no fiction and did not enjoy music or art. She did not marry. She was a strongly religious person; her sole social life was connected with church activity and her sole recreation was religious reading. Her physical health was excellent. Mentally and emotionally, she considered herself very well adjusted and so did everybody else.

Not psychotic, not neurotic, Miss Elsie had no obsessions or compulsions, but she represents a completely rigid personality. By some standards, she led a perfect life; by other standards, her life was sadly incomplete. She was a model of propriety and decorum. Also she was a bore. Some might think her life represented a perfect passport to heaven. Others would say that if this was the way to get to heaven, it might be better to decline, for an eternity in the company of people like Miss Elsie might be considered a reasonable facsimile of hell. Miss Elsie deprived herself of pleasure; she had no fun. She deprived herself of contact with adventure, challenge, and creativity; some people consider these to be the essence of the zest of life.

Discussion of the rigid personality brings us to a couple of complex and controversial areas: religion and sex. The rigid personality may have trouble in religious expression or sexual expression or both. The rigid person is frequently inhibited; inhibitions often involve sex or religion or both.

It is difficult for an American, no matter what his racial, ethnic, or religious background, to escape two strong strands in our national heritage: the Judeo-Christian ethic and the Puritan influence. These strands, primarily religious, permeate the cloth of our culture everywhere; they tend to be restrictive and inhibitory. Yet the American has another force in him, the heritage of revolution. Our forefathers came to this country in the spirit of revolt against the older taboo, seeking freedom of speech, religion, and opportunity. But, fleeing an older restrictive moral environment, the pioneers brought with them a newer one. It is an American national characteristic to display a conflict between these two opposite forces: the spirit of revolution and the heritage of inhibition. Such a conflict, it might be noted, is not unlike that of the individual adolescent, and in a sense America has always been an adolescent nation. This conflict gives us, as a nation and as individuals, our variety, our vitality, our vigor, and our strength. It also gives us, both as nation and as individuals, tensions which can produce anxiety, guilt, and neurosis. Such tensions are apt to be greatest in persons with a rigid personality.

The Judeo-Christian ethic is a major force in our culture, affecting the individual no matter whether he personally is Catholic, Protestant, Jewish, Zen Buddhist, Muslim (black or otherwise), agnostic, atheist, or whatever. The ancient Jewish tribes were a fiercely monogamistic folk; the Old Testament is full of stricture against adultery and fornication. Jesus of Nazareth preached forgiveness of sin, including the sexual; one of His closest female friends had been a prostitute; He believed in the sanctity of married love and the importance of children. However, Jesus did not marry; there is the mystery or legend of the Virgin Birth; the writings of later saints, especially St. Paul, seemed to condemn all sexual relation. St. Paul wrote that it was better to marry than to burn but seemed to suggest that it was still better not to burn at all. In Christianity, there sprang up an association of chastity and celibacy with sanctity and at least an implication of sex as sin.

The contemporary American may not be a descendant of a Puritan but the culture in which he lives has this ancestry. The Puritans developed the sex as sin concept one step further to imply that any pleasure—eating, drinking, dancing, playing—is a sin.

We have, therefore, in our cultural heritage the instinctive feeling that bodily pleasure is a sin. When the infant is taught conventional inhibitions, the price he must pay for membership in society, he is given the potential for shame or guilt whenever he overcomes the inhibition and violates taboo. Toilet training, taught to the infant, is apt to be based on shame and guilt for violation of convention. Since, anatomically, the organs of excretion and of reproduction are in close proximity, it is easy for genital and excretory function to be confused on subconscious emotional levels, both being identified with dirt and sin. This association was vividly brought out in the work of Freud, and it is psychologically valid. The obsessions and compulsions of the rigid person, being exaggerations of inhibition and taboo, are very often expressions of sexual function as dirt or sin. Although I wouldn't say that Donna's fear of stepping on pavement cracks has a Freudian implication—and I think a true Freudian would say just this —I think it is apparent that Donna's fear of dirt and germs, her pathological bathing, her implied frigidity have this implication. The rigid personality may show no obsession or compulsion but may be a person who has repressed sexual expression, who has strong religious expression, and who bases his life on high moral ethical standards; such was the case in Miss Elsie; surely correlations between the religious and the sexual are hinted in Miss Elsie's proper life.

In adolescence, as we have said, the individual tries to learn a delicate balance between the force of taboo required to fulfill his social need and the force of transgression needed to express his individuality. The psychopath learns half this lesson only. The rigid person learns his social lesson too well, often at the expense of the expression of his individuality. In this sense, at least, the rigid personality is opposite to the psychopathic personality. Rigid people can get themselves tangled up in matters of religion or in matters of sex or both together.

Frank (Case 31)

Frank was a bachelor, a quiet respectable bank teller. He was generally well liked: not gregarious but reasonably social. His propriety was perhaps excessive; he blushed easily; he was uncomfortable at any mention of the phenomenon of sex; there was something of the "old maid in pants" in him.

Frank seemed to believe that sex and reproduction were such absolutely private matters that they should never be mentioned. He did not believe that discussion of the subject should ever be set down in print. He made something of a nuisance of himself in this regard. He bothered the local librarian, demanding that certain volumes be removed from the shelves. He bothered the local postmaster about certain communications in the mails. He bothered druggists and news dealers about some of the books and magazines they sold. When an attempt was made to introduce an elementary course in sex hygiene at the high school, Frank led the campaign against it. Without question, Frank was against sin. To some, it seemed that Frank was against sex. It sometimes seemed that Frank was against freedom of speech.

Frank was a rigid personality with rigid inhibitions of a sexual nature. Miss Elsie, a similarly proper person, excluded the things in her life against which she was inhibited and reached a reasonable compromise, for her, by ignoring such subjects altogether. To ignore sex was not enough for Frank; in fact, he placed an undue emphasis on the subject in his life in a negative fashion; he made it his business to try to exclude such subjects from the lives of others. Together with his inhibition, Frank showed an inclination toward revolution; suppressing his own revolt wasn't enough, and he was preoccupied with suppressing it in others. Sexual inhibition was something of an obsession with him, and censorship something of a compulsion.

We'll deal with censorship later in another connection, but at this point we'll pause to deal with the censor. I myself am a person of reasonable propriety, but I am a writer, and a censor is the bitter natural enemy of the writer.

The censor is a rigid personality in whom the conflict between taboo on the one hand and transgression on the other is intense. Inhibition wins, but at the price of severe repression of the urge to revolt. If this uneasy balance should be tipped only slightly in the opposite direction, the censor himself would display the sexual excesses and variations he so fears in everybody else. He tries to protect himself against any influence which might disturb the balance. He seems to think everybody else is in an equal state of delicate balance, and that everybody else needs protection: therefore his attempts at censorship. However, he protests too much and gives himself away. The society he clamors to protect does not itself feel threatened and does not clamor for such protection. The censor presumes to impose on society two boasts: first, that he himself is moral enough and strong enough to resist temptation which would be too strong for others (and he must read all the dirty books to decide which ones should be censored); and second, that he is wise enough to decide what another man should and should not read. In general, the man in the street is not fooled by the censor. The man in the street recognizes that sex is here to stay and is not alarmed by the dirty condition of his own mind; the man in the street knows that dirty books, or any other temptation, can always be obtained underground by the person who wants them badly enough and that the mere act of prohibition increases circulation of the prohibited article by invoking human curiosity. The man in the street senses that the censor, obsessed by the dirtiness of what he is trying to censor, is the man who has the really dirty mind. In the long run, the censor has little or no effect on society; the banned book of today may be the classic of tomorrow. In the short run, the censor stirs up a lot of nuisance, irritation, and legal complication. He is the sort of rigid person who is obsessed and compelled to force his own obsessions and compulsions on others of more stable temperament.

Gerald (Case 32)

Gerald was a dentist. He was also a strong churchman. He belonged to one of the popular Protestant sects, attended all church services, participated actively in church work, and gave the impression that he would rather have been a clergyman than a dentist. The minister had to recognize Gerald as one of the most faithful of the flock, but the minister did not really like or trust Gerald. Gerald was too ardent. His notions of church ritual and dogma were rigid and fixed, and if there were any deviations from Gerald's concepts of the righteous and the proper, Gerald would protest, loudly, publicly. Sometimes the minister felt that his own life would be easier if he submitted his sermons to Gerald in advance for clearance and approval.

Within the higher echelons of the church was a certain prominent bishop with advanced and somewhat radical ideas, a figure of national interest whose provocative opinions appeared in the press frequently. Gerald was personally offended by the opinions of this bishop which Gerald felt were blasphemous. Gerald took it upon himself to mount an attack against this bishop. Gerald gave speeches whenever two and three were gathered together in one place. He wrote letters to the editor. He wrote letters to other bishops and, in fact, to every ordained minister in the church. He had broadsides printed up which he mailed to every taxpayer in his town. He harangued his poor patients in the dental chair. Before long, Gerald was recognized as a religious "nut" and avoided by everybody whenever possible, including the local minister.

Gerald's obsessions and compulsions were in the religious sphere. A more detailed account of Gerald's history would suggest that he also had obsessions and compulsions within the field of sex and that his sexual and religious ideas were inappropriately mixed. Some of Gerald's public pronouncements had a vivid and even embarrassing sexual flavor. The particular issue upon which Gerald attacked the bishop was that of the Virgin Birth.

Analysis of the relationship of religion to sex and of religion to neurosis and psychosis is a tricky area where one must tread gently in order to avoid offense. Certain statements on religion, deemed sane and sensible by some, will sound blasphemous and sacrilegious to others. It is not my intention to stir up a controversy in this area, and I will confine myself to a few generalities which should not sound blasphemous to those whose own thinking is not too rigid.

I feel that man has a deep instinctive religious need which must be satisfied in order for him to attain his full potential of maturity and adjustment. I concede that certain systems of philosophy ordinarily considered atheistic, including sincere genuine atheism, may satisfy this need. I also concede that many modern men and women banish all religious thinking and ritual from their lives and still reach mature adjustments, but I feel that such people do not reach their full potential; I have often seen such people suddenly develop great religious need when faced with serious illness in themselves or their family. A lack of faith does not support in the emergency. I have also seen a lot of people, faithful members of a church, regular attenders of the services, who seem to participate in church activities as a social function, rather than a matter of faith; I have seen such people develop severe religious need, unsatisfied by their church, in the face of emergency.

In my opinion, man must believe in something. I don't think it makes a great deal of difference what he believes in, if the faith is genuine. In God's house, it has been written, there are many rooms. There are many religions and within each religion many sects; if the entire dogma of any given sect was correct, that of any other sect would be incorrect; I do not think one small group of men possess monopoly on total truth. I think that every intelligent man of faith possesses part of the truth, and that only part of the truth is available to any living man.

Furthermore, I believe that every man of good faith must

show as complete tolerance as possible for the faith of every other man. A missionary tendency is inherent in many sects; I think it appropriate within limits when addressed to ignorant or primitive peoples, to the young, to those genuinely seeking spiritual guidance. When missionary zeal is such that it must proselyte, that it must convert a man of another belief by persuasion or force, then I think the missionary is showing obsession and compulsion.

I think that man has a sexual need. I do not think his sexual need is as basic and essential as his religious need. It should be obvious that many persons sublimate their sexual need into other channels and reach mature adjustment. Some persons sublimate sexual expressions into religious expressions; and for some it seems to work well. I am not convinced that fulfillment of the religious need requires suppression, inhibition, or sublimation of the sexual need. Personally I am not convinced that celibacy is mandatory for sanctity. I have been interested to note that in sects where the long weight of historical tradition requires celibates in the priesthood, there is a mounting rebellion against this requirement, and I think it likely that mandatory celibacy for priests may become obsolete in time. I am inclined to think that full maturity requires appropriate expression of both religious and sexual needs. The two needs are closely linked in our subconscious minds, but these needs are not identical; expression of the one does not fully compensate for expression of the other. It is often dangerous when religious expression is mistaken for sexual expression, or vice versa, although many expressions do contain elements of both.

Anybody who has visited an institution for the insane will know that many of the residents show intense and bizarre religious expression, often tinged with sexual overtones. As a corollary, it should be evident that certain bizarre religious expressions are not true statements of faith but signs of neurosis or psychosis. When sexual expressions are put forward as a religion, this may also be an expression of insanity. Religion with excessive sexual coloration and sexual expressions masked as religion may be seen in members of the clergy, and such confusion may represent an occupational hazard in that important and difficult profession.

In this "swinging" generation, the problems of inhibition, the Puritan influence, the taboo, may appear to be archaic. Certainly the forces of revolt and transgression appear to be gaining over those of taboo and inhibition. But excess of transgression is no more healthy than excessive inhibition. The conflict continues. The ardent "swinger" is no more happy or adjusted than the zealous Puritan, and the reason is much the same; both are rigid personalities; both are caught in a conflict they do not resolve. The "swinger" is made unhappy and maladjusted by the residual force of taboo within him which is not overcome, just as the Puritan is unhappy because of his suppressed rebellion. Because of our historical and religious heritage, I think the rigid personality in conflict with himself is a rather characteristically American problem. Transgression solves it not a bit better than taboo. Here, as throughout biology, adjustment is a state of appropriate balance between the opposing forces.

11

The Hostile Ones

The fight-or-flight reaction is basic to survival of the organism. The "flight" element is accompanied by the emotion of fear or its low-grade chronic form, anxiety. "Fight" is manifested by aggression or hostility. Hostility is therefore present in all of us, although civilization requires us to suppress it; we tend to be ashamed of the emotion because hostility is uncivilized and often we do not know how to manage it. Although complete suppression of hostility may sound like the desirable goal, hostility can only be suppressed down to subconscious levels, not eliminated, and at subconscious levels can cause us considerable trouble. Emotional maturity demands, not suppression of hostility, but a channeling of hostility into beneficial or at least harmless outlets. The advantages of sports and games and all competitive types of activity lie in such a constructive channeling of hostility.

We have been speaking of taboo and transgression frequently in the last two chapters. Let us now focus on these terms more sharply.

Strictly speaking, taboo implies the set of interdictions, primarily religious, imposed upon the members of a primitive tribe, or, in modern man, the residual inhibitions and superstitions from the heritage of such taboo. More generally speaking, referring to modern man, we imply the total mass of interdictions and prohibitions, some written into the law, many unwritten: the things we "ought not to do." Some taboo is quite logical, and some illogical. Taboo will differ from individual to individual, and in the same individual from time to time.

The primary taboo of primitive peoples is religious in nature. The influence of religious taboo is less strong on modern man. The intent of the primitive religious taboo was not so much to deprive an individual member of the tribe of his pleasure-seeking as to avoid offending the gods. Many ancient gods—and in some societies most of them—were rather inclined to encourage the pursuit of pleasure, and many religious festivities involved bodily indulgences and pleasures, often to the point of orgy. Yahweh (or Jehovah), the ascetic God of an ascetic monotheistic people, was less inclined to look with favor on pleasure-seeking, and the subsequent God of the Calvinists and Puritans looked with disfavor on pleasure. The heritage of religious taboo of modern man tends to exert an inhibitory and prohibitory effect on pleasure-seeking with the consequence that many of us are apt to feel guilty over pleasure-seeking, as if in pleasing our bodies and senses we were offending God. Since we do desire pleasure, we are apt to indulge ourselves in spite of our guilt and thus we set up a conflict within us between the subconscious forces of taboo, and the urges to overcome taboo which we may call transgression.

Beyond the religious implications, taboo served to protect the safety of the tribe, prohibiting the individual from actions which might endanger the tribe. The modern equivalent is patriotism. Patriotism of an individual is apt to vary widely according to the degree of threat to the safety of the nation and the degree to which the individual agrees with national policy. On Pearl Harbor Day, American patriotism ran universally high; in recent turbulent times, it has often been quite low. An American student of the '40s might line up at the recruiting station to volunteer, while a similar student of the '60s might burn his draft card. Despite varying degrees of individual patriotism, high treason remains the most serious crime in the formal body of written law. Perhaps this explains our interest in the spy who, protecting the highest taboo of his own country, violates the highest taboo of the enemy, thereby living the taboo-transgression conflict at its most intense.

Closely following patriotic taboo, in both primitive and modern man, is the injunction against death or injury of another member of the tribe: murder and its lesser equivalents of assault and battery. This taboo, and an urge to transgress against it, is always operative in our subconscious minds. Our natural hostility often tempts us to kill, or at least injure, the individual who blocks us or thwarts us; since those who block and thwart us most often are those with whom we are in closest contact, our aggressive impulses are often directed against those whom we ought to love. Our interest in murder and in violence of all kinds is instinctual; to some extent our study of the subject, in fiction and in factual news accounts, serves as a harmless channel for diverting our hostility.

Of lesser importance to primitive man but influential in a capitalistic society is the taboo against violation of property rights. The law takes all forms of theft, direct or indirect, very seriously. It is not always appreciated that the true motivation for theft is often not the desire for easy acquisition of the property but is the expression of hostility against the owner.

There are taboos to protect the right of privacy of the individual, especially bodily privacy and particularly sexual; there is a great mass of taboo associated with sex and strong forces of transgression against such taboo.

Finally, there is a long catalog of what might be called minor taboo, operative in custom, etiquette, and social behavior, which differs according to the background of the individual and which changes according to the circumstances in which he finds himself.

The sum total of taboo of the various kinds in us keeps telling us "don't" all the time. There is a lengthy list of the things we should not, must not, ought not to do. Our reward for staying within acceptable confines of taboo is partly personal: an absence of guilt and shame, a feeling of self-respect and integrity. Part of the reward comes from others who give us trust, confidence, and respect, and from society which supports and protects us. Presumably, if we conform to all taboo, we should attain a state of happy adjustment with ourselves, others, and society. However, such full conformity would block us from many pleasures and goals, sharply restrict and inhibit our lives, and prevent us from expressing our identity and individuality. There is an instinctive need to violate taboo, and this force of transgression, within certain reasonable limits, is normal; complete suppression of it is inclined to be abnormal and tends to produce a dull frustrating inactive life.

We have looked at the rigid person and some of the problems of the rigid personality; this person has a strong taboo sense and represses his urges to transgression. We have looked at the psychopath; he apparently lacks a social need; the psychopath accordingly does not enjoy the rewards of taboo and expresses himself with free transgression. We are now looking at persons who do have a social need and a feeling of taboo but in whom the urge to transgression is stronger. These are the hostile people, inclined toward acts of violence, which acts bring them into conflict with society and the law. Such a person has not learned to handle his hostilities in a constructive way. The immediate purpose of his transgression, his acts of violence and crime, obvious to himself, is free gratification of individual pleasures, needs, and goals. It is not obvious to him that his ways are primarily an expression of hostility. Most of the various pleasures, needs, and goals can be obtained in ways which conform to the taboos of society. It is possible to get around a person who is blocking

you without killing him; if you kill him, you remove him
from your path but the consequences of the act of murder
will block you even more effectively. The bank robber may
dream of wealth but it is bank presidents and not bank rob-
bers who retire prosperous.

Society deals with hostile transgressing individuals by punishment. The punishment itself is an act of hostility. The
theory, which sounds reasonable, is that punishment de-
ters crime. Actually, historical experience shows that the
criminal is never deterred by the fear of punishment. Legal
punishment, in fact, acts reversely; the more strict and punitive it is, the greater the incidence of crime. The criminal
exerts hostility against society; legal punishment, itself hostile,
increases the hostility of the criminal. The non-criminal man
is deterred from crime, not by fear of punishment, but by his
own conscience, responsibility, and desire for social approval.
The non-criminal man has a taboo sense stronger than his
transgression urge. Reinforcement of taboo sense therefore is
the logical deterrent of crime rather than a hostile punishment system which increases forces of transgression.

Henry (Case 33)

Henry was small and his father was big. His father was strict,
a policeman of the type inclined to be stringent and tough with
criminals. He was also a tough stringent father. Henry was a good
little boy; he had to be, for his father would thrash him for even
the most minor of transgressions.

In school, he seemed like a bright youngster, although he
was an underachiever with marginal grades, and he was cooperative, offering no disciplinary problems. He obviously did
not like school, however, and he dropped out as soon as it was
legally permissible for him to do so. He had some musical talent
and was able to support himself as the leader of a rock and roll
group. Twanging the guitar did not seem to be a sufficient outlet
for his aggressions, however, and he tried his hand at burglary.
He was caught, jailed, and then released on bail pending trial.

Immediately upon his release from jail, he broke into a series of hunting camps, stealing rifles and shotguns. He was caught again. In the jail again, he fashioned a reasonable model of a revolver out of soap, carved with a razor blade, blackened with shoe polish; with this counterfeit weapon, he made a jail break. After an extensive manhunt, he was caught again. Although he had sworn not to be taken alive, he surrendered rather meekly; he was caught by a policeman of the same strict school as his father, and the arresting officer roughed him up despite his lack of resistance. He served a prison term and was released before his time for good behavior. Following release, he broke parole, fled to a city in another state, and collected himself another armory by breaking into sporting goods stores. Caught in the act one night, he shot it out with the police in a spectacular running battle over rooftops. In the course of the skirmish, he wounded a policeman and was himself wounded.

He is presently confined and presumably will remain so for some time. If he receives good psychiatric attention during his confinement, he may be rehabilitated; if not, it seems likely that, upon his next restoration to society, he will kill a policeman, a policeman like his father, which may have been his subconscious motivation from the beginning.

We think of the criminal as one who breaks the law. However, mere lawbreaking in and of itself is not enough to stamp a man as criminal. There are many laws not taken with great seriousness by society, and in fact all of us violate the law now and then, either in ignorance or with appreciation that the law does not deserve our serious attention. Society will punish us more severely for violation of certain taboos not illegal; we will injure our social reputation much more by rude behavior or unseemly language than by flagrant violation of parking ordinances. The law itself makes a distinction of seriousness between the misdemeanor and the felony. Certain misdemeanors will do us great damage socially—such as, for example, repeated indecent exposure by a male exhibitionist—whereas certain felonies may be lightly regarded, even admired by society—income tax evasion, for example, taxes being a legal taboo against which most of us have a strong desire to transgress. For a man to be considered a criminal implies repeat transgression of the law, serious transgression of the law, and knowledge of the wrongfulness of such transgressions; to boil this down into psychological terms, we perceive that the criminal shows habitual hostility toward society.

Ingrid (Case 34)

Ingrid was a wealthy society matron. She was not in any need whatever of creature comforts. She was apparently a sensible normal well-adjusted person. However, she compiled a record of multiple arrests for petty larceny in stores. She was widely known among local merchants as a kleptomaniac, and whenever she appeared in a store with an umbrella, the clerks became watchful and alert. An umbrella will conceal many small articles without suspicious bulging. No charges were ever pressed against Ingrid, and she was customarily released shortly after her various arrests; customarily, her husband reimbursed the stores considerably in excess of the value of the goods Ingrid had lifted. It was customary that Ingrid, when arrested, was carrying considerable amounts of cash, much more than she would have needed to buy the articles she had stolen. It was also customary for Ingrid to throw away all the small articles she had lifted as soon as she got home. She did it, she said, "for kicks."

Considered on logical grounds, in terms of acquisition of property, kleptomania makes no sense. The crime is different from that of the starving man stealing his loaf of bread. Almost invariably, the kleptomaniac has no need for the articles he steals, can usually afford to buy the articles, and often has no interest in the articles themselves; it is the act of stealing which seems to give pleasure. Only when considered psychologically as an act of hostility and aggression does kleptomania make any kind of sense.

We tend to think that easy gain is the motivation for the various kinds of theft, but this is rarely the case. On purely practical terms, it is usually easier to work for money or property than to steal it and theft has an in-built blocking device: most thieves are caught and in jail can enjoy none of the benefits of money or property. The successful thief is often unable to enjoy his gains; he is inclined to spend extravagantly without much pleasure and often will give money away, in unnecessary tips, to friends, even to charity. It is the act of theft itself which gives the thief his pleasure, and his act is an expression of hostility. The hostility is easy to see in the mugger, and it is apparent in armed robbery. The aggressive element is more subtle in the quiet stealth of the burglar and even more subtle in such passive forms of theft as embezzlement, forgery, and counterfeiting, but it is there.

The psychotic, psychopathic, and mentally deficient criminals cannot appreciate the wrongful nature of the act. Some crimes are accidental, although a great many accidents are subconsciously "on purpose." Some crimes are committed impulsively in the heat of the moment, but the impulse is an uncontrolled burst of hostility. The neurotic, in confusion, may break the law as part of his neurotic expression. But most crimes are committed by persons who have to be classified as "psychiatrically normal"; these persons are manifesting social hostility through transgression.

It has been said that approximately 2 percent of criminals are psychotic and the same percent mentally deficient; 5 percent neurotic; 26 percent psychopathic; and the remaining 65 percent fall into the class of "psychiatrically normal." These figures are derived from what is perhaps the most extensive study made of criminals, an experience of a quarter of a century, an evaluation of more than seventy thousand persons convicted of felony at the Court of General Sessions of New York City.

We customarily think of crime as an illegal immoral act, of the criminal as an inhuman immoral person, and of punishment as a deterrent. We think in terms of rehabilitating the criminal by making him "pay" for his crime, by setting up sufficient pain, grief, shame, and remorse so that he will mend his ways. However, such moral judgments do not relieve hostility in the criminal. If we consider that crime, psychologically, is an act of transgression, of hostility, we can prevent crime more effectively and rehabilitate the criminal more successfully by seeking outlets for the constructive, or at least harmless, release of hostility. Conventional thinking, which basically is hostility against the criminal, increases hostility of the criminal, thereby increasing the incidence of crime.

A classic study of the psychology of crime is the interesting book by Walter Bromberg entitled *Crime and the Mind*. Dr. Bromberg makes the valid point that the student of crime should attempt to be objective and should rid himself of conventional concepts of guilt and punishment; he should view crime, not as an inhuman act, but as an example of very human behavior, a purposeful and personalized act in the human drama.

Crime is much like drama. In a play, there is conflict, tension, climax, and resolution. The basic conflict in the criminal is that common to us all: the clash between taboo and transgression. Tension increases as urges toward transgression grow. The crime itself is the climax. The resolution may permit the criminal to "get away with it"; often it involves the traditional dramatic elements of pursuit and capture, of guilt and punishment. We might think of such antisocial behavior not as "games people play" but as "plays people act." Many lives seem to lack intrinsic drama. The game of life, played by the rules, is inhibiting, frustrating, and dull. Crime puts drama into the play. The criminal stages his play "for kicks." The kick is the pleasureful release of tension produced when transgression overcomes taboo and hostility is discharged. Storage of hostility causes unpleasant tension; aggression releases the tension.

Discussion of activity "for kicks," the release of tension by transgression against taboo, reminds us of normal behavior of the adolescent. Teen-agers, normally, do a good deal of such "acting out" in their behavior. Crime, to a considerable extent, is adolescent. Most crimes are committed by teenagers and young adults, and the adult criminal often shows the personality of fixed adolescence. We are not saying that teen-agers are necessarily latent criminals; obviously most adolescents are responsible adjusted young persons growing toward mature adjusted adulthood. However, transgression and hostility against taboo is most likely to be expressed in antisocial behavior at this stage of life. The normal adolescent will sow a few wild oats; in fact if he does not, his repressions and inhibitions may cause him trouble in later life. In the normal horseplay and exuberance of youth, property is apt to be destroyed and the peace disturbed. Rebellion and hostility is normal for the teen-ager. He must test his weight and strength against society, to find out what sort of a person he is; he must hit the taboo standards of his parents a good hard lick to see if they ring true; he must experiment with various vices and indulgences to see whether they are good or bad for him. If the situation can be viewed objectively, it is amusing to see parents shocked and offended when their teen-age children sow the same oats that the parents sowed at a similar age; likewise, it is amusing to see how often a teen-ager, hostile and rebellious over the taboo standards of his parents, grows up to have the same taboo standards himself. The war between wild youth and proper age has gone on since the cave man.

Adolescence is the time when the individual must set up his personal taboo standards. He must wean himself away from dependency on his parents and discover his own identity; this is what adolescence is all about. He cannot turn to his parents for advice, for this is the child's way, and he seems to turn against them. He seems to demand the right to complete freedom without responsibility. He must learn that there is no freedom without responsibility and that irresponsibility is not free. By instinct, he is fiercely idealistic, romantic, altruistic, and intellectually honest at this age; he looks at the adult world, and finds it not altogether good, and dreams of better things. When idealism is frustrated by adult practicality, romance by adult cynicism, altruism by adult selfishness, and honesty by adult hypocrisy, he wishes to strike out at the adult world. On the other hand, he is uncertain of himself. Viewing the accomplishments and acquisitions of adults, he doubts his own ability to accomplish and acquire that much.

I recently read a prediction that, by 1970, sixty-one percent of the population would be age twenty-five or less. I'm not sure of the validity of this prediction, but within the near future, if not now, more than half of the population will be in this younger age group. Add to this the fact that a substantial and growing percent of the population is age sixty-five and over. This means that a diminishing minority of the population, less than a third, is in the age group of twenty-six to sixty-four. Perhaps it will soon be necessary to use adults exclusively in management, teaching, and supervisory capacities with the work being done by the juvenile and geriatric groups. The juvenile and geriatric groups may also have to become more productive. Can one quarter of the population support the other three quarters?

We hear much of the American "cult of youth." Traditionally, America has been a nation of youth and rebellion. We have tended to admire physical grace and beauty, to discount wisdom and experience, to fear the aging process. The sublimal bombardment of advertising which strikes us from all sides tries to sell with appeals to youth and sex; we are urged to buy this product or that product because its use will make us younger or more sexually attractive or foster a "swinging" life. I think the present advertising emphasis is not so much because we envy and admire youth, but because youth, now being in the majority, constitutes the major merchandising market. I am not sure that youth is admired now.

The young of this generation are in protest; I doubt if they are in protest against the older generations. Why should the majority protest against the minority? We don't exactly have a small ruling class holding the masses in slavery; young persons have as much freedom as they need and more than they can sometimes handle. I suspect that the young may be in protest against each other. When more than half of the population is young, where is the advantage of youth? There is a great deal of competition in youthful grace and beauty, and the young try to conceal it under a uniform that would not be out of place on the Bowery. They try to conceal their sex. The boys wear long hair and the lines of their faces are softer. The girls wear short hair and pants, and the lines of their faces are harder. It is difficult to tell the one sex from the other, and it almost seems as if a neuter condition was the objective. Because youth is so plentiful, it seems difficult for any young person to rise above the mass and find his or her own individual identity; the competition is too great; and the cult of youth worship may be dying from the sheer weight of numbers. Perhaps age, wisdom, and experience may come to be admired. This might be a good thing.

In the meantime, the song of protest and the act of transgression often represent a call for help. Transgression should be recognized as the dramatization of a personal predicament. Forces creating the predicament should be studied, and channels for the socially acceptable release of hostility should be encouraged and developed. This approach, not punishment or moral condemnation, is the antidote to transgression.

12

The Young Ones

The taboo-transgression conflict, which operates in all of us from early childhood on, is most intense during the adolescent years. When the child becomes the teen-ager, his parents can play only an indirect supporting role; the time of direct parental influence has passed. As the twig is bent, so grows the tree. This is what conscientious parents have suspected and feared. If the adolescent turns out well, this means that he was loved sufficiently and raised properly, which is reassuring. If he turns out badly, ergo, he was loved insufficiently or raised improperly or both. No child turns out perfectly, matching an ambitious parent's hopes and dreams. When imperfections are discovered, the parent has a sleepless night. Help, Dr. Spock! And please speak softly, Dr. Freud!

The importance of the early home environment on future emotional adjustment can hardly be denied. However, it should not be exaggerated to the exclusion of other factors. The child of conscientious loving parents in a good home environment can turn out badly. The parent must not necessarily assume the entire blame for any bad result, just as he cannot claim the entire credit when things turn out well. A good deal of the responsibility for the adjustment of an individual must rest upon that individual himself, not on his parents or the home environment. It is obvious that many bad apples come from good barrels and that many fine individuals were raised in very poor environments.

If you dig into the early history of a neurotic, you will find evidence of childhood trauma. This, however, does not prove that childhood trauma causes neurosis. If you dig into the early history of a mature stable individual—provided he will let you dig there—you will also find evidence of childhood trauma. Childhood is traumatic, and so is every other stage of life. The adjustment of an individual depends not only on his parents and his home environment but upon the things which happen to him after he leaves home and, most importantly, upon the sort of person he is.

I remember my first assignment to the newborn nursery when I was in medical school. Not being a father myself at the time, this was my first contact with very young infants. One of my classmates, assigned to the nursery before me, told me he did not enjoy working with newborns. "They're all alike," he told me. "There's no variety." I entered the nursery expecting to encounter twenty or thirty carbon copies. What I found was twenty or thirty tiny individuals, each quite different. I mean not only physical variation but distinctive personality differences. In the first few hours of life, even before he has been introduced to his mother, the baby is an individual with a personality of his own. Some are lazy and some ambitious; some good-natured, some irritable; some full of fun and some serious; some friendly and some antisocial. Within the same newborn nursery, there is the same environment. There is only one possible Freudian trauma which might shape personality in the first few hours of life —the recent passage through a birth canal, experienced by all. But each comes into the world different.

My medical practice is almost exclusively adult; I do little pediatrics and no obstetrics or well-baby care, and I seldom follow my patients from birth into adult life; however, there have been a few of my patients whom I have observed shortly after birth and followed through the years. In these patients, there are personality traits which I first noticed in infancy which remain unchanged fifteen and twenty years later, despite the varied home environments in which the children have lived.

The person we are today is, to a considerable extent, the same personality as on the day of our birth. Our conscientious parents should not blame themselves for all the mistakes and maladjustments we have been making since. Similarly, we ourselves as parents should not blame ourselves for all the mistakes and maladjustments of our children. Freudianism, literally applied, would tend to blame the parents for everything, and parental guilt seems to be something of a national neurosis, but honest observation tells us that environmental influence does not change basic personality.

This is a youthful nation. The majority of the population is young, and in America youth has been king. I think the time has come to give a little more sympathy to parents. Parenthood is no easy road. Much has been said and written about the harmful effects of the parent upon the child. Perhaps enough has not been said about the traumatic effects of a child upon a parent. The family tree is not a one-way street; psychological influences can extend down as well as up.

Joan (Case 35)

Joan had one child, a sweet cheerful bright little boy. When the boy was five, he developed an acute severe illness with convulsions and coma, probably a meningitis. He survived the illness physically but suffered mental retardation as a consequence; for the rest of his life, he did not mature mentally beyond the age of five.

We have encountered the child before: Donald, the retarded child, Case 5 in Chapter 3 of this book. We are now looking at his mother, Joan.

The care of Donald became the sole occupation and preoccupation of Joan's life. She had no further children. She said, with some pride, that she had never spent a single night outside her own home since the day Donald was first taken ill. Thereafter, she always slept in her own bed and she slept alone, except on occasions when she took Donald into her bed to comfort him. There was another person she might have taken into her bed for comfort from time to time—her husband—but she did not.

People generally admired Joan, her courage and fortitude in the face of catastrophe, her single-minded devotion to her retarded son. Yet Joan was a cripple, socially at least. Her son absorbed all of her time, and she gave none of it to anybody else. Furthermore, in the interest of being a good mother, she resigned from the role of wife. It can be said, with justification, that the disease which disabled the son mentally disabled the mother emotionally. It can be suspected that Joan brought to a catastrophic situation emotional equipment not fully capable of handling it.

Let us take Joan back a generation. Her mother died when she was very young. Her father, a shy and introverted person, did the best he could to be both father and mother to a brood of three. Joan's two brothers provide no case history material for this book. Joan, the baby of the family, was her father's pet and darling; he showered affection upon her which she returned in kind.

Joan's father could not bring himself to believe that Joan was growing up. She entered adolescence; he continued to think of her as a child. Before Joan's father was aware that Joan was interested in boys in general, or any boy in particular, Joan's interest had become considerable. Joan pursued her interest in boys in general, and one boy in particular, secretly. She did not quite understand what she was doing. She vaguely understood that she was doing wrong, but her secret wrongdoings gave her quite a "kick." No psychologist or psychiatrist considered the evidence in her case, but in retrospect one might suspect that Joan's transgressions were an expression of hostility. Whereas boys often express transgression by breaking the laws of property, girls usually express it through sex. Perhaps Joan's hostility was not directed against her father; she appeared to love him; perhaps the hostility was against her mother, hostility at the absence of a mother, a mother who wasn't there because she was dead.

At any rate, Joan became pregnant. She married the boy in question. Her child was named Donald, of course.

Joan's father could never accept Joan's husband, her marriage, or her child. He attended the wedding, a small private ceremony, but after it he suffered a sort of breakdown. A shy and introverted person to begin with, he later became a recluse. He shunned dealings with people. He did not see Joan again.

It might be understandable that Joan should want no more children after Donald, considering what happened to him. However, the odds against another child being retarded as a complication of meningitis are no better than a million to one. Most parents with a single retarded child would wish to have a normal child when the chances for one were good. It must be recalled, furthermore, that Donald was normal for the first five years. Normally, the majority of parents will have a second child before the first child is five years old if both parents are healthy. It might be suggested that Joan had an unhealthy attitude toward motherhood. Considering the circumstances under which she entered motherhood, an unhealthy attitude might not be considered unwarranted. Some blame could be attached to Joan's unhealthy home environment and to her father who, though he loved her, could not bear to teach her to grow up.

We are looking in both directions along this family tree. Granted an unhealthy influence of the father upon Joan, how about the influence of Joan upon him? Joan's transgression crippled him; as an apparent consequence, he severed his social relationships.

Let us take the generations back another step. Now we look at the mother of Joan's father: Joan's paternal grandmother, and great-grandmother of Donald, whom we shall call Katherine. Katherine was a physically sensuous woman, a possessive woman, a demanding woman. She gave much love, physical and otherwise, to her husband and also to her only child, a son, who later became Joan's father. Katherine lived in the last century, in Victorian times, before popularization of the work of Freud. Then, it was generally considered that a woman was a lady, or she was not. A lady might have romantic, sentimental, or even passionate attachments, but she did not have lust or sexual desire. She was a passive recipient of sexual desire, the masculine prerogative, from the one man whom she served as proper wife. Katherine was a lady. She had never heard of Oedipus. Being accepted as a lady by all, accepting herself as a lady, and acting within the frame-work of conduct expected from a lady, she acted naturally, with-out guilt or shame. It was never considered that love for a son was in any way unladylike, and Katherine loved her son. It did not occur to her that physical expressions of love for her son could possibly harm any of her relationships. It was natural for her to kiss and pet and fondle her son, which she did as he grew from child toward man; she did not consider it unnatural to take her son into her bed at night if he awoke, screaming, from a nightmare. It did not occur to her that her possessive and some-times physical love might be bad for the boy. It did not occur to her that her love for her son might be harmful for her husband, that her husband might feel himself in competition with the son, that the husband, a rather shy and quiet man, might feel his own masculinity threatened by the son. Katherine noticed, of course, that her husband came to bed with her progressively less and less after the birth of the son and, soon, did not come to bed with her at all. Katherine understood enough of what have been called the "facts of life" to realize that, under these circumstances, there would be no more children. She would have liked more children, but it would have been unladylike for her to take any positive steps to lure her mate into her bed. The matter of lust and desire was the male prerogative; a lady did not encourage it. She transferred a good deal of her natural affection from her hus-band to her son. It did not occur to her that this could cause the son any harm. She noticed that her son was a shy introverted quiet sort of boy: just like his father, in other words. This was natural, wasn't it?

Katherine, in all innocence, set up a classical Oedipus situation. Presumably this did affect the son, who, in later life, faced with a stressful situation, became a recluse. An unhealthy emotional adjustment of Katherine's son was passed along to his daughter, Joan, but then, since Joan had no more children after the retarded Donald, the interlocking family trauma stops.

This family tree is quite amenable to interpretation on classic Freudian terms, of course, and can show examples of unhealthy parental influence upon adjustment of the child. Look in the opposite direction, however, and you can see examples of unhealthy influences of the child upon the emotional adjustment of a parent. Donald's father lost a wife when Donald became retarded. In a very similar fashion, Katherine's husband lost a wife as she transferred affection to their son. That son, in his turn, suffered severe disruption of social relationships when his daughter committed a sexual transgression.

We do not wish to construct the plot of a Gothic novel from the four generations of this particular complicated family tree. Consideration of it, however, should raise the point that unhealthy psychological reactions can be passed in both directions along a family tree. The generations interlock. There is a feedback phenomenon in human interrelationship.

Freud's observations are valid and useful in understanding many situations, including many aspects of the family we have been discussing. Freudian ideology, however, is not a very reassuring guidebook for the raising of children from the point of view of the conscientious and anxious parent. Dr. Spock is more reassuring and, incidentally, far more practical. The child can be the source of just as much trauma to the parent as the parent to the child. Most modern mothers are now equipped to discuss Freud intelligently over cocktails in the living room and are sufficiently aware of things in the bedroom not to create classical Oedipus situations, consciously at least. Most modern mothers, however, consult Dr. Spock in the nursery, which is healthy. It is even more healthy when a mother, and father, recognize that the child is born with certain unique personality characteristics of his own which the environment does not change.

13

The Old Ones

Winnie (Case 36)

Winnie was a famous man, aggressively successful in several fields. He had a zesty jubilant approach to his affairs and was noted for his personal courage, indomitable spirit, and lusty appetite for adventure, conflict, hearty food, strong liquor, and big cigars. He lived past his ninetieth birthday. Outwardly and in public, he appeared to retain most of his vitality in the later years, though battling through a series of disagreeable and potentially disabling physical illnesses.

Those who lived with him, however, saw a different man in the last few years of his life: disagreeable, suspicious, demanding, fearful, garrulous, obstinate, and depressed. His passing caused regret and grief among the public. Those closely associated with the old warrior must have felt relief that death had finally found him and might have thought it fitting if he had passed away a number of years before.

Willie (Case 37)

Willie was a famous man with an international reputation in his special field. His private life was not serene; he was a homosexual; he had one brief and stormy marriage. Despite his known inversion, however, he had a large circle of admiring friends and acquaintances and was highly regarded in international social circles. He was generally considered an urbane sophisticated charming personality.

Willie also lived beyond his ninetieth birthday. In his final years, his personality ceased to be considered attractive, and he became a difficult disagreeable person.

"I have been a horrible and evil man," he said at the age of ninety-one. "Every one of the few people who has ever gotten to know me well has ended up by hating me."

Apparently trying to prove the point, he flew into rages, shouted obscenities, alienated friends. He attempted to disinherit his only child, engaging in an ugly court action against her, revising his memoirs to include some highly unflattering remarks about her.

"Dying is a very dull dreary affair," he once had said. "My advice to you is to have nothing whatever to do with it."

Yet, it might seem that it would have been better if Willie had had something to do with death a number of years earlier.

Winnie was better known as Sir Winston Churchill, and Willie as Somerset Maugham. Interestingly, these two gifted vigorous men were born in the same year, 1874, and lived almost exactly the same long span of life. Both were successful, active, and busy long past the average retirement age, but both were compelled to endure a final stage of painful disagreeable senility.

Oliver Wendell (Case 38)

He was the son of a famous father. The first half century of his life was not undistinguished; he was a lawyer of considerable accomplishment; his achievements, however, were not such as to accord him a distinguished place in history, and it seemed likely that he would be remembered only as his father's son. His real career began at the age of sixty-two, when most men are nearing retirement. The final thirty years of his life were truly distinguished and earned him a place in history in his own right. The older he grew, the better he seemed to get. His final year on the Supreme Court, when he was ninety-one, was one of his finest, and he did not miss a single session of the court that year. We are speaking of The Great Dissenter, of course: Oliver Wendell Holmes.

Leonard (Case 39)

Leonard isn't famous, but he shared one thing with Churchill, Maugham, and Holmes: longevity. In this regard, he beat them. As I write these words, Leonard is a hundred years old and still going strong. Always a vigorous man, he is still vigorous, and his mind is clear as a bell. He lives alone, taking care of himself, as he has done since the death of his wife a generation ago. He has always cut his own hay by hand in the back pasture in summer; he still does. He cuts his lawn; he cuts his firewood; he shovels the snow out of the driveway in the winter. Leonard had several sons; they always said they never could keep up with him, physically or mentally, and they still can't. Two of his sons, in fact, have died of old age.

To paraphrase George Orwell, while all men are equal, some are more equal than others. This is especially true where longevity and vigor are concerned. Some men are prematurely old and senile in their forties; some, like Leonard, never seem to wear out, and some, like Justice Holmes, improve with age. For some, the geriatric period really is the golden age, the best years of life; I am sure George Bernard Shaw thought so. Many, like Churchill and Maugham, must endure distressing senility before the end. For some, the senile sessile period can be amazingly long. I knew an old lady who was admitted to a nursing home at the age of seventy: half blind, half deaf, too weak to get out of bed. She lay all day in the nursing home bed, apparently unaware of anything around her, like a vegetable. She lived to be a hundred. She vegetated in that nursing home bed for a full

generation, thirty years. Visit any nursing home and you will
see many vegetative old people like this; there are more of
them each year. It seems to me ironic that, in this public
health conscious day, when we are so afraid of cancer, when
we do such desperate and radical surgery in the hope of pro-
longing life, when the medical profession seems to feel that
death is an awful stigma, so many people survive into advanced old age, long past any enjoyable or useful life. For so
many, death would be a friend. Care of the sessile and senile
invalid is arduous and very expensive.

The basic cause of geriatric degeneration is hardening of
the arteries, arteriosclerosis. The higher brain centers concerned with thinking lose their function from insufficient
oxygen due to partially blocked blood vessels, while lower
brain centers essential to life continue functioning. Many
theories have been proposed, but we do not know the cause
of arteriosclerosis; many regimens have been prescribed, but
we do not know how to cure it or prevent it.

There is, certainly, a hereditary influence, which seems
operative in alternative generations. Osler, father of modern
clinical medicine, said that the secret of longevity was to
choose your grandparents carefully. It has been suggested—
and I think it probably true—that if arteriosclerosis could be
prevented, man's natural life span with full vitality and vigor,
with good physical and mental powers (and in men, at least,
full sexual potency), might very well extend a hundred and
fifty years. It might be added that anybody who lived for a
hundred and fifty years would almost undoubtedly have
had cancer, so we must cure cancer too if we wish to prolong
longevity. And one might wonder who would want to live for
a century and a half, especially if he had to spend more than
half of this span in retirement.

The symptoms of senility are familiar: peevishness, irritability, suspicion, garrulousness, inflexibility, slovenly dress
and personal hygiene, poor attention span, diminished social
awareness, clear recall of ancient events combined with poor
memory for recent happenings. The senile person does not act

senile at all times; he may be gracious, charming, and interesting for short periods of time and may carry off a public appearance very well. People who live with the senile individual know too well that such good moments are the exception and not the rule.

The senile person may seem largely unaware of his senility or, at least, is reluctant to admit it to himself. A particularly sensitive situation arises when a person in authority grows senile: the surgeon getting careless, the judge beginning to lose his judgment, the professor or the minister becoming a garrulous bore. A mandatory retirement age is sometimes a godsend in managing such people. Creative individuals whose work is solitary and does not involve close contact with others can often continue their work, in decreasing quantity but consistently high quality, even in the face of considerable senility. It may be said that work defers senility and old age, while retirement causes rapid aging. In this regard, a mandatory retirement age does great disservice to the individual, and it often does disservice to society, depriving us of the experience and judgment of many vigorous old people. It would have been a pity if George Bernard Shaw, Michelangelo, Winston Churchill, Somerset Maugham, or Justice Oliver Wendell Holmes had retired at the age of sixty-five. Particularly fortunate is the individual with the second business, hobby, or creative interest, who can retire from one activity into another. With the increasing span of geriatric years most people can expect, it would seem strongly desirable for every man, and woman, to develop such a second interest in which he and she can occupy body and mind after retirement. Fishing, golf, travel, sitting in the sun are all very well for a few weeks, but sheer recreation is insufficient to sustain interest in life.

Very often the disabilities of age are increased by degenerative changes in organs other than the brain. Many geriatric people are disabled by arthritis, by the residuals of stroke, by fractures. Though we can't prevent the arthritis, the stroke, the fracture, it is amazing how much functional ability can be restored with modern techniques in rehabilitation and physiotherapy. It is tragic how relatively few such people have had the opportunity of receiving proper rehabilitation and physiotherapy. Too many people resign themselves to disability without making an effort to overcome it, and too many young persons do not seem to know the benefits of such therapy to aging relatives. Also very troublesome is loss of function of special sense organs: eye and ear. Many elderly persons face increasing blindness and many more increasing deafness. Treatment of aging changes of the eye, cataract and glaucoma, is often very good today; too many elderly persons avoid eye care through fear or ignorance. Even more frequently neglected is deafness. Although eyeglasses are accepted as normal appendages today, there seems to be a stigma against the hearing aid. Partial deafness of the elderly brings with it a rather specific paranoid reaction and social difficulties often thought to be due to senility alone. The average American would never buy a pair of spectacles over the counter without a prescription, but he will often buy a hearing aid in this fashion. By consequence, his hearing aid may not be fitted to his hearing loss, in which case it will be unpleasant and confusing for him to wear. There are a great many hearing aids lying unused in bureau drawers throughout the country. Also, people fail to realize that a hearing aid is a machine. A pair of glasses requires no maintenance, but a hearing aid with a broken wire or a dying battery does not work.

The two most dire problems of age are the fear of death and loneliness. Many old people are perfectly adjusted to the increasing possibility of their own death, and many welcome it, but many seem to be more afraid of it than ever. In age, a lack of faith does not sustain, and here, most poignantly, the inability of an individual to satisfy his religious need becomes apparent. Loneliness in old age is inevitable. The geriatric person often has outlived his mate, his friends, sometimes his children. Making new friends among younger people is neither easy nor satisfactory. The solution is new friends in the geriatric group. Not infrequently, marriage is the answer; one is often surprised at the marriage of two elderly persons long past the age of passion, but such a marriage has the usual effect of increasing the years, and enjoyment of the years, for both. This fact might be offered as proof that passion is not the essential ingredient for marriage. On the other hand, young people might be surprised, and maybe even shocked, if they knew how much sexual activity really does occur in geriatric marriages. Marriage is the solution only for some; for many, the retirement village and similar communal developments for the elderly is the answer.

Our span of years, and our enjoyment of the later years, is not within our own control, but here, as everywhere, there is much the individual can do to better his chances in the environment. Here, as everywhere, emotional maturity, understanding of self, awareness of others, are priceless ingredients. Resignation to disability merely fixes the disability. To enjoy, we must create; to create, we must struggle to overcome our limitations, a struggle which can never be entirely successful; and to find satisfaction, we must overcome dissatisfaction at our lack of complete success. These axioms, incidentally, are just as valid for the young as for the old. It is later than we think.

14

The Misplaced Ones

James and John (Case 40)

They were brothers, brought up on a farm. Their father was determined that they should learn to farm in the modern scientific fashion, and he sent them to the state university where they majored in agriculture. When John graduated, his father bought an adjoining farm for him; he did the same for James two years later.

John liked people, but he did not like farming, and he disliked a rural environment. He deeded his farm over to his brother and moved to the city where he found employment in a real estate and insurance firm. He did very well and he soon became a partner.

James, on the other hand, liked farming. He ran his own farm and that which had belonged to his brother and, eventually, that which had belonged to his father too. James developed chronic asthma. After study, it was discovered that he was allergic to a number of agricultural plants. Upon physician's advice, James gave up the farms and moved to the city. He found employment in his brother's real estate and insurance firm. He no longer wheezed, but he hated city life. Soon, he moved back to the country and took up farming again. He wheezed, but he was happy.

James and John were lucky. Each found himself misplaced, in a career to which he was unsuited. Each was wise enough to realize this and to choose the suitable field, even though in James's case it meant enduring a chronic medical disease.

Modern life has a tendency to misplace us. In a complex technological world, better careers require long specialized training. It is often necessary for the student to choose his specialty early, before he has much understanding of his own tastes and trends. How does one know whether a given specialty is suitable until one has tried it? Having tried it and not liked it, does one have time to learn another specialty or the courage to throw away the past in favor of the future?

Tom, Dick, and Harry (Case 41)

They were all physicians. They interned together at the same teaching hospital and each took a residency there. Tom was a pediatrician, Dick a gynecologist, and Harry a surgeon.

After residency, Tom, the pediatrician, established his practice in a small city. He was a gifted and intelligent man, well versed in his specialty; he always had something of value to contribute at conferences and teaching rounds at the hospital in which he had staff privileges. He kept up with the latest advances in his field. He published a number of papers in the medical literature and was author of a moderately successful pediatric text. When other pediatricians had professional problems, they asked Tom for advice, but they sent him no referrals. When non-pediatricians were worried about their own children, they sought Tom's advice but they did not ask him to see the children. Tom was a doctor's doctor but not a child's pediatrician. His practice volume was small and his income low. Small though his practice was, Tom dreaded office hours and suffered through them anxiously. He was most happy talking shop with other doctors. Tom liked diseases of children, but Tom did not like children. He was afraid of them. His fear was communicated to the small patients and they in turn were difficult, tearful, and uncooperative, which made his problems worse. People sometimes wondered why he was a pediatrician.

Dick, the gynecologist, got along with women well in his consulting room; he was gracious, charming, and sympathetic, and his female patients liked him on first contact. In the examining room, however, it was a different story. The pelvic examination, bread-and-butter in the gynecologist's routines, seemed to make him nervous, which made his patients nervous too. Probably for this reason, his practice was also small. It was never clear to his associates whether Dick liked doing pelvics too little or too much; there certainly seemed to be some sexual factor operative; but at any rate his professionalism left him in the examining room. Dick had a military obligation and he entered the Army. The Army doesn't need many gynecologists, and Dick was assigned to a large base hospital in an administrative capacity. Most doctors have a hatred of administrative work, but Dick liked it, and he did well. He decided to make the service his career. He rose rapidly in rank and eventually became a general. In the Army, he did no pelvic exams.

Harry, the surgeon, also entered private practice. He was an immediate success. His patient volume was heavy from the beginning. He loved surgery, but the pace and pressure of 18-hour days was too much for him, and he had a breakdown, part physical and part emotional: a combination of hypertension and anxiety. During convalescence, he did some woodcarving. Harry had always been clever with a knife. People liked the clever eagles, owls, and ducks he carved, and Harry began to sell them. He never returned to surgery. He became a professional full-time woodcarver; he didn't make much money, but his anxiety left him, and his blood pressure remained in normal ranges without medication.

Here are three examples of misplacement within the medical profession. Some physicians are not suited for the medical profession at all; this is not too difficult to understand; many are doctors' sons, pushed into medicine by family tradition; some were originally motivated by a praiseworthy but unrealistic idealism. It is more puzzling to see a good doctor in the wrong medical specialty. All physicians begin with general training and have a chance to sample each specialty before a decision must be made. There seem to be some doctors who choose a specialty for which they are unsuited. I have known unstable psychiatrists; latently homosexual urologists; gynecologists who were misogynistic; pediatricians afraid of children; and surgeons without mechanical aptitude. Such men seem to have a compulsion to do, each day, jobs which are difficult for them, perhaps as a means of proving their own value and worth. This is neurotic thinking; physicians are by no means immune to neurosis. Similar misplacement occurs in every profession.

Morris (Case 42)

Morris never had to work for a living; he inherited a fortune at an early age. Many men of independent means feel a responsibility for the money which they did not earn and devote themselves to philanthropy or to public service of some type. Morris felt no such obligation. He devoted himself to having fun.

It is perhaps expected that the playboy will marry unwisely and often. Morris seemed to be trying for the record in this regard. The last I heard, Morris had married nine wives, had been divorced by nine wives, and was about to get married for the tenth, if not the final, time. All his wives were young, blonde, and long-legged; none seemed to be overly intellectual.

One must suppose that sexual desire alone was not the motivation for Morris's multiple marriages, for presumably a man with Morris's money could satisfy a taste for young long-legged blondes without the necessity of marriage. The institution of marriage must have been attractive to Morris. One must suppose that a person so often divorced has traits undesirable in a husband. One suspects sexual perversion. None of the wives ever brought up such a possibility in divorce court evidence, however. Apparently his ex-wives liked him, for he remained good friends with all of them.

Why did Morris marry? He didn't know. Perhaps he was looking for the unattainable. Why did his wives leave him? Many women remain married to unattractive, psychotic, cruel, alcoholic, or deviated men; there is no evidence that Morris was any of these. There is one absolutely uncongenial trait in a husband which most women cannot tolerate; this is egocentricity, a sort of self-centeredness, which prevents the man giving any of himself. There are men who enter marriage only to take; such men are misplaced in marriage, which must be a give and take relationship. It seems likely that Morris is an example of this kind of extreme egocentricity.

Nat and Nell (Case 43)

Nat and Nell were man and wife; they seemed to have every ingredient for successful marriage except one. Nat was born and raised in a small town; he loved small towns and hated city life. Nell was born and raised in a city; she liked city life and hated small towns.

Nat and Nell maintained their marriage, and their life was like a ping-pong game: two years in the city, two years in the country; then back to the city; then back to the country; and so forth. They loved each other and could not bring themselves to separate, but each was unhappy in the other's chosen environment, and neither was sufficiently resilient to compromise to the needs of the other in this respect, so one or the other was displaced geographically at all times.

Misplacement, in job or career, in marriage, in geography, is often seen in persons not apparently neurotic or psychotic. In a minor degree, it is inescapable. One has free choice, but, lacking the gift of prophecy, one cannot predict the ultimate destination of a road selected, and once started down a road it may be difficult to turn back. One gets into a rut. The rut may be unpleasant, but it seems more unpleasant or too expensive or too dangerous to escape it. Serene and mature adjustment to ruts is part of practical lifesmanship.

Serious misplacement, in a person not neurotic or psychotic, could be thought of as a failure of education. The essence of education may be defined in the Socratic injunction: "Know thyself." The man who does not know himself is very likely to become misplaced. Complete self-knowledge being beyond us, some misplacement is inevitable; we endure it if we are mature; and we must be mature to make the best of it.

Serious misplacement, too, may be a function of inadequate self-expression. Self-knowledge is not enough without self-expression, and self-expression requires a certain amount of courage. There is a phenomenon, applicable to the artist, which has been called "creative courage." The artist must have basic knowledge of the fundamentals of his field; he must display some mastery of his medium; he must be aware of trends and fashions and formulas of his day. However, this alone is not enough. If he is to be more than a hack or a drudge, the artist must find courage to go beyond trends, fashions, and formulae; he must use his medium to express his personality in his own individual way; otherwise, although he may be solvent and acceptable and even popular, his work will not endure.

Creative courage may be necessary in areas other than the creative arts. Otherwise, misplacement will result. Misplacement, whether accepted with cheerful resignation or with bitter discontent, may often imply mediocrity. Mediocrity is not a major sin; few of us can be creative artists; most of us must labor in the salt mines, anonymously and without distinction; but we cannot say that we have really lived unless we make some effort toward education and self-knowledge and unless we can find the courage to make occasional expressions of our individuality.

15

The Addicted Ones

The God of Puritans and Calvinists looked with disfavor on pleasure-seeking, considering pleasure the equivalent of sin. Few of us are Calvinists today, but few of us can escape all traces of a Puritan heritage. Pleasure presents us with a paradox. Considering ourselves realists, emancipated from the restrictive inhibition of the past, we like to believe that pleasure is man's prerogative, provided that the pleasure is innocent, provided that our pleasure does not injure or restrict the freedoms of others. Man, who must endure pain and suffering, would seem to be entitled to the pursuit of happiness, including pleasure. Yet, as we seek pleasure, we tend to be anxious and guilty. As part of our means of relieving tension in our pursuit of pleasure, we tend to formalize and organize our recreations, setting up rules and regulations in our sports and games, thereby making out of the recreation a business and giving it the appearance of gainful constructive activity. That pleasure for its own sake can be gainful or constructive seems to elude us.

Consider for example fishing. The traditional image of the sport is the barefoot boy, with pole cut from a sapling, a can of worms, a hook, some string; he lies on the bank in the warm sunshine, looks up at the clouds, and dreams; if he hooks a fish, he may not even notice it. It is difficult for a modern man, even a modern boy, to fish this way. Now he must buy a Fiberglas pole, a spinning reel, a special type of tested cord, lures, a license, a boat, and a guide. We make of fishing a technology with a special science of its own.

In golf, it is not enough to thrash away in the bunker. We take lessons. We have a handicap. We engage in tournaments. For many a middle-aged man, his golf score is more anxiety-provoking than the state of his business.

In the game of bridge, it is not enough to release aggressions by overbidding and wild daring play. The laws of Goren are as inhibitory as the Ten Commandments. People spend their lives working anxiously for Master points.

We also tend to approach personal gratifications and indulgences with anxiety. "Everything I enjoy is illegal, immoral, or fattening."

Caught in the paradox, driven toward pleasing his body and his senses but anxious and guilty at his sin, an indulging man is threatened by addiction. The addicted man is trapped by a habit of indulgence; the habit itself in moderation is pleasant; the habit may be harmless, though many things which give us pleasure do involve a risk; the trouble with addiction is that the habit rules the man, distorting his other relationships. Knowing he should give the habit up, for his own health and safety, but unable to give the habit up because of an inner compulsion, the paradox begins to hurt him on both horns. Sometimes he comes to a bad end on account of the substance to which he is addicted. Most of the substances to which humans become addicted may be used with safety, as well as pleasure, for long periods of time, a fact to which reformers and moralists customarily are blind. The efforts of the reformer, attempting to get immoderate people to give up their indulgences, are usually based on dire predictions of disaster to the addict—a fact which the addict knows from personal experience to be at least partially untrue—and are most often phrased in moral terms of pleasure-as-sin. Moralists seldom succeed. Their efforts increase anxiety, rather than relieve it; since the indulgent person indulges to relieve anxiety, moral preachments tend to make the habits worse.

Pleasure for its own sake is healthful on emotional terms, if not pursued exclusively, if combined with constructive work and meaningful social relationships. In proper balance, pleasure seems to increase efficiency in work and fluency in social relations.

In itself, a habit is not bad. Even granted the risk of a habit, life can't be entirely safe, for life is a risk operation, and something is bound to get us in the end. It might be better to be done in by an old familiar habit which has given us decades of pleasure than by some chance or impulsive act of stupidity however well intentioned.

The trouble with the reformer is that he maintains his own ascetic existence is to be desired or admired. The person with a habit does not desire or admire the ascetic life. The trouble with an addict is that his abuse of the habit tends to spoil the pleasures of indulgence for everybody else. Humans tend to develop habits. Perhaps we should not feel guilty or anxious about our habits unless we are guilty and anxious about the human condition and its inevitable mortality.

Paul (Case 44)

Paul developed Buerger's Disease, a rare condition characterized by progressive gangrene of the tips of the extremities. In the course of the next few years, multiple amputations of fingers and toes were required. Paul was a heavy cigarette smoker. It was carefully explained to him that the patient with Buerger's Disease has a peculiar sensitivity to tobacco. If he continued smoking, his disease would progress, and further amputations would be required. If he stopped, it was likely that his disease would not progress. Paul seemed to understand the situation, but he continued smoking and further amputations were necessary. He lost his remaining fingers and toes. He still smoked even when he had no fingers left and somebody else had to hold the cigarette to his lips for him.

There are certain diseases where the use of tobacco causes progression of the disease. The rare Buerger's Disease is one. More common is arteriosclerotic gangrene, with or without diabetes. A third is the increasingly common and serious lung condition, emphysema. Tobacco is not the chief cause of these diseases, but it obviously has a bad effect on patients with these diseases, and such patients are customarily advised to stop smoking. Most of them prefer loss of the pleasures of tobacco to further increasing disability, and do stop smoking. The few who do not may be regarded as genuinely addicted to tobacco.

In speaking of addiction, it is customary to distinguish between true medical addiction and psychological addiction. In true medical addiction, the body becomes so accustomed to the addicting substance that it requires the substance for continued health, and withdrawal of the substance causes severe symptoms and real physical disease. In psychological addictions, such a physical withdrawal syndrome is lacking. To my mind, the distinction between medical and psychological addiction is not very important. Some substances officially considered addicting under our Harrison Antinarcotic Act cause serious withdrawal syndromes, especially heroin, morphine, and a number of the other opium derivatives; and some, considered narcotic under this law, cause little or no withdrawal symptoms, such as codeine and marijuana. Tobacco is considered non-addicting, but every smoker knows that there is a definite withdrawal syndrome when he stops smoking, although, admittedly, it is much milder than a morphine withdrawal syndrome. To my mind, the essence of addiction is psychological and the degree of withdrawal symptoms is not directly correlated with the degree of addiction. Tobacco is addicting. It is not difficult to stop smoking—

Mark Twain boasted that he had done so a thousand times—but most smokers start again.

Current public opinion accepts the fact that cigarette smoking is very dangerous to health. The Surgeon General tells us so; the American Cancer Society tells us so; even the pack of cigarettes now carries a printed warning to this effect by law. Despite this public opinion, consumption of cigarettes continues to increase. Why? Does the average smoker not believe the Surgeon General or the American Cancer Society? Is he consciously trying to commit suicide by smoke? Or is he so addicted that he really cannot stop?

The average healthy cigarette smoker is in a different position than the patient with Buerger's Disease or emphysema. The healthy smoker has no present disease; he feels well and he likes to smoke; the hazard to his health lies in the future, over some distant horizon; he prefers his pleasure now and will take his chances with disease when the time comes; after all, sometime before he gets cancer of the lung, he might get run over by a truck.

Actually, I think the Surgeon General, the American Cancer Society, and certain propagandizing members of my profession have sold the public a bill of goods in this regard. I think, also, the public suspects the lie. If cigarettes were so dangerous, I believe that most smokers would stop. Most smokers with arteriosclerosis or emphysema, to whom tobacco is obviously and manifestly dangerous, do stop. The actual fact of the matter is that tobacco, like most pleasure-giving substances to which mankind becomes addicted, is safe, for most people, most of the time. Not even tobacco's most bitter enemy can maintain that one cigarette has ever caused any person any physical harm at any time, whereas one cyanide pill would have finished him and, in fact, one dose of LSD may put him into the asylum permanently. Furthermore, excepting the patients with certain specific diseases we have mentioned, ten cigarettes or a hundred cigarettes or a thousand cigarettes do the smoker no harm. The possible harm of tobacco for the healthy smoker only follows decades of daily continuous use. This harm, of which we hear so much, is lung cancer, of course.

Almost all patients with lung cancer have smoked cigarettes. Does this mean that all cigarette smokers get lung cancer? By no means! The incidence of lung cancer in cigarette smokers is about one in four hundred, a quarter of one percent. The risk of lung cancer to the female smoker is negligible. Though women do rarely develop lung cancer, it occurs as frequently in non-smoking as in smoking women. In men, about one cigarette smoker in two hundred and fifty gets lung cancer. Out of every two hundred and fifty cigarette smoking men, two hundred and forty-nine of them will not get lung cancer.

Why do a few cigarette smokers get lung cancer while most do not? We don't know. Which cigarette smokers will get lung cancer? We cannot predict. What is the factor in cigarette smoke which causes susceptible males to get lung cancer? We do not know. Until we know these things, perhaps we should spend less time and energy frightening the public. The scare approach, obviously, does not work. The smoker continues his pleasure, but his pleaure is mixed with fear. The combination can, and often does, produce neurosis. Neurosis causes a thousand times more pain, expense, suffering, and disability than cancer. That label on the cigarette pack strikes me as ridiculous. It would be equally valid to label every automobile as possibly dangerous to the health of the user, and this would not exactly stop people from using automobiles. Perhaps we should also label mattresses, for most people die recumbent upon one.

Cancer is a horrible disease. Some day, we will learn to cure it and prevent it. We cannot now prevent it. The treatment results in a cure now and then, but not very often, and the treatment is often worse than the disease. This is a heretical remark from a member of my profession, but I feel that a fatalistic attitude toward cancer is warranted in light of our present ignorance. By fatalism, we could hope to reduce the enormous incidence of the neurosis

associated with cancerphobia. In the meantime, I question
the wisdom of spoiling pleasure for the many in the vain
hope of saving the few.

Ethel (Case 45)

She was born fat, they say. She was a fat little kid. She grew
fatter in adolescence. As an adult, she grew fatter and fatter and
fatter. She died at the age of forty-four, at which time she weighed
more than three hundred pounds.

Should obesity be included in a chapter on addictions?
All living things need food, a fact not true of any other
addicting substance. It seems to me, however, that the compulsive eater who overeats beyond nutritional needs is psychologically addicted; and overeating strikes me as the most
common and serious of the addictions. Obesity is not compatible with longevity. How often have you seen a person
who is at the same time fat and old?

Americans have become very conscious of the dangers of
obesity in recent years, and many of us are calorie counters.
In fact, many Americans become neurotic in the opposite
direction, counting calories obsessively, going on compulsive
diets, and depriving themselves of pleasure with the fork.
In general, I think, the calorie-consciousness is good for us,
and largely accounts for the vigor, vitality, and youthfulness
of so many of our senior citizens. I might note that I
consider it more healthy psychologically, and no less healthy
physically, to indulge in an occasional feast and compensate
for the extra calories by reduction for a few days afterward
than to be totally ascetic and avoid the banquet table altogether.

In regard to obesity, I think there are two kinds. There
is the person, ten or twenty pounds overweight, who becomes
aware of his increasing corpulence and decides to do something about it. For these people, weight reduction is relatively easy; a few weeks on a diet does the trick. I think

any nutritionally sound diet works as well as any other, and simple calorie reduction without a formal diet does equally well. Fads and fashions in diet crop up regularly, often outlined in books which invariably seem to become best sellers. Most of such fad diets, and the books which describe them, are fraudulent, because they imply that there is a special way to lose weight by eating as much as you like. This, of course, is not true.

The other type of obese person, many pounds overweight, has always been aware of the problem, has "tried everything," and never loses weight. These are the addictive eaters. They do not necessarily eat much at any given time; they eat all the time; they are the constant nibblers. These people will not adhere to any diet and they will not stop nibbling. Also, they do not live long. The addictive eater cannot, or will not, give an honest dietary history. They will tell you what they eat, and you must multiply the calories they claim by two or three to get the truth. Obese people seem to be pathological liars, in regard to food at least, and they may be related to the psychopath. I have often been amused when addictive eaters tell me they "eat like a bird," which they often do; this remark is true, though not in the way intended, for birds have a high basal metabolism rate and must eat almost constantly.

I have largely given up trying to treat the compulsive eater in my practice. Dr. E. B. Astwood, in an article called *The Heritage of Corpulence* (Endocrinology 71:337–41, 1962), proposes that obesity, at the present time, is an incurable condition. I agree with him. Let the fat woman enjoy herself: for her short time.

Another common American addiction is coffee. Many Americans tend to think that coffee is as bland, and as necessary, as water. The British traditionally have the same attitudes toward tea. Coffee and tea are both pleasant and stimulating, and the pleasures of these beverages to the multitudes are great. In excess of perhaps five cups a day, I do not consider these beverages safe, and I think the 10-

cup-, 20-cup-, 50-cup-a-day people are in danger. In these ranges, these beverages often induce hypertension. In my opinion, coffee addiction in this degree is potentially more dangerous to health than cigarette addiction.

Alcohol is the most controversial of the substances to which man can become habituated. The opinions of those who drink and those who don't often seem at complete variance on this subject. The benefits of alcohol are obvious to most people who use it; this is the best sedative we know and the best tranquilizer; it eases emotional tension, relaxes physical fatigue, serves as catalyst to song and dance and laughter and courtship and business and politics and social conviviality. It may do more than Milton can to justify God's ways to man. The dangers of alcohol should be equally apparent to those who drink as well as those who don't. There is the state of drunkenness which is a danger to any person drinking. And there is alcoholism, a public health problem of major proportions, a very distressing and difficult problem on individual levels.

The immediate primary effect of alcohol ingestion is a relaxation of inhibitions, a softening of the harsh corners of reality, and a pleasant physical euphoria. This is the stage which the sane drinker seeks to achieve and maintain when drinking. In this stage, basic social conformity and maturity of judgment is retained; cerebration is not impaired and in fact emotional receptivity and imagination may often be increased; and in this stage physical coordination and reaction time is not significantly impaired. In fact, many overly reactive people have better physical coordination after a drink or two.

A sense of physical well-being and euphoria is pleasant, and the pleasure alone might justify the use of an intoxicant if the risks are not too great. Is a relaxation of inhibition and softening of reality advantageous? In theory, perhaps not, for the mature man should be able to cope with inhibitions and reality. In practice, for many people in these tense and nervous times—and in all other times which have also been tense and nervous—a temporary vacation from the stress and care of life seems to serve as a partial antidote to neurosis and promote emotional well-being. Used for such purposes, for pleasure and relaxation, alcohol's advantages seem to outweigh its liabilities for the nineteen drinkers out of twenty who do not have a drinking problem. Used as a crutch or as a medicine, alcohol is dangerous.

Like all substances used habitually by men over the centuries, alcohol is safe from the physical point of view. In terms of immediate direct toxicity, alcohol is not as safe as tobacco. The smoker cannot hurt himself at a single sitting. It is possible to kill yourself with drink at one sitting through the direct toxic effects of alcohol on the brain. This is possible, though difficult, and alcohol is much safer than the sedatives and tranquilizers in this regard. Sedatives and tranquilizers have often been used successfully for suicide. For most persons, it is literally impossible to commit suicide with alcohol. In my professional experience, I have seen this happen only once, a physician who drank three fifths of vodka on an empty stomach in two hours. The Welsh poet, Dylan Thomas, presumably killed himself in this fashion; just before entering his terminal coma, Thomas is believed to have consumed eighteen highballs in less than an hour. Most persons pass out long before they have consumed a lethal dose of alcohol, and the margin of safety between coma level and lethal level for alcohol is much greater than for most of the anesthetics used in an operating room. The toxic effects of alcohol on brain tissue, at lower levels than the lethal one, are temporary and reversible; some hours after cessation of drinking complete sobriety returns; this is not true of cerebral intoxicants such as the hallucinatory drugs where a single non-lethal dose may produce permanent damage of the thinking apparatus. Even after long continued daily use, alcohol is safe from the point of view of physical toxicity. Although the point is controversial and some experts do not agree, the weight of evidence seems to indicate that chronic use of alcohol does not cause any physical disease directly. In this regard, alcohol is safer than tobacco. There are a number of diseases where alcohol is an important contributory cause, but the evidence continues to suggest to the majority of observers that these diseases are caused by nutritional and vitamin deficiencies associated with the poor diet of the alcoholic and not by the direct effect of alcohol itself.

Although alcohol, physically, is safe to use, its use is often obviously dangerous. The line between the safe stage of relaxation and the dangerous stage of drunkenness is thin, and even the sanest of drinkers risks overrunning his end point from time to time. As any drinker knows, his capacity, and his ability to judge his own capacity, differs considerably under different circumstances. Drunkenness is unpleasant, as well as dangerous, and the sane drinker seeks to avoid it. The social drinker, learning from experience, is apt to become more temperate and moderate in his drinking patterns as he grows older; for the person with a drinking problem, obviously, the reverse is the case.

The state of alcoholism is difficult to define. Experts have been trying to set down definitions and diagnostic criteria without marked success. Despite difficulties of definition, the alcoholic is easily recognized. There are obvious personality disturbances in him when he is drinking, and some of these disturbances may be recognized in an alcoholic who is not drinking. He uses alcohol for a different purpose, and with a different result, than the social drinker. Prohibitionists are inclined to feel that the heavy social drinker is just one step short of being alcoholic, but unprejudiced observation should suggest that the amount of alcohol consumed is not the criterion of alcoholism.

Winnie (Case 46)

Winnie began drinking in early adolescence and continued to drink until shortly before his death. His capacity was astonishing. During the long span of approximately seventy-eight years, he drank every day, and his minimal daily intake was a bottle of brandy.

On one occasion, this Naval Person, as Winnie often called himself, was aboard a British vessel and was conversing with the officers. The question arose as to whether Winnie, in a lifetime of heavy drinking, had consumed enough brandy to float the ship. After mathematical calculation, it was decided that he had not but that he had consumed sufficient spirits to fill the vessel's substantial holds.

"I have taken more out of alcohol than alcohol has taken out of me," Winnie is reported to have said.

We have met Winnie before, of course. We are again speaking of Sir Winston Churchill. I have never heard it suggested that Winnie was an alcoholic, though his total lifetime consumption of alcohol had been equaled by very few human beings. It hasn't been suggested that alcohol shortened his life. I don't think anybody would have the temerity to suggest that drinking reduced Churchill's accomplishments in any of the several fields in which he was a distinguished success.

Rose (Case 47)

Rose was a disreputable person of the lower social order, a prostitute. She was obviously alcoholic. Everybody who knew her recognized her as such. Rose's average daily consumption was two bottles of beer. On this amount, she appeared to remain continually drunk. If she tried to consume three beers, she could not walk. It was impossible for her to consume four bottles of beer at a single sitting; before the fourth beer was finished, Rose would pass out.

Rose and Sir Winston Churchill offer a marked comparison, not only in life achievement, but in alcoholic capacity. Such a comparison is evidence that the amount of liquor consumed is not in itself the measure of the alcoholic.

The social drinker, even the heavy social drinker, functions efficiently on all levels. The alcoholic, including those who drink lightly and even when not drinking at all, has distorted relationships. The bottle may be a pleasant part of the social drinker's life, but it is not the dominant or central part. The alcoholic is dominated, in all areas, by his bottle.

The alcoholic appears to be a conscience-ridden man. He is basically defensive. He may show his defensiveness with compensatory arrogant hostility or, more frequently, with a whining servile self-pity. It is not enough for the alcoholic to achieve relaxation of his inhibitions and tensions; he pushes himself through the stage sought by the social drinker until he has drowned his critical faculties. The consequences of his drinking make him even more defensive and self-critical which drives him to anesthetize himself still further, creating a typical and difficult vicious circle. The difference between the alcoholic and the social drinker is perhaps most clear-cut in the early hang-over stage. On awakening after a heavy night, the last thing a social drinker wants is a drink; and a drink is the first thing an alcoholic needs on opening his eyes. The alcoholic does not like himself and he cannot bear to face himself.

It is my opinion that alcoholism is incurable until it cures itself. It is also my opinion that alcoholism does cure itself with reasonable frequency. The group called Alcoholics Anonymous uses the phrase "rock bottom." When the alcoholic touches rock bottom, it is not difficult to help him, for he has already developed motivation to help himself. Before he is so motivated, no matter what he may promise in remorse, no form of therapy seems to offer much except "drying out" of a temporary nature.

The work of Alcoholics Anonymous is highly commendable; it is one of the few therapies which has a reasonable frequency of success. However, the approach of Alcoholics Anonymous is not theoretically ideal, because they do not attempt to cure the disease, only to control it. A basic premise of A.A., which is shared by a majority of professional workers in the field, is that alcoholism is incurable; "once alcoholic, always alcoholic"; the controlled alcoholic should never dare to take another drink.

A few professional workers in the field believe that alcoholism can be cured, and that cured alcoholics can become safe and sane social drinkers. I concur with this point of view. I have seen a few alcoholics cure themselves. If a cure is to be desired, rather than control, the alcoholic almost has to do it by himself, since there are so few professional workers who admit that the condition can be cured.

A final incidental note on the alcohol controversy. Some prohibitionists base their argument on religious grounds, maintaining that it is un-Christian to drink. This argument must amuse the monks of certain religious orders who manufacture some of the finest wines and liqueurs. Religious prohibitionists seem to forget who turned a gloomy wedding feast into a joyous celebration by changing the water into wine. Perhaps they forget what beverage was consumed at the Last Supper. Even St. Paul, author of so much taboo in the name of Christ, wrote: "Drink no longer water but use a little wine for thy stomach's sake and thine often infirmities." (1 Thimothy 5:23.)

There's an addiction common in modern life which might be called the habit of "the valley of the dolls," to borrow the title of a recent best-selling novel on the subject: addiction to sedatives, often barbiturates for sleep, often combined with tranquilizers in the daytime, and not infrequently combined with amphetamines or other "pep pills" in the morning. Such an addiction is often begun at the suggestion of a physician, for relief of symptoms from neurosis, with drugs on his prescription. The extent of drug usage gets out of the doctor's control, often without his knowledge. Until recently, pharmacists were willing accomplices to this addiction, freely refilling the prescriptions to their own profit. Recent law prohibits such indiscriminate refilling, but the patient can still get around this by consulting a number of doctors and using a number of drugstores.

These drugs are very helpful for the management of neurotic symptoms under proper control. There are occasions when their use may be very helpful and healthful for anybody. As an addiction habit, these drugs are more expensive than alcohol, less safe, and less effective. The margin of safety between coma and lethal levels is much smaller than with alcohol, and sedatives have often been used suicidally. They are implicated in the half-accident half-suicide which we have discussed before. Some of these drugs, especially some of the more potent tranquilizers and the "pep pills," have serious physical toxicity effects. Physically speaking, the barbiturates are safe for habitual use. Perhaps the chief danger of "valley of the dolls" addiction is the masking of an underlying neurosis which deserves psychiatric care.

Narcotic addiction is a serious social problem in certain areas, slum neighborhoods of big cities, and frightening epidemics break out from time to time in school and college populations. Individual problems are apt to be encountered in two groups: in patients accidentally addicted by their doctors, and in the medical profession itself where doctors, nurses, and orderlies have easy access to the drugs.

Narcotics are very important in medicine: the chief weapon against the most awful symptom of injury and illness, pain. Narcotics seldom seem to addict a patient with real pain; when the pain is gone, there is no desire for further narcotic. Addiction occurs when narcotics are used for symptoms of neurosis or as an expression of antisocial hostility. Once addicted, it is almost impossible for the addict to break his habit alone; physical withdrawal symptoms are too severe.

The popular image of the crazed and raving "dope fiend" is false. The addict receiving his drug is not violent; he is content to dream the hours away. He becomes violent when deprived of his drug; then he will kill and steal to get it.

In overdosage, narcotics are lethal; in therapeutic doses, there are unpleasant side effects but these disappear in the habituated person. Addicts using unsterile needles often develop local abscesses or generalized blood poisoning. Certain infections can be transmitted when addicts share a common syringe: malaria and hepatitis. Administered with sterile technique in proper dosage, narcotics are safe, and physical disease does not follow chronic use.

Treatment of narcotic addiction is very poor indeed. The addict can be weaned away from his drug, but almost invariably he returns to his addiction. Narcotic addiction, like true addiction to almost anything, is virtually incurable although, from time to time, an addict does cure himself.

Since narcotics, properly given, are safe; since the addict with sufficient drug is happy and socially acceptable; since he will kill and steal when deprived of his drug; and since addiction is virtually incurable, why should addiction be considered a crime? Why is the law so strict in prohibiting narcotics? The law itself plays right into the hands of organized crime. It is easy for a pusher to addict some underprivileged slum youth who takes the drug at first partly out of curiosity and mostly as an expression of antisocial hostility. Once hooked, the addict must have the drug, which the pusher can then sell to him at enormously inflated rates. Without the law, if the narcotic was cheaply and freely available, the association of narcotics with crime might disappear, and the number of addicts might become quite small. Until recent years, this was the experience in England where there was no antinarcotic law, and the British used to point with pride at the absence of a narcotic problem in their country. Recently, they have been having increasing numbers of youthful addicts in Britain too, so the solution may rest more in the taboo-transgression conflict of the young than in the matter of availability of drug.

It is not generally appreciated that narcotic usage has been illegal only in this century. Our Harrison Antinarcotic Act was passed in 1915. Before that time, narcotic addiction was legal, respectable, and common. A surprising number of our ancestors took their daily laudanum, freely available at every pharmacy, with no more stigma than if they were taking snuff. The Chinese, of course, have smoked opium since early history. Our Harrison Act, in fact, was a so-

ciological reaction against a Chinese habit. In the era between the Civil War and World War I, the great railroad-
building era of the West, gangs of Chinese laborers were
imported, and kidnapped, to build the railroads. Many of
these coolies were addicted to opium, and the supply of
opium was limited in this country; tong wars resulted over the
opium supply. On account of violence in Chinatown, narcotics and violence became associated in the popular mind,
and the Harrison Act was the consequence. As a consequence
of the Harrison Act, narcotics became associated not only
with violence but with crime. A narcotics addiction is not
to be encouraged, for such an addiction seriously interferes
with the capacity of the addict for doing constructive work,
but when an addiction is considered as a crime, then it
is in fact likely to become one.

The current newsworthy drug dilemma concerns the so-
called hallucinogens or psychedelic drugs. These drugs are
not medically addicting. They are not apt to be used on a
daily habitual basis and so they differ from the other substances we have been discussing. There is another important
difference: these drugs are not safe. There is no toxic danger
in one cigarette, one drink, one sleeping pill, or even in one
injection of a sixth of a grain of morphine. One dose of
LSD, even in the minimal dosage required for any detectable
effect, may induce a permanent psychosis. And, though LSD
may have been used many times safely in the past by an
individual, this is no guarantee of safety to him, for his next
dose may cause serious permanent disease. Hence, it is not
likely that hallucinogens will have any widespread general
use, since most persons do not wish to make themselves
insane. Hallucinogens are a serious problem as long as they
are vended as a current fad and while articulate advocates do
urge their general use.

The mildest and safest class of these drugs includes morn-
ing-glory seeds, nutmeg, and marijuana. The latter, though
officially classified as narcotic under the Harrison Act, is
not physically addicting. More potent and dangerous are

bufotenine and psilocybin, both derived from mushrooms; cohoba, which comes from the bark of a tree; and peyote or mescaline, derived from a cactus. In a class of its own, both for potency and danger, is LSD.

LSD stands for d-lysergic acid diethylamide tartrate. The base from which LSD is synthesized is ergot, the rye fungus, which also gives us drugs very useful in obstetrics and in treatment of migraine headache. Derivation of LSD from the ergot base is a fairly simple chemical extraction. The drug was first synthesized in 1938 by a chemist in Switzerland working for the international drug company which manufactures most of the ergot derivative drugs. The properties of LSD weren't known until five years later when the discoverer, by accident, inhaled some fumes of the drug and induced in himself the typical delirious state. It was originally thought that the drug produced an artificial schizophrenia. LSD-induced psychosis is like schizophrenia; a chemical closely resembling mescaline is found with some regularity in the urine of schizophrenic patients; but the LSD psychosis is not identical with schizophrenia and the drug has been disappointing in work with schizophrenia. Unlike most drugs, LSD apparently has little or no physical toxicity, and enormous doses may be ingested without producing physical injury or death. It exerts its typical emotional effect in tiny trace doses, and increasing of the dose does not increase this effect. One person can carry sufficient LSD to hallucinate the entire population. Material saturated in an LSD solution, such as a handkerchief or an undergarment, may be worn or carried about and subsequently cut into small pieces; chewing on such a piece of cloth will give enough LSD to produce the desired effect. LSD is metabolized by the body almost immediately, and cannot be detected in the system after ingestion, and so presumably it is a metabolic breakdown product which produces the effect, not LSD itself. Presumably the metabolite enters into the epinephrine-norepinephrine-serotonin-monoamine oxidase system we have discussed before.

The psychological effect of hallucinogens is to break up

normal chains of association. Since association chains built up from our education and experience produce our maturity and judgment, the drugs cause instant immaturity. They also block anticipation of future events, producing distorted sensory images out of context with the past and future. To some people, this is an intensely exciting experience; to others it is intensely frightening. A distorted timelessness suggests a popular philosophy which emphasizes the importance of the moment while discarding the past and future, and advocates of this philosophy naturally desire an LSD experience. This philosophical approach is particularly appealing to certain immature pseudointellectual young persons and for this reason the drug became fashionable to the very persons to whom it is most dangerous. Such persons have incomplete and inadequate association chains, have not grown from past experiences, and are afraid of future events, and consequently are most vulnerable to LSD effects. The more mature a person, the less apt he is to have bad effects from hallucinogens, but such persons do not desire to be hallucinated. LSD can precipitate latent neurosis and psychosis, including schizophrenia, and one dose can produce long-lasting or even permanent disturbances. For this reason, LSD is dangerous. I think it both wise and mandatory that the drug be kept out of amateur hands, although I hope that its use for research purposes under proper scientific control may continue, for LSD may be the key to unlock a very important door.

The importance of LSD seems to lie in study of the causes of psychosis and elucidation of the neurophysiology of the emotions. I doubt if it will be helpful in diagnosis. There have been reports on its use in examination, as an aid to uncovering material concealed in the subconscious mind, but since LSD blocks association trains, its use in this connection would only lead, I should think, to instant confusion. I doubt if LSD will be important in therapy. The experience to date has been disappointing.

One intriguing therapeutic use for LSD has been suggested: in the terminal phase of the dying patient, where the blockage of anticipation of future events might relieve fear at the final stage of life. I would think religion was the preferable antidote. Used in this way, LSD might be thought of as instant religion. As a matter of fact, some articulate advocates of LSD suggest that its usage should be religious and have attempted to build a religion around it. Alcohol, opiates, and hallucinogens have been used from time to time in religious experience. Personally, I would feel that a meaningful religious experience should involve clarity of mind, and I would tend to reject as meaningless hallucinations induced by a toxic drug. Of course, many saints, zealots, and mystics seem to be psychotic. Perhaps we can see truth only through hallucination. If truth lies in visions and voices, LSD may be a drug of choice. Most of the happiest people I know work under the presumption that truth is amenable to logic and reason. Incidentally, many of the happy adjusted people that I know do have what are called bad habits, but none of them use LSD. It might be preferable to confine our habits to substances relatively safe: tobacco, coffee, and alcohol.

16

The Bothered Ones

Sigmund Freud, a patient, thorough, modest scholar, examined a group of hysterical women in greater depth and with greater perception than other psychiatrists. He noticed something which earlier psychiatrists had overlooked: the factor of sexual conflict as cause and expression of neurosis. At that time, females were generally considered to be of two kinds: ladies, who were believed to have no sexual needs or demands, and the other kind, considered to be so immoral and depraved as to deserve no serious consideration. Freud started a revolution, which has been going on ever since.

As a consequence, discussion of sexual matters, in conversation and in print, previously unthinkable, became commonplace. Freudian concepts began to influence and then to dominate all areas of the creative arts. A school of psychotherapy arose which first came to be the major approach to psychiatry and still commands an important influence in the field. As a result of the revolution, light was cast into many dark areas. People began struggling to free themselves from the harmful effects of sexual repressions and inhibitions with beneficial results in many individual cases. We entered an era of sexual sophistication. We have not yet, however, entered an era of sexual maturity. Old moral standards were cast aside, but new moral standards have not appeared. The result may have been enlightenment; it has not, however, been peace of body or of mind. A harmful element of repression has been eliminated; a new and harmful element of anxiety has entered the bedroom. Major emphasis has been placed on sex as a mechanical biological phenomenon; consideration of the importance of psychology in sexual relations, the starting point of the revolution, has, in the process, become overlooked.

The tone used by Freud originally to report his revolutionary theories was casual and disarming. Then fame and controversy overtook him. Later in his career, he began to re-examine his earlier concepts and painfully to reverse some of them. Toward the end of his career, he reported some observations which should have been rather obvious in a tone of naïve astonishment.

"However strange it may sound," he wrote, "I think the possibility must be considered that something in the nature of the sexual instinct itself is unfavorable to the achievement of absolute gratification."

Some of the later sexologists appear not to have noticed this observation as they labor under the premise that sexual satisfaction is mandatory to man's emotional health.

A considerably more sophisticated and urbane writer, C. S. Lewis, made essentially the same point as follows: "Lust is more abstract than logic; it seeks (hope triumphing over experience) for some purely sexual, hence purely imaginary, conjunction of impossible maleness with an impossible femaleness."

Some contemporary sexologists do not appear to know that they are attempting to observe, record, and measure the impossible. It has been said that every individual, privately, considers his or her own sex life to be unsatisfactory. Freud became vaguely aware of the fact, and Lewis stated it urbanely: sex inherently involves dissatisfaction. Sex is a biological tension state. There are long periods of continence during which the tension grows; moments of release which may be very pleasureful but which also may be very distressing; short periods of relaxation following release which may be very peaceful but which also may be characterized by sadness and desire for death; and then another growing period of tension. If man must achieve satisfaction in such a tension state, the pursuit of emotional health through sexual gratification will fail in all but a few moments of any given lifetime.

George Bernard Shaw, a complex man who did not exactly come to terms with sex in general or the other sex in particular, suggested that sex is a cruel trick played on us by Mother Nature in the interests of continuing the race.

There are other means of obtaining bodily pleasure, relaxation, and satisfaction which do not involve the tensions and dissatisfactions inherent in sex. Without the compulsive nature of the sexual drive, it seems likely that men and women would pursue other gratifications where satisfaction is more consistent and predictable, in which case the race would become extinct.

In fantasy, man looks back on his moments of sexual gratification and magnifies them in duration and extent far beyond what happened in actuality. He looks forward to such moments in future of far greater duration and intensity than past experience should lead him to expect. When he reports on his past sex history, he is very likely to exaggerate. When he dreams of his erotic future, his dream exceeds the chances of probability. And yet sexologists, in all seriousness and without humor, observe and report and study such sexual fantasies as if they were scientific fact.

Pornographers attempt to draw such fantasies. If we can disengage ourselves from our own fantasy, we can ascertain that such erotic fantasies are, in fact, impossible. A number of persons have attempted to report the secret aspects of their erotic lives in autobiography. Such autobiography sounds joyous, lusty, and triumphant, but there is a false note in it. One senses the frustration of the autobiographer. Not only does he attempt to describe the undescribable, he attempts to pursue the unattainable and especially to prolong something which, by its very nature, must be short and temporary. There is a certain maximum of sensory gratification that any individual can attain. This peak is not impossible for any individual to attain; satisfaction beyond the peak is impossible for every individual. Levels higher than the peak, time durations longer than a few minutes, do not exist in the physiology, can only exist in the psychology, in the fantasy itself.

There is a modern erotic autobiography which is more candid and erotic than either Casanova or Frank Harris, written by a man using the pen name John Phillip Lundin, and bearing the simple title *Women*. As do all erotic autobiographers, Lundin describes with great zest his pleasures with multiple uninhibited female partners. But yet the subtitle of this book is *Autobiographical Reflections of a Frustrated Male*, and, in the final chapter, Lundin admits that he has been an unhappy man. All erotic autobiographers look back and seem to say, "I really should have kissed them more," and yet, at the time, if the account can be believed, the autobiographer kissed them so much and so often that he passed the point of satiety to become exhausted or even disgusted, and then his sole remaining desire was to move along and try to attain the unattainable with somebody else. Those who do achieve relative satisfaction are not compelled to write about it, or to report their histories to the sexologist, and they have no desire to move along.

There's a lengthy erotic autobiography, written by an anonymous Victorian gentleman, entitled *My Secret Life*. This classic was long unavailable to the general reader, the few existing copies having been kept strictly under lock and key, but it has recently become available in a new edition. After describing erotic experiences at great length, the anonymous author comes to the following conclusion, "Regarding love's mysteries, there is nothing mysterious about it, except in the psychology." This same conclusion is one which the erotic autobiographer, the pornographer, and the sexologist ought to be able to reach. It is a conclusion which is not beyond the grasp of any intelligent logical adult.

There has never been any particular mystery as to what a man wants in sex. His biological drive is to impregnate as many available females as possible. Social considerations, jealousy factors in other males, and the differing biological drive of the woman make it impossible for him to impregnate every attractive woman he encounters, so he accepts a compromise. If his compromise is relatively acceptable, he is adjusted in this regard. If he cannot attain a reasonable compromise, his drives force him into difficult and dangerous social situations. When he is young and immature, he attempts to play the field, with varying degrees of success, never complete. As actuality fails to attain his erotic ambitions, he becomes discontent, restless, and frustrated. If at this point he fails to mature, he may continue the adolescent sexual pattern throughout his adult life, remaining, like John Phillip Lundin, the frustrated male. The "Casanova complex" is a recognized psychiatric entity. His frustration may lead him to hate the objects he is driven to love—women in general and in particular—in which case his sexual pattern assumes one of the deviant or perverse expressions. He may find himself trapped into marriage by a shotgun. He is more likely to choose a female that he likes as well as desires and he marries her, half reluctantly and half by strong desire. In marriage, if he is lucky and can adjust to the differing needs of his partner, sex becomes an important, but not the sole important, aspect of his marriage and his life. Sex is the expression of his love, but the love is more important than the sex, and sex is deferred or abandoned altogether when the circumstances and the needs of the partner so dictate. Such a man may privately believe that his sex life has fallen short of the perfectly satisfactory, but this does not bother him. His love for his wife and for his family is of far greater importance and satisfaction. He has come to terms with his biological drives, and he knows, though he may hesitate to admit it, that his life has been far more satisfactory than that of Casanova, Lundin, or Frank Harris.

What about the woman? There is much more mystery here. Freud, after plumbing the depths of female psychology for thirty years, rather plaintively remarked that he had not uncovered any satisfactory answer to the basic question: What does a woman really want?

A relatively valid answer to this problem was supplied by a more sophisticated and urbane observer five hundred years before.

Perhaps we can suggest this answer best in the form of a case history. The original observer told it as a story. The case histories we have utilized earlier in this book have been largely factual and true. The one we are about to give is not true, though I believe it is quite valid. I will use no true case histories in this chapter on sex. I believe that sexual histories as related to doctors in the office, as written in books, and as reported by sexologists, lie largely in the realm of fantasy, and, for the most part, are not true.

The Young Knight (Case 48)

One day, the young knight was galloping over the medieval plains and he encountered a desirable young damsel. With the hot blood of youth, he leaped from his horse and raped her on the spot. He was apprehended in the act and dragged before the king and queen for punishment; the usual sentence was death. The king found him guilty. The queen was struck by the grace and beauty of the youth and urged the king to be lenient. "Boys will be boys," she said. In order to please her, the king suspended sentence for a year but he gave the young knight a riddle to be solved. One year to the date, the knight must return. If he had found an answer to the riddle, he would be free; if not, he would hang.

The king thought the riddle could not be answered. It was:
What does a woman really want?

The knight was joyful. He spent the first few months of his
freedom enjoying himself. From time to time, he thought about
the riddle. No ready answer occurred to him. He consulted seers
and sages and wizards and women of varying ages. No answer
was supplied.

At length the year was up. The young knight had no answer,
and despondently he returned to the castle, prepared to die. On
the plains, he passed an old witch. He stopped to speak with
her; perhaps she knew the answer he was looking for; she was
the last chance he had.

Yes, the witch declared, she knew the answer. She would tell
him if he would grant her one favor. The knight gave his promise.
The witch whispered the answer into his ear. It seemed to be
what the knight was looking for. The witch said that she would
ask her favor only if the answer to the riddle was found acceptable, and she went along with him to see the king and queen.

The knight presented himself.

"Have you found the answer?" said the king.

"I have, sire," said the knight.

"What does a woman really want?"

"Sire," said the knight, "what a woman wants is this: that
she should be desired by her husband as if he were her lover."

The king looked at the queen; the queen looked at the king;
they looked around the court; there seemed to be general satisfaction on every face. The answer was accepted and the knight
was free.

Then from the back of the court, a voice spoke up: "Just a
minute!" It was the witch. She reminded the knight that he owed
her a favor. The knight acknowledged the debt. What was the
favor?

"Marry me," said the witch.

The knight was flabbergasted and depressed. Rather than
marry this horrid ugly old woman, he would rather have been
hanged, but he had given his word, and he had no choice. The
king married them immediately.

That evening, alone with his bride, the knight felt most reluctant to go to bed with her.

"Just close your eyes and make love to me," said the witch.

The knight closed his eyes, got into bed, and made love to her, manfully trying to forget her ugliness.

"Now," she said, "open your eyes."

He did so. To his astonishment, the knight saw in the bed with him, not a horrid ugly old witch, but a beautiful and desirable young woman. He fell in love with her immediately, and they lived happily ever after.

I'm sure Chaucer wouldn't mind my retelling this story, for he often told retold tales, although, of course, he tells it better than I do. This is the subject of one of the Canterbury Tales.

The biological drive of the female is not to make love to every passing man but to select the strongest, bravest, and most fertile male available and then to cling to him. The differing and somewhat opposing drives of male and female are part of Nature's trick to strengthen the race. Recognition of and adjustment to the difference between male and female is the secret of successful relationship between the sexes. Promiscuity is not natural or normal for the female, and selection of a new partner is not desired unless the new partner seems to be stronger, braver, or more fertile than the present one. Desirability of a male to a female is measured by the intensity and devotion with which he courts her; to keep her he must continue courting her; she will often tease or provoke him to make him prove his love; if he does prove himself with courtship, she will do her best to give him pleasure and satisfaction, and he in turn will find himself satisfied and pleased with her. The pleasure and satisfaction given to male by properly courted female is considerably greater than that which he may try to seize by force. Chaucer knew this very well; Freud never discovered it.

A major milepost in the revolution after Freud was the

work of Kinsey and his group. The late Alfred C. Kinsey was a careful statistical taxonomist whose early work was in the field of classification of insects. Why he turned from entomology to human sexual behavior is not exactly clear. The two famous so-called *Kinsey Reports*, published in the early '50s, were based on interview techniques with volunteers, and the statistics derived thereby are treated as if they were fact. The possibility of human exaggeration and fantasy in this area is not considered. Neither is the phenomenon of love; in the index of the *Report* on women, there are many references to "orgasm" and not a single reference to "love." To focus on the phenomenon of orgasm without reference to the psychology of love is to consider an aspect of the subject which has never been mysterious, as the anonymous Victorian author of *My Secret Life* had discovered.

Kinsey did not consider himself a moralist. He was a scientist; morals and ethics had no place in his work. The public, fascinated by statistics on sexual outlet lined up like insects transfixed to the dissecting board, took the data and began to apply it to possible moral and ethical standards of conduct. From this, a concept arose which has been called polymorphous perversity. This concept, focused on the orgasm, considers any activity leading to orgasm as equivalent, and postulates that any sort of sexual outlet is equally normal and natural for the human. This implies that variety in sex is healthy, and gives encouragement to the promiscuous and deviant individual. Such a philosophy was accepted with enthusiasm by certain immature males, since both promiscuity and deviant behavior represent immature masculine behavior. The concept was not as willingly accepted by women. Orgasm is quick and easy for the majority of men, but neither quick nor easy for the majority of women. The focus on the mechanical phenomenon of orgasm as if it were the entire basic constituent of sexual activity brings anxiety to women who know they may not uniformly achieve it, and to men who wish their partners to attain full satisfaction. Failure to achieve orgasm tended to give the woman a feeling of incompleteness or inadequacy, and the male who failed to bring his partner to climax had a similar feeling of inadequacy. Emphasis on the importance of orgasm and the concept of polymorphous perversity therefore brought anxiety into the bedroom, and anxiety does not assist the achievement of sexual satisfaction in either male or female.

Following Kinsey, the revolution was carried forward through many books by many authors. The courts progressively began to open doors previously closed by censorship, and frank books on sex, both fiction and non-fiction, began to appear, including many hoary old pornographic classics which had long been burrowing underground. In March of 1966, the Supreme Court tried to close the doors again by upholding the conviction of Ralph Ginzburg, a decision which caused shock and horror in the liberal wing of the literary community. Ginzburg's books, by the Court's admission, were not pornographic; the new and rather weird concept suggested by this decision is that a person may be jailed for publishing material which is not obscene if his advertising suggests that it is obscene. Followed to the letter, such a dictum might suggest that most commercial advertising is obscene, since sexually exciting images are so frequently used by Madison Avenue. The Ginzburg decision obviously will not be used that way, and its final effect on freedom of the press may be fairly minimal. Freedoms once gained are not easily relinquished.

We have previously said that the censor is the natural bitter enemy of the writer. Most writers take the position that freedom of speech and freedom of the printed word is decidedly a good and healthy thing, and that censorship of all kinds is unhealthy and dangerous. This is my natural position. I think that anything one man writes should be available to another man to read. I think that anything which can be written—and I really do mean anything—is of at least potential value for the understanding of life, people, and the faces that we meet. I think certain material should be kept out of the hands of children and insane persons, just as one would like to keep liquor and the automobile out of these same hands, but I believe that the sane adult should have free choice of what he will and what he will not read.

The question of the psychological effects of pornography is an interesting and controversial one. As suggested in the quotation from C. S. Lewis, the pornographer attempts to describe that impossible conjunction of imaginary maleness with imaginary femaleness, those rarefied areas above the natural peaks of excitement, and such material, pretending to be so realistic, is on the contrary quite abstract and unreal. It does not affect the actual mechanical physiology of sex. It does affect and enter into the fantasy. Is this good or bad?

Psychologically speaking, fantasy is good to the extent that it relieves tension from the harsh edges of reality as a temporary escape or vacation. As a permanent guideline, fantasy is dangerous. A good reason for recreational reading is vicarious enjoyment of experiences one cannot accomplish in the flesh. One may read about the thrills, excitements, and dangers of shipwreck; this does not mean that the reader desires to be wrecked at sea; he might in fact take all possible precautions against being caught in a shipwreck. Reading about certain exotic or deviated sexual experiences does not necessarily mean that the reader wishes to run right out and indulge himself in such a sex experience. He might take considerable precaution against trying such an experience, using such reading as a means of understanding certain impulses and reactions in himself and others as a guideline to sane and healthy living, not as a road map to sin. On the other hand, sex is a tension state and a good deal of sex is psychological; reading which increases psychological tension might have dangerous consequences to the psychologically disturbed. There are certain things which have strong potentials for both good and bad, depending upon use: such as fire and gunpowder and barbiturates and alcohol and gasoline. Perhaps pornography might be included in that class. One thing which might be fairly stated: to an emotionally stable adult reader, small amounts of pornography in the reading diet are interesting, amusing, revealing, and exciting; in more than small amounts, such reading is monotonous, depressing, and dull, because such prose is based upon premises basically fantastic and false. The true aphrodisiac is not found in print. That which arouses desire in the male is the female, and vice versa, and censorship can never ban the major factor causing erotic fantasy.

The most recent milepost in the present revolution is the book called *Human Sexual Response* by Masters and Johnson. This book is on the best-seller list as I write these words, and it has been there for quite some time. Obviously many people have read it. It does not seem to be causing the general discussion and controversy that followed publication of the *Kinsey Reports*. Perhaps we have become too sophisticated for controversy in this area.

Less than one percent of the Masters-Johnson book is devoted to the psychology of sex; the remainder concerns anatomical and physiological functions. If you look in the index for the word "love," it should appear between "lethal factor, vaginal" and "lubrication, vaginal," but it is not there.

In common with the *Kinsey Reports*, the Masters-Johnson book was not written for a general audience, but was primarily intended for medical readers, and hence a good deal of it is incomprehensible to the general reader. In common with the Kinsey books, the Masters-Johnson study was developed from an essentially abnormal group of subjects with data presented as if applicable to the general population. The normal person does not volunteer to reveal the secrets of his intimate private life to an interviewer; the normal person does not volunteer to perform a sex act before witnesses.

Medically speaking, the findings of the Masters-Johnson study do not seem to be especially new or surprising. Is it any great surprise that there is an increase in the rate of breathing and pulse, an elevated blood pressure, and sweating during sexual excitement? The so-called "sexual flush," a measles-like rash on the skin, is a phenomenon not often noticed but one which does not appear to have great practical significance. It is interesting to the gynecologist that vaginal lubrication comes from general outpouring from the entire mucous membrane, rather than a specific secretion of the glands of Skene and Bartholin as was previously believed, but again the importance of this finding seems limited.

The fascinating and slightly horrifying aspect of the study lies in the methods and not the results. It is the concept of exposing what has always been a private intimate reaction to the public scrutiny of camera and scientists in a laboratory that stimulates the imagination. The investigators approached the problem cautiously and carefully, obviously aware that any hint of lasciviousness or lust in any aspect of the investigation would cause a scandal and prevent further investigation altogether. It is obviously commendable that propriety was so scrupulously maintained; and yet, when any trace of lasciviousness or lust has been removed, can such a sex act be considered normal?

Sexual excitement was induced in the laboratory by a variety of techniques. The frequency of the various techniques utilized is not stated, which is bad science. Natural coition in a variety of positions was studied, but apparently only rarely. This can be understood. Not too many married couples could be expected to volunteer, and moral considerations would prevent study of relations between two persons not married to each other. Also, natural coition would prevent observation and measurements of genital organs which was one of the primary objectives of the study. It is not stated but one presumes that manual masturbation was the method of choice in males. In females, that technique was useful in the beginning, but the method of choice became what the authors refer to as artificial coition, which involves the use of a machine. I suspect that it is the horrified fascination and fascinated horror in thinking of this machine which placed the book so solidly on the best-seller lists. Leslie H. Farber, of whom we will speak further in a moment, outrageously suggests that this machine was inspired by a limerick: stated euphemistically, the one about the young man from Racine who invented a loving machine and found it was easy to clean. Masters-Johnson state that the equipment was created by radiophysicists; it seems like an unusual creation for men in that specialty.

The most thought-provoking finding of the Masters-Johnson study is the fact that, once female volunteers had become accustomed to the machine, climax could be obtained with it regularly. This is in contrast to the well-known fact that women do not attain climax consistently under natural conditions. It has been suggested that the efficacy of the machine is due to the lack of fear of pregnancy from it. I am not sure this is a valid suggestion in view of the ease and prevalence of contraception today, especially "the pill." One wonders about the factor of exhibitionism. A female volunteering for a study of this type would have to be somewhat exhibitionistic, and could not be prudish or greatly inhibited. Does this imply that only an exhibitionistic female is able to achieve full femininity? This would be in accord with the neo-Freudian philosophy that sexual repression is the great cause of human unhappiness. On the other hand, however, although there is no laboratory confirmation, general experience tends to suggest that many shy and modest women are able to achieve full sexual response when inhibition has been cast away in the name of love and there seems to be some suggestion that uninhibited exhibitionistic women are not necessarily good bedroom companions. The most obvious explanation for efficiency of the machine in inducing orgasm in contrast to the irregular occurrence of orgasm in natural coition lies in the differing reaction time of male and female; the machine can continue to supply stimulation long enough to result in female climax, and a male often cannot. Should we derive from this explanation the concept that, for a woman, a machine is better than a man? Masters and Johnson give the case history of a divorced woman who volunteered for the study because it gave her a socially acceptable outlet for release of sexual tension. If machines should become universally acceptable, would males be used only for companionship and money, and, in the bedroom, only rarely for the specific purpose of procreation? One must presume that even the most satisfied female volunteer in the Masters-Johnson lab would prefer good marital relations to any consistently satisfying machine, and accordingly the premise must be stated that there is more to sex for a woman than consistent achievement of mechanical orgasm.

Masters-Johnson state that all their findings emphasize the similarity and not the difference between male and female sexual response. And yet, the most obvious thing one could say about men and women is that there is a difference (and the entire French Parliament rose and shouted in a single voice, "Viva la différence!"). A major source of anxiety in our society is the presumption that women should act like men: in sex, in business, in society. When a woman tries to act like a man, it really doesn't work.

Criticism of the Masters-Johnson study is skillfully and neatly brought out in a wonderful article by Leslie H. Farber, which first appeared in the excellent Jewish magazine Commentary, is reprinted in the book called The Commentary Reader, and appears in an expanded form in Farber's book The Ways of the Will. The title of Farber's essay is "I'm Sorry, Dear," which refers to the bedroom scene, both comic and tragic, when the two sweaty lovers fail to achieve climax at the same moment. Farber points out that the frustration of this situation is set up by undue emphasis on orgasm in women. Equal political rights for women have led to clamor for equal sexual rights for women; achievement of orgasm is regarded as the hallmark of maturity in women, and failure to achieve orgasm is considered as prima-facie evidence of immaturity and neurosis. The male learns to resist his rush toward pleasure if it seems that he will be premature, says Farber; if he is premature despite such efforts, he attempts to bring his mate to a similar release although he is in a natural fatigued refractory period. The female is not apt to be deceived by this attention, but she tries, both for her sake and his, to fulfill her sexual franchise. "It cannot be easy for her to ignore the irony that her right to orgasm may depend upon her willingness to be diddled like a perverse underwater edible whose shell refuses to be pried open," says Farber.

It was Freud who first laid emphasis on female orgasm at a time when such a thing was not acknowledged to exist. He made the distinction between two kinds of female orgasm, the clitoral and the vaginal, and sexologists have been discussing this distinction ever since. Kinsey recognized the distinction and elaborated upon it in great detail. Masters and Johnson, on the other hand, find that there is no such distinction and state that vaginal and clitoral orgasm are not biological entities. This is probably the most interesting finding of the Masters-Johnson study to sexologists.

"Orgasm" is an ugly-sounding word. It is derived from a Greek root meaning "swelling with fluid"; as such it is descriptive of the male climax, perhaps of the female climax too. It seems reasonable to suggest that a sexual climax of a similar nature to the male response occurs in women. To imply that this response is identical in male and female seems to me to be a mistake. Perhaps we need a different word. For, it seems to me, it is the difference and not the similarity between the responses of men and women which is important. I agree with the French Parliament and not with Masters-Johnson.

It is Farber's guess that orgasm has always been an occasional but not a regular or even essential part of the female sexual experience. He suggests that orgasm occurs regularly only during masturbation; the Masters-Johnson study, which essentially is a study of masturbation, would tend to confirm this suggestion. Farber further states that the woman, before the days of scientific sexology, did not have a great anxiety at not attaining orgasm during natural relations and was perfectly content with the mystery of her difference from the man, in fact not wishing it otherwise. The male, says Farber, also preferred the mystery of difference and became interested in the mechanics of orgasm only when the vital difference was lacking, as in masturbation.

Scientific investigation of biological phenomena is important; it leads to vital and practical information regarding health and disease. Biological investigators must fight a tendency to regard their studies as truly scientific; it is very difficult to eliminate all variables and to measure psychological influences. In sex, it is still the psychology that is mysterious, and the mystery may be considerably more important than the measurements.

The most sensible book of modern sexology I have encountered is *Love and Orgasm* by Alexander Lowen. Dr. Lowen puts too great a neo-Freudian emphasis on orgasm for my taste, but he does consider love. The word is in the index of his book, and it is in the title, and in the title Dr. Lowen puts it first. He says that it is the mystery of love which lies at the heart of the sexual act. Here, it seems to me, sexology is beginning to return toward sanity.

One of the great psychiatrists of this century was Carl Jung, whose work has not received the popular attention it deserves. Jung was never interested in popularization, and he chose to approach each patient as a unique individual problem. Jung was one of Freud's disciples, but he had a falling out with the master, and his work branched off in a different direction, concentrating on the psyche rather than the sexology. One of Jung's basic beliefs was that subconscious emotional reactions are often expressed in symbols, and that such symbols are a heritage from the folklore, superstitions, and emotions of the past.

To take a Jungian approach, I would like to suggest a symbol to represent something sexologists may have overlooked. I refer to the unicorn. The unicorn is a white stallion with a Freudian phallic horn in the middle of his forehead, who figured richly in mythology and early Christian thinking. He was a fierce creature under most circumstances but very gentle in his mating habits. No man alone could capture him but he would lay his head peacefully in the lap of a virgin. Medieval theologians used the unicorn as a symbol of the power of love, sometimes as a symbol for Christ, and as a symbol of the meekness which may inherit the earth. Presumably the unicorn is exclusively male, for female unicorns are not mentioned; perhaps the female unicorn is shy and elusive, never seen by man, visible only to a male unicorn in love. According to one theory, the unicorn became extinct in The Flood; some said he was thrown out of the ark and drowned. It is not exactly clear how he got onto the ark in the first place, animals having been admitted there in pairs, and there is no good explanation as to why he was thrown overboard. Perhaps Noah, when drunk one night, tried to study the mating habits of his passengers and the unicorn objected fiercely to scientific sexology. At any rate, when modern sexologists consider sex without love, it seems to me that they are drowning the unicorn.

Love without sex is possible and rewarding. There are a number of love relationships in which sex plays no part. There are a number of other love relationships, especially incestuous ones, in which, because of social factors, sex can play no active part; Freud studied the conflicts set up by these relationships in detail. Sex without love is possible and brings rewards of pleasure and the relief of tension. On account of the basic difference in biological drives, sex without love is far more apt to be rewarding in male than in female. The prostitute, except in fiction, finds no joy in her profession; nymphomania is a distinctly unpleasant condition; the mistress and the adulteress seek not sexual satisfactions but rewards of a monetary or social nature. Promiscuity is more apt to be rewarding to a young man than to an old one; one of the most pathetic figures in the human comedy is the aging and increasingly impotent philanderer. Sex with love approaches the maximum of human sensory experience. Although sex with love may be found outside of marriage, it is more apt to thrive within marriage. Marriage is a tricky game; it is most apt to succeed when both partners are faithful to each other and have faith in each other; accordingly the old-fashioned standard of premarital chastity and postmarital fidelity is most likely to result in maximum sensory experience. It is difficult for a young person to postpone his adventures in achieving maximum experience; if he postpones it, he fears that he may miss it altogether. He rationalizes that, since sex is an art which requires practice before perfection can be reached, it is better to bring some sophistication and practice to the marriage bed than to appear as a bumbling amateur. As a physician in an area popular for honeymoons, I can testify from considerable experience that the honeymoon is often a traumatic experience, physically and emotionally, to either or both parties. However, early premarital adventures are also traumatic, and they often set up psychological barriers which make very difficult or impossible subsequent satisfactions either inside or outside of marriage. There is a fact which the young cannot appreciate because the experienced do not mention it: namely, it takes years and decades of practice and experience with a single partner to attain maximal sexual satisfactions. It is not experience with one's own physical reactions which is essential; it is experience with the physical and psychological reactions of the partner that increases satisfaction. Accordingly, wide variety of superficial sexual contacts, while it may produce sexual sophistication, does not produce sexual maturity. Fidelity works better. The factor of human jealousy, a subtle but important emotion, often poorly understood, will tend to undermine satisfaction when the partner knows that the individual has been, may be, or will be unfaithful.

When love relations exist but sex outlets are, for one reason or another, unavailable, the stored-up biological tensions need not necessarily induce neurosis. Such energy can be diverted to other creative outlets. Considerable amounts of the best creative work and art are given impetus by such energy. This phenomenon has been called sublimation; it was noticed and studied by Freud.

When sexual activity is individualized, separated from contact with a partner, the process of masturbation occurs. A healthy effect of modern sexology has been to remove the stigma from masturbation. The phenomenon is no longer considered immoral, deviant, or destructive to health. Kinsey popularized the fact which physicians had long recognized: that masturbation has been practiced by almost every male and by the majority of females. It is psychologically harmful when the practice induces a guilt reaction. As a major outlet, it is probably harmful because it concentrates on the self which makes more difficult concentration on the partner in a heterosexual relationship. If orgasm is regarded as the essence of sexual behavior, masturbation is more consistently satisfactory than coition, certainly in men, and almost undoubtedly, as suggested by Masters-Johnson, in women. If there is more to sex than mechanical orgasm, masturbation is an immature and incomplete sexual expression.

Sex is often intimately associated with love. It is also often intimately associated with hate. As Somerset Maugham had reason to know from his own life experience, the line between hate and love is thin as the razor's edge. Even in the most perfect association between two partners, elements of irritation, resentment, anger—hate equivalents—filter in. If hard-core pornography can be examined with emotional detachment, it will be recognized that what is passed off as love expressions are in fact expressions of hatred upon the sex partner. In pornography, the recipient of the sexual expression has a body but no person and no face and is degraded and abused by the experience. The common dirty words for love relations are dirty because they are thinly disguised expressions of hate.

If the various perverse and deviant patterns of sexual behavior are considered as expressions of hatred, the psychological dynamics are not difficult to understand. Deviant expressions attempt to degrade, depersonalize, or destroy the sex partner.

The hatred face of the coin bearing the face of love on the other side is derived from fear. This fear seems to stem largely from an inability to define and recognize the three-sided role of woman, a paradox which bothers both men and women. The woman is, in her time, mother, wife, and lover. The wife is the companion. The mother is holy, chaste, and pure. The lover is indulging in sexual activity which is the opposite of holiness, chastity, and purity. It is difficult for any of us to reconcile the fact that our own mother once engaged in a sex act, although obviously she must have done so. Religion reinforces the paradox by emphasis on such things as the Virgin Birth, the Immaculate Conception, the holiness of chastity and the sinfulness of sex. The mature adult comes to terms with this paradox, though perhaps never entirely. The immature person who cannot resolve this psychological dilemma may express his fear and hatred of woman through perverse or deviant behavior. In *Love and Orgasm*, Dr. Lowen states that a man cannot love a specific woman unless he loves women in general, and that a woman cannot love a man until she has come to terms with the reality of her own body. Dr. Lowen also considers that homosexuality is the great tragedy of our age.

Homosexuality in the female, lesbianism, does not appear to be a major tragedy. Presumably it is more common than male homosexuality. In any community, there are pairs of women living together as man and wife, and the relationship seems to be accepted calmly enough. Of course, many single women live together without any lesbian relationship, but one can sense lesbian attraction when one encounters it, and lesbians do not work very hard at concealing such inclinations. Lesbians are not notably happy individuals and they are not notably popular, but they are often acceptable and useful members of society. There are more females than males in the general population with the disproportion increasing. There are not enough men to go around. Society may tacitly accept that if polygamy is not acceptable lesbianism may be an inevitable substitute in certain cases.

The male homosexual is not accepted with equanimity. We are painfully getting beyond the concept of homosexuality as degeneracy or vice and beginning to accept it as personality disorder; eventually we may get rid of the legal concept of homosexuality as crime, although the law always lags far behind social opinion. Homosexuals themselves try to proclaim their activity as equivalent—equally normal and equally healthy—to heterosexual relations. The concept of polymorphous perversity seems to add justification to such a proclamation. The average citizen, however, knows that the "gay" life is not gay, quite the opposite, in fact. Anybody who has stumbled into a "gay" bar or party will hear the air full of hate expressions very thinly masqueraded in the name of love. Homosexuals are sensitive, very often articulate and talented, and the case they make for "Greek love" may sound quite convincing. The sight of a Wilde or a Gide viciously squabbling over a stupid dirty Arab boy puts the lie to any beauty in such a relationship.

I would think that the tragedy of homosexuality, aside from emotional distortion within the individual, would be the distorting influence upon our arts and culture. Since homosexuals are talented and articulate, they tend to dominate the arts out of all proportion to their numbers in the population. A good deal of modern fiction, drama, movies, television is homosexually oriented. The consequence of this is to drive men out of the audience. The readership for fiction and the Broadway audience is feminine. The women in novels and on the stage are apt to be cruelly distorted. It may be surprising that women so readily accept the homosexually drawn cartoon. One gets the impression that, in general, men like both women and other men; women like men but not women; and homosexuals hate both men and women. The cause of this phenomenon apparently lies in our inability to reconcile the three-sided role of woman.

Homosexuals wish to accept their condition as a biological alternate in which conversion is neither possible nor desirable. Therapists used to consider homosexuality incurable. Present evidence indicates that homosexuality is amenable to treatment and cure if and when the individual accepts his own abnormality and is genuinely motivated to change it.

An excellent counterattack to proclamations of the beauty and normality of homosexuality—if one should be needed—is the book called *The Caricature of Love* by Hervey Cleckley. This is the same Dr. Cleckley who wrote the classic study of the psychopath.

The various individual deviations of Krafft-Ebing do not seem worth cataloging. They are either incomplete and immature heterosexual expressions or homosexual equivalents. There is, however, one sexual variation—actually a double variation—which deserves attention. The specific sexual deviation is rare, but psychological elements in it are almost universal, exerting important influences on behavior both sexual and non-sexual. I refer to what sophisticates sometimes call S-M, meaning sadism-masochism. The two conditions are always correlated, though opposite.

When I was younger and trying to become a novelist, I read some advice in a writer's book which struck me as very true: if you want to hold the interest of your reader, fill your story full of sadism, the one element the reader can't resist. Whenever I have tried to use this advice in a novel, I have misused it, which may explain why I have never had great popular success as a novelist, but I still consider the principle valid. The key scenes in most of the very popular stories, novels, movies, plays are sadistic. We seem to need a shot of sadism in our entertainment as a tonic. It is instinctual for us to get vicarious pleasure from the fantasy of torturing and killing the enemy and of being captured and tortured by the enemy. We must only make the distinction between "good guys" and "bad guys." Good guys must escape in the end, bad guys must get their just deserts. This is the basic ingredient of the story; it is a basic ingredient in life. Our concept of justice hangs from this hook; this is the justification on both sides for each and every war, for each and every competition in any kind of arena. The principle by no means is confined to fantasy. Sadistic acts continuously occur. Even the most civilized, who rarely practice physical sadism, engage in psychological sadism a good deal of the time.

In many ways, sex, normal heterosexual sex between loving partners, is a sadistic-masochistic act. The male drive is sadistic, the female drive is masochistic. Our life is often oriented by such principles. If we do not strike out against certain hostile forces, such forces may overwhelm us, and if we cannot accept certain punishments, the misery of life and death would be too great to be endured. Religion is basically masochistic. Christ consciously provoked sadism from His own people which led to His crucifixion, and He welcomed pain, suffering, and death as the means of rising above pain, suffering, and death to immortality. He advised us to turn the other cheek and to love our enemies. The meek are supposed to inherit the earth. This is love, in its purest form, but it is also masochism in its purest form, and masochism may be considered equivalent to love as sadism is to hate. Much of psychology and psychiatry rests on this same dynamic interplay. Freud identified the two forces: Eros, the creative force of love, and Thanatos, the destructive force of death—this is the same thing.

The prophet of sadism, for whom the condition was named, was of course the Marquis de Sade, sometimes called "divine," sometimes considered the "anti-Christ," an obvious sexual psychopath. "It is necessary to keep coming back to de Sade again and again," wrote Baudelaire. Baudelaire was himself a sadomasochist, which could explain his preoccupation with the Marquis, but the student of human behavior and motivation must consider the same source. The actual writings of de Sade may be dismissed. There is a cult of hero-worship of the Marquis, a group which deems him a great writer and philosopher. He was not a great writer: long passages of verbose self-justification alternate with equally long passages of sexual psychopathy which are far more emetic than erotic. He was not a great philosopher: his arguments are contradictory and redundant and poorly phrased. But he does represent a concept which must often be taken into account if human behavior is to be explained and understood.

The sadism of de Sade is more abstract than logic; it is even more abstract than lust; carried to the ultimate, it goes beyond sex, desire, cruelty, and lust into an emotionless nullity. He often speaks from the viewpoint of Justine and other victims, but Justine and the other victims are unreal; these are not people any of us see and recognize; they are faceless uninhabited slabs of flesh, without personality, without inner person, existing only as a matrix for orifices to be violated. The heart of the philosophy lies in denying to the victims their persons, their identity, and their reality. By this process, the whip-bearer asserts and affirms his identity and reality, his own immunity to pain, suffering, and death. The moment that the victim seems to be real, the whip-bearer is also threatened and then he must turn the cheeks of his face and his buttocks to become the masochist himself. Such a role reversal is not allowed in fiction. If Goldfinger should become real and show real suffering as he gets his just deserts, then James Bond is not a hero any more. Role reversal does occur regularly and consistently in life; when it does, the holy war is holy no longer, the punishment no longer seems to fit the crime, and we must accept equivalent punishment ourselves if we can ever face ourselves in any mirror. Such a polarity explains much paradox of human behavior. This is the important thing de Sade tells us. His writings tell us only half of it. His life tells the other half. His actual sadism was minimal. The worst mutilation he actually accomplished was the dropping of some hot wax on superficial lacerations on the breast of a masochistic prostitute well paid for her pains;

you don't have to look very far in history to discover worse sadism than that. To de Sade, the actual fact of his long imprisonment by a society which did not understand him was as important to him as any fictional tortures he did not commit, despite the fact that his philosophy proclaimed that society should not and could not understand him. In fact, therefore, the sadist spokesman was a masochist.

How about primary masochism, the willing victim? There is something puzzling about the seeking of pleasure in pain, for pain is not pleasant after all. The specific inversion of sexual masochism is rare, but masochistic impulses are almost universal.

For the sexual inversion, the following explanation of the psychological mechanism has been given: it is not the pain which gives sexual pleasure; pain is sought as a punishment for pleasure found in sex; the masochist, accepting punishment first, can thereafter enjoy the pleasure without guilt, having paid for it in advance. There is a psychological verity here: we often do enjoy things more when we have rendered payment in advance.

The prophet of masochism—Leopold von Sacher-Masoch, the nineteenth-century German novelist for whom the condition was named—represented the viewpoint of the passive male transvestite under the domination of a sadistic woman. There is an interesting psychological implication in role reversal in a heterosexual relation. On the other hand, this is the mirror image of sadism, rather than the analogue. If sadism is analogous to the male sex drive, we would expect the spokesman for the masochistic willing victim to be a woman. Only recently has she appeared.

I refer to the author of a book written in French and published in Paris in 1954 under the title *Histoire d'O*. An English translation has been published in France, but customs regulations prevent its importation into this country. However, another English translation of the same original, different in style but identical in content, was published in America in 1965 under the title *Story of O* and is freely available. The author of this tale is Pauline Réage, a pen name. The true identity of the author has been carefully concealed, but the book was obviously written by a woman and it is also obvious that the author is a skillful novelist although she has written no other books under that name. *Story of O* is well written; I consider it an important book; and I hereby warn the gentle reader to stay away from it, for it is strong stuff. Only the sophisticated reader should tackle it and he is warned that this is a disturbing book.

The tale concerns a young woman named "O," who, in the name of love for a man named René, consents to torture and abuse in the de Sade manner. The details are quite explicit, less bloody than de Sade but more convincing, because Réage writes much better than de Sade and because this victim is quite real. It is not the details alone which are disturbing in this book, for the sophisticated reader does get used to the crude candid brutalities which frequently appear in print these days; and it is not realism which disturbs us, for the plot is fully as much in the realm of fantasy and unreality as *Justine*; what is disturbing is the psychological implications.

Justine pretended not to be a willing victim. "O" is always asked in advance of each act of torture and abuse if she will consent, and she always does. She consents in the name of her love for René. She consents without question, for no other reason than that her lover has made the request. Such blind consent is implicit in love; one does consent to any sort of inconvenience, abuse, pain, or suffering in love if the act will satisfy any pleasure or need of the lover. The reason why René should desire to see "O" tortured and abused by others is not even raised (as, in fact, a lover would not raise it); to an impartial observer, the reader, René has no true "love" for "O," even though he frequently proclaims that he has, for the true lover does not wish to see the loved one tortured and abused, but the story is told from the viewpoint of "O" and she is consenting in the name of love.

The problem of consent in love disturbs us. We are in-

clined to be afraid that when the lover has satisfied his
pleasure or need at our expense, he or she will then abandon us, seeking satisfaction elsewhere, and leaving us alone
with our scars and wounds. This is the dilemma of the virgin
in the parked car or in the honeymoon bed and it is a
dilemma sometimes faced by a pregnant woman nearing the
time of her confinement. The same dilemma is equally valid
in the case of men and equally applicable to non-sexual human relationships.

After "O" has been subjected to torture and abuse in the
name of love for René, his love for her, and her love for him,
for which the strange game has been played, evaporates, and
René disappears from the story. This does not seem to bother
"O." She does not take pleasure in pain; abuse and torture
is always highly unpleasant at the time and she is afraid of
it; but she does come to enjoy the act of consent and the
state of being a passive recipient for humiliation and abuse.

This also disturbs us. To accept life, we must accept the
fact of death and suffering. To accept love, or any responsibility, we accept with it inevitable future moments of suffering from love or responsibility. We are afraid that the acceptance may become more important to us than the love for
which it was given, which is exactly what happens in the
case of "O." By welcoming abuse and self-destruction, we
may come to seek our own abuse and destruction, which in
the last analysis implies that we may prefer suffering to joy
and seek death in preference to life. This does happen to "O."
Having consented to each successive abuse as offered, she
finally requests the ultimate abuse, her own death, and presumably is granted her request.

This is the Devil's point of view, much more subtle but
much more real and frightening than de Sade's abstractionist.
Is the consent of love, in actuality, the pursuit of death? Does
the acceptance of suffering in the name of another imply
destruction of the self? The more you give, the less you have
to give, until you have given yourself away, destroyed by the
suffering you have given in the name of love until you are

degraded and depersonalized down to a nullity? This happens to "O"; she becomes null and void, a zero, as suggested by the alphabetical letter of her name.

Such a fear of depersonalization and destruction in the name of love may be why we are afraid to seek love blindly. This may be why we would like to enjoy sex as a momentary pleasure out of its natural context as reproductive process and expression of love. This may also be why we are unable to accept religion blindly and receive the joy from it which sustained our ancestors. If we live from moment to moment, taking pleasure as it comes and accepting inevitable pain of the moment, then at least we do not give ourselves away and destroy ourselves in the process. We are afraid that pain, suffering, and death may have no meaning. The dilemmas raised in the Book of Job remain as puzzling as ever. Without meaning, the pain, suffering, and death will only render us null and void, like "O."

There is an answer to the Devil's argument, fortunately, and it lies in the significance of love. If love is a give-and-take affair, a children's game of hide-and-seek, a two-headed beast where each separate head feasts on the other to satisfy pleasure and need, then Pauline Réage may be correct. However, what Pauline Réage describes is not love but perversion; there is one vital capacity of love which the invert, in his immaturity, cannot bring himself to face. The answer may be stated in religious terms. As we have noted, religion is pure masochism of a kind. The unpenitent thief cried, "If Thou be The Christ, save Thyself and us!" But Jesus remained upon His Cross. Love does not take the cheap miraculous escape but remains upon its Cross.

If we look around, we can see everywhere people in love where love has long since lost any physical element of pleasure, excitement, or release. The love partner may have become old or sick or crippled or insane or unlovable, but love continues to enrich both partners. Love remains upon its Cross.

The unicorn was the symbol of the fierce gentleness of love

and that meekness which may yet inherit the earth. When we try to enjoy sex without love, when we exploit another person sexually or non-sexually for our own pleasure or need, when we refuse to consent to responsibility or love out of self-protection or -defense, we drown the unicorn. In the consent or the giving, however, we must avoid the trap of confusing the act of consent with the person for whom consent was given: this is the perverted masochism which can reduce us to a nullity, just like "O." Without responsibility and love, sex may be the cruel joke played on us by sadistic Mother Nature in the meaningless interests of continuing an animal race which will soon become extinct. The body is a perishable commodity; bodily pleasure and bodily pain are both self-limited and temporary. Love with responsibility, which implies the capacity to remain upon a Cross, contains the seeds of our immortality.

17

The Nervous Ones

Dr. Albert Ellis is an articulate spokesman for a liberal system of sexual ethics, and his writings on sex have drawn fire from representatives of a more conservative philosophy. His work in the field of neurosis is less controversial and less well known but I think his writing on this subject is perhaps the most rational and lucid available.

When asked how many people are neurotic, Dr. Ellis will reply: approximately one hundred percent. He modifies this sweeping generality by saying that perhaps twenty or thirty percent of the population is neurotic but that any individual is potentially neurotic. As a definition of neurosis in this connection, Dr. Ellis considers a person neurotic who falls below his potentials because of excessive or inappropriate emotional reaction. It has often been said that half of the patients visiting any doctor's office have neurotic symptoms without organic disease and that three quarters of them have symptoms which are at least partly neurotic. My personal experience would tend to confirm this axiom. As a cause of the symptoms which make an individual feel ill and which reduce his efficiency at work and play, neurosis is the most common, even more frequent than the common cold.

Since neurosis is so frequent, one might presume that it is easy to recognize and diagnose. A great deal of the time, however, the diagnosis is made by exclusion. The patient's presenting symptom is accepted at face value; physical examination and laboratory tests are done to find a physical cause for the complaint; if no physical cause can be found, the symptom is then presumed to be neurotic. Diagnosis by exclusion represents insecurity on the part of the diagnostician; the doctor is naming as neurotic the symptom for which he cannot find a cause.

Psychiatrists should understand neurosis best, but they also seem insecure about making such a diagnosis. As a non-psychiatrist is afraid of missing organic disease, the psychiatrist is afraid of overlooking psychosis. Some psychiatrists escape the dilemma by failing to acknowledge any difference between psychosis and neurosis, an attitude which ignores the growing body of evidence suggesting that all psychosis has an organic cause. Some psychiatrists even maintain that there is no such thing as emotional illness and that all irrational and inappropriate behavior results from irresponsibility in a selfish person; this strange position would imply that there is no place for psychiatry in medicine and that management of all behavior problems is in the province of education. A good many psychiatrists cloak their insecurity by the use of vague nebulous terms or by devising their own private system of nomenclature, which does not increase public confidence in the profession. Strangely, psychiatrists are able to treat neurosis with considerable success despite their reluctance to diagnose it; neurosis will often respond to psychotherapy of almost any school. I have heard several psychiatrists state that they have often obtained good results from treatment when they didn't know what the trouble was.

If neurosis is so common, why should there be a problem in diagnosis? The difficulty is intrinsic in the nature of the disease. Since there is no physical disease, there are no physical changes to observe, measure, and record. The patient is disturbed by a problem which he cannot face; if he could admit the problem and bring himself to face it, he would be well on his way to solving the problem and curing himself. The first step in treatment is bringing the patient to accept the real nature of the difficulty. Accordingly a neurotic patient will reject the diagnosis of neurosis as the cause of his complaints. Non-psychiatristic physicians pretend to diagnose some mild elusive physical condition and pretend to treat it with sedatives or placebos while starting the first stage of psychotherapy. Psychiatrists use a different approach; they attach no diagnosis; when the patient asks what his trouble is, he is met with a dignified and noncommittal silence. This happens to work. It does not increase public confidence. The public is inclined to believe that any kind of psychotherapist works in ignorance, darkness, and confusion.

There is a general inability to accept the fact that the emotions can and do produce almost any sort of symptom and mimic almost any disease. Furthermore, the emotions can and do cause, and increase susceptibility to, most physical diseases. The interrelation of body and mind is apparent in the so-called psychosomatic and stress diseases; these diseases are so numerous and so complex that we cannot do them justice in a short space and will not discuss them in this book. The mind and body also interlock in the various diseases considered strictly physical. It is obvious that any sick person may suffer emotional consequences as the result of his illness. It may not be so obvious, but it is equally true that a person with good emotional adjustment is resistant to physical disease while poor emotional adjustment increases susceptibility to physical disease. If we can bring ourselves to accept the fact that emotions produce most of the symptoms which bother us and that emotions are a primary or contributory factor in causing most of our physical illnesses, the recognition of neurosis becomes very much more acceptable. Neurosis cannot be detected by physical examination, measured in the laboratory, or silhouetted by X rays, but it can be diagnosed positively by symptoms and signs. The symptoms are the patient's complaints and the signs are his behavioral and social maladjustments.

The basic neurotic manifestation is anxiety. This is a disagreeable sensation to the patient and it causes him to act inappropriately. We must make a distinction between fear, nervous tension, and anxiety. Fear is a protective reaction against potential danger. Fear may be inappropriate, out of proportion to the actual danger, but the fearful man can identify what he is afraid of. Fear makes him cautious, and his caution reduces the danger. When the source of danger is removed, fear disappears. Nervous tension is anticipation of an important approaching situation, which may or may not be dangerous; the person may fear the situation or he may look forward to it with pleasure; he knows that it is important to him, and his tension prepares him to meet the situation at his best. Anxiety is chronic distress without appropriate cause; the patient may feel fearful but he can identify no specific danger and no specific important occasion. Anxiety is inappropriate and illogical. The patient knows that it is not appropriate, and he exhorts himself, telling himself there is nothing to fear, but his anxiety persists despite his efforts to overcome it. Exhortations from others have equally little effect. Anxiety is inaccessible to exhortation because it is the result of conflict on subconscious levels.

A major sign of neurosis is what used to be called hysteria and is now often called somatic conversion. This means the conversion of emotional anxiety into an actual physical symptom or sign. To some extent, the patient makes himself physically sick. A physical illness is more acceptable to him than an emotional conflict which he cannot face and he turns his disability into something he can see and accept.

Self-defeating or self-blocking behavior is another major sign of neurosis. The patient has within him an unresolved emotional conflict. Until this conflict is resolved, he is unable to pursue some of his normal life goals. To the impartial and perhaps unsympathetic observer, it seems as if the patient was blocking or defeating himself and causing his own failures and unhappiness. To the patient, a thwarted incomplete and even unhappy existence is more comfortable than facing the emotional conflict he cannot resolve.

Life is full of problems requiring decision and a choice, minor ones occurring every moment and major ones quite frequently. Often, we make the decision and take action upon it. The decision may be appropriate, furthering our goals. It may be inappropriate and we may suffer the consequences, which may be anything from minor irritation to disaster. The consequences of an unwise decision do not, however, cause neurosis. Faced with a problem requiring choice, we may defer decision until some later date; we may be able to find an alternate route around the problem so that a choice is not required; we may ignore the problem in the hope that it will solve itself. Any of these approaches may deal with the situation very well, or any of them may bring adverse consequences; but none of them cause neurosis. We may feel insecure about our choice of approach to a problem or we may lack confidence in the wisdom of a choice already made; in this event, we conduct an internal debate. Such a debate on conscious levels is healthy and mature; this is the way in which we translate experience into wisdom. If the debate has within it some element which we cannot bring ourselves to face, we are in potential trouble. It is normal for us to push unpleasant subjects, out of the conscious mind, down to subconscious levels. Such a rejection of the unpleasant is part of our normal adjustive mechanism; it permits us to recover from disaster and tragedy and prevents morbid preoccupation with past unpleasantness. It is healthy to push an unpleasant happening, once finished, into the subconscious mind. It is not healthy to push unresolved conflict into subconscious levels. When we do so, we plant the seed of potential neurosis.

For such a seed to grow, it must fall on proper soil. There is a wide individual susceptibility to neurosis. The susceptibility has nothing to do with intelligence, for neurosis is seen on all intelligence levels. Neurotic susceptibility depends on certain qualities which might be called sensitivity, awareness, and imagination. By sensitivity, I mean inner emotional reactivity to external stimuli; some persons are emotional and reactive while others are phlegmatic. By awareness, I mean reactivity to the emotions of other people; some persons are empathic to the emotions of others and some oblivious. By imagination, I refer to the quality of being able to anticipate the various possibilities which could arise out of a given circumstance; some people have this in high degree and others lack it.

Sensitivity, awareness, and imagination are among the best of human attributes; accordingly, some of the most valuable, talented, and creative people are inclined to be neurotic. When neurosis develops, it tends to block talent and creativity but it is out of a person's most important characteristics that his neurosis may develop.

When the seed of unresolved conflict falls upon a soil of sensitivity, awareness, and imagination, a neurotic impulse appears. Many persons have brief and transient neurotic periods, lasting only a few hours or a few days; often, they can sense the cause of the resultant anxiety as due to unresolved conflict, can dig into their own subconscious minds and find the conflict and resolve it, thus curing their own neurosis. Some time may be wasted, some hours spoiled, but these transient neurotic periods do not cause much self-blocking or defeat. When the neurosis becomes fixed, lasting for months or years at a time, disability may be prolonged and serious. There appear to be other factors which tend to prolong and fix the neurosis.

Freud, investigating the nature of man's neurotic disabilities, uncovered the factor of sexual conflict. He also emphasized the importance of emotional trauma in early childhood. Both of these were important revelations. Putting the two together, he evolved a theory of sexual trauma in childhood as cause of neurosis, and here credibility begins to break down. To ascribe all neurosis to childhood sexual conflicts would appear to be false emphasis. At least four other non-sexual factors which tend to fix and prolong neurosis can be identified.

One, seen in early life, is parental rejection, lack of love from parent or parent substitute, which certainly gives much trouble in later life. A second, set up in childhood and operative from then on, might be termed perfectionism, the overly strict taboo sense seen in the rigid individual. A third factor, with onset in adolescence, is misused hostility, inappropriate use of transgression to express the individuality. Finally, there is the factor of the cumulative effects of failure, grief, and loss. We are all subject to such blows, and we recover from them, but each recovery leaves a scar, and in later life the cumulative effects of a series of these episodes may tend to perpetuate neurosis. I am sure the cumulative effects of failure, grief, and loss are more important in fixing neurosis in the middle-aged and elderly than any childhood sexual trauma long forgotten.

Since transient neurotic episodes are so common, there are a number of ideas, axioms, and postulates which are in common usage and widely accepted that are neurotically based. Such ideas, axioms, and postulates are easy to accept as true; they offer reassurance and justification for our various lack of successes; they take the sting away from our transient minor neuroses. If used as guidelines for decision-making and choice, however, they encourage neurosis. Let us list a few of these neurotically based and neurosis inducing fallacies:

(1) A person should be loved by everybody.

(2) Accomplishment is the measure of value and worth.

(3) Failure in one area implies failure in every area.

(4) People should treat us better than they do, and things should go better than they have been going.

(5) Since an important happening once influenced our life, it will always influence our life.

(6) One has no control over the emotions and must give in to them.

(7) One has complete control over the emotions and should never give in to them.

(8) Worry in advance will prevent pain or difficulty at the time.

(9) Freedom is the right to do exactly as we please.

(10) All men, being equal, deserve equal rewards.

(11) Men and women, being equal, have equal responses and needs.

(12) Tomorrow will be better.

Whenever a person discovers that he has been reassuring himself with any of these axioms, or guiding his decisions by any of them, he should suspect himself of neurosis. It would be nice if people loved us more and treated us better. It is possible that worry in advance may help us lay down plans to reduce pain or difficulty. Tomorrow may possibly be better, but it may also be worse, and is rather likely to be much the same. The neurotic seeks a world which might be, should be, ought to be, but, unfortunately, isn't. The adjusted person makes the best of things as he finds them, using sensitivity, awareness, and imagination to adjust to reality; the neurotic uses them to create unreality.

The world we find is not the best of all possible worlds. The love, which is the best we can find, is not the best of all theoretically possible loves. We cannot be complacent with reality. We must do what we can to improve things as we find them, but we should not expect total success. To protect ourselves from the pain of our failures we may need to escape from reality from time to time, but we should make such escapes a temporary vacation and not a permanent way of life. Some of the escapes are likely to be escapes from conflict we cannot resolve, and therefore we should expect to find ourselves neurotic from time to time. We should come to recognize the expressions of our own neurosis, and having recognized a neurotic expression, we should dive to the roots of ourselves in search of the conflict, for if we permit our neurosis to be permanent, we will permanently block and defeat ourselves. Often, we can resolve our own neuroses. When we can't, we should seek professional help. We may criticize psychiatrists, and there is much in psychiatry to be criticized, but the fact remains that most psychiatrists cure most of the neurosis they see most of the time. We should not be ashamed of our neurotic tendencies; they come from our sensitivity, awareness, and imagination, of which we should be proud; but we should use these qualities creatively. Neurosis is the great destroyer of creativity.

18

On Living with a Neurotic Person

It's impossible to avoid living with a neurotic person. Given the frequency of neurosis, one must frequently encounter the neurotic: in husband or wife, in a child, in parent or relative, boss or associate or business contact, friend or social acquaintance. A good deal of the art of getting along with people is the art of getting along with neurotics.

The importance of learning this art is partly self-defense. A trying aspect of dealing with a neurotic is that such dealings may induce neurosis in oneself; in this sense, neurosis is contagious.

Perhaps the key to the secret is the simple recognition that neurosis can and does frequently exist. We are inclined to accept the behavior we encounter in other people at face value. If they act difficult, we wonder why; if they are offensive, we wonder what we have done to cause offense; if they get mad at us, we become defensive because they are mad, or we get mad in return. We are apt to become disturbed by behavior which we sense to be illogical or inappropriate. We expect people to act in their own self-interests, putting their best foot forward while at the same time remaining within the confines of acceptable social behavior and taking the rights and privileges of others into consideration. When a person puts a bad foot in our face, we are inclined to think that we may be in some way to blame. When people act in an antisocial way toward us and abuse our rights and privileges, we tend to think that we have been tactless or rude or selfish in our dealings with them. Thus, an illogical or inappropriate reaction from others induces an illogical or inappropriate reaction from us, and this is the mechanism by which neurosis may be considered contagious. If we can identify disturbing action in others as an expression of neurosis, then we are more apt to accept it with equanimity and deal with it much better.

The recognition of neurotic reactions in others, though sometimes obvious, is by no means simple. Experienced psychiatrists hesitate to diagnose neurosis, and it would be presumptuous for us to claim we can spot neurotic behavior at a glance. It is even more presumptuous to think that we can determine the cause, or identify the unresolved conflict, in the neurotics that we meet; it takes the experienced expert weeks and months and years to uncover the roots of any individual problem.

We can see anxiety in people; this strongly suggests neurosis; chronic anxiety, as distinguished from fear or nervous tension, is usually a symptom of neurosis. Somatic conversion is a matter for the expert to uncover, but a pattern of self-blocking or self-defeating behavior is often more apparent to a friend or relative than it is to the psychiatrist, and such behavior is usually of neurotic origin.

There are a number of characteristic ways in which neurotic persons may act, by which we may suspect a neurotic tendency. Dr. David Shapiro, a clinical psychologist, has coined the phrase "neurotic styles" in a book bearing that title, and I think this is a useful concept. Dr. Shapiro considers four of them: what he names the impulsive, the hysterical, the obsessive-compulsive, and the paranoid styles. Impulsive behavior and hysterical behavior are obvious phenomena, and are frequently seen in the neurotic. Obsession-compulsion is a little bit different, I think, and we have already discussed this type of behavior in a chapter of its own. Likewise we have discussed paranoid behavior; certainly this is seen in neurosis but its presence must always suggest psychosis, especially schizophrenia.

In considering neurotic behavior patterns or styles, one might first think of the various types of behavior commonly associated with immaturity: impulsive, irresponsible, moody, procrastinating, theatrical, melodramatic, exaggerating, exhibitionistic—such behavior is normal in a certain degree in young persons and it has a certain charm in persons who are entitled to be immature because of tender years. Some persons remain immature throughout adult life. Perpetually immature persons are not necessarily neurotic, though many are. However, in a person who has shown characteristics of maturity and subsequently develops immature personality traits, neurosis may be strongly suspected.

One then might consider types of behavior commonly associated with the neurotic phenomenon of somatic conversion. Hypochondria, whining, griping, inadequate or inert behavior associated with complaints of physical ill health, especially if long continued in a person not obviously ill, suggest neurosis.

Finally, there are patterns of behavior associated with and partly responsible for the self-defeating and self-blocking elements of neurosis. Irritability and touchiness, specific phobias, nervous agitation and hysteria, inappropriate jealousy, evasive mannerisms, a gift for making enemies and losing friends and disrupting social gatherings: these are some of the ways in which the neurotic blocks and defeats himself. A neurotic wishes to be loved, respected, and admired by the people that he meets, as do we all. If he adopts styles or mannerisms which shock, offend, disturb, or irritate people, he is not likely to be loved, respected, or admired. He acts in this fashion, not because he wishes to irritate, offend, or disturb people, but because he has something to hide, his subconscious unresolved conflict which he is hiding from others and himself. His styles and mannerisms are devices for concealment: a mask, a smoke screen, a red herring, a diversionary tactic. Although the neurotic cannot state this position, he prefers to alienate people than to have people discern the nature of his problem, and this is why he acts in the typical illogical inappropriate manner.

If we recognize the neurotic style for what it is—a concealment device—we are much less apt to be shocked, offended, disturbed, or irritated by the way neurotics act. It is in just this recognition that smooth relationships with neurotic persons depend. We do not need to diagnose neurosis and we do not need to know the cause if we can recognize the typical neurotic styles. We may find it difficult to understand why a person should choose to be anxious, make himself physically sick, and block or defeat himself, but we should be able to understand that concealment of his dilemma is more important to the neurotic than popularity in social relationships.

A book has been written by Laura Huxley entitled *You Are Not the Target*. I don't think much of the book, but I consider the title to be the basic secret of dealing with neurotic persons. Neurotics often seem to direct shocking, offensive, disturbing, or irritating behavior at you. However, the neurotic is not aiming anything at you. He is hiding something from you. If you let yourself become the target, you thereby induce a neurotic reaction in yourself. Sir William Osler recommended that all doctors cultivate equanimity. Anybody will find that equanimity is the priceless ingredient in dealing with neurotic persons. In the modern jargon, youth often tells itself: don't lose your cool. This is another definition of equanimity.

Dr. Albert Ellis, mentioned earlier, wrote a book called *How to Live with a Neurotic at Work or at Home*. I consider this the best self-help psychology book I have encountered: short, readable, rational, lucid, and wise, equally applicable to neurosis in others and in the self. Dr. Ellis makes the extremely important point that, if one expects to live peacefully with a neurotic, one must expect him to act neurotically. This may sound easy and obvious, but in practice it is neither. Again and again, we seem to expect the neurotic to act as if he were well adjusted and we show disappointment and distress when he does not. Half the trouble in the world, says Dr. Ellis, is because there are so many people acting neurotically, and so many other people who don't understand that a neurotic will act neurotically. We tend to blame the neurotic for his behavior. We think he "ought" to act as if he were not disturbed. Since he is disturbed, he will act that way, a fact which should not in turn disturb us.

Dr. Ellis supplies further helpful advice in this connection in another, and perhaps surprising, place. Offhand, one would not expect a book called *Sex and the Single Man* to contain sound advice on living with neurotic persons, but Chapter 8 of the book does just that. Here, Dr. Ellis points out that love, once won, cannot be guaranteed to last; he refers to love by a woman from a man's point of view, but the comment is equally valid the other way around and valid in social relationships not involving sexual love. Having been loved by a person, one cannot be sure that love will endure, and rejection by the loved one may occur. Such a rejection often is the result of neurosis. When rejection occurs, one is entitled to endure pain and sorrow from the loss, but one should not react to such a loss as a catastrophe nor should one blame the previous lover for what has occurred. When the rejecting person is neurotic, which is so often the case, one must appreciate that the neurotic person may lose most of his or her capacity for love as a result of the disturbance. Therefore, the rejection is not "his fault," "her fault," or "your fault"; it is the result of the disease. Finally, one should appreciate that the neurotic person may recover; when recovery occurs, the ability to love is restored.

If a relationship with a neurotic is too difficult to be accepted with equanimity (some are), if there appears small likelihood that the neurotic will recover (some don't), then one must seriously consider discontinuing the relationship.

In marriage, this may mean divorce. In blood relationships that cannot be broken by divorce, physical separation may be necessary. In employment situations, this might mean changing jobs, and in casual social relationships, this might mean changing friends. Divorce of any kind should not be undertaken lightly; it is an expensive process, financially and emotionally. It means discarding a portion of the past and it is an admission of partial failure. If the relationship has been valuable, all feasible methods of salvage should be explored before the ship is sunk. If distortions of the relationship have been due in part to neurotic expressions from oneself, which often may be the case, one's own neurosis must be treated, before irreversible steps are taken to dissolve the relationship, for if one carries neurosis away from a broken relationship, the divorce will make things worse, not better, and any new relationships may be jeopardized in the same way. But sometimes dissolution of the relationship is the only way toward peace of mind.

Often it is impossible to dissolve a relationship with a neurotic person; circumstances are such that one must continue to deal and live with him. In this case, one must often pull away from him or her emotionally in order to avoid entrapment in the web of his or her neurosis. Is it possible to live and deal with a neurotic while being emotionally detached from him? Yes, it is. Is it possible to love a neurotic who rejects you? Yes, it is. One might think that a close relationship means emotional entanglement and that love means total emotional engagement, but this is not the case. Even in a mature love relationship, some degree of emotional detachment on both sides is healthy. Complete and total emotional engagement with another person is not possible; what may seem to pass for it is an unhealthy sort of possessiveness, which itself is neurotic. In a mature relationship, each party retains his identity and respects the identity of the other. Two persons don't fuse toward one; they reinforce, making something more than two.

Perhaps the best way to live with a neurotic is to treat

him. I scarcely suggest that we all become psychiatrists or that we practice amateur psychiatry, but we must practice amateur psychology. Neurosis is extremely common; professional psychiatrists and clinical psychologists are in short supply; the professionals in the field can handle only a very small percent of neurosis. Professionals in many other fields treat neurosis constantly, whether they are aware of it or not: non-psychiatric physicians, marriage counselors, social workers, judges, teachers, lawyers, ministers, personnel specialists, management experts; so do parents; so do friends; and so, in fact, do we all. We must, unless neurosis is to paralyze the world.

How does one treat a neurotic when professional help is unavailable? Basically in the same way the professional does: you listen to him. You don't advise him, or preach to him, or debate with him, or argue with him: you listen to him. You just listen: sympathetically but impersonally and impartially, without emotional engagement. A great many neuroses will respond to this technique alone and it is not a difficult technique to acquire.

In addition, one can use what might be called selective encouragement. When the neurotic shows interest in any healthful outgoing activity—work, hobby, recreation, social activity—he should be encouraged. Lack of interest in such an activity is not actively discouraged or preached against but simply ignored. Encourage the healthy tendencies; ignore unhealthy tendencies.

Finally, we may consider something which has been called "reality therapy," a technique sometimes very helpful to psychologists, both amateur and professional. This phrase was coined by a psychiatrist, Dr. William Glasser, in a book bearing that title. Dr. Glasser presents his concepts as an effective psychiatric treatment different from other techniques generally accepted and based on a new theory which is generally not accepted. Dr. Glasser is one of the psychiatrists who believe that there is no such thing as emotional illness and that all inappropriate and illogical behavior is the result of irresponsibility by selfish persons. I do not myself accept this theory and I don't think it worth discussing at any great length, but part of his treatment approach seems to be useful to both professional and amateur therapists. This approach might be stated as Dr. Glasser does not state it: sometimes the neurotic needs a good swift kick in the ass. A cartoon that appeared in *Playboy* magazine says the same thing: it shows the psychiatrist reaching over the couch and giving the head of the patient a good stiff whack with his fist while saying, "Maybe *that* will knock some sense into you!" Dr. Glasser phrases the concept along these lines: people have the need to love, to be loved, and to feel they are worthwhile; these needs can be met satisfactorily only in ways which do not deprive others of their needs; the responsible person takes the needs of others into consideration; and disturbed people must be taught such responsibility. The therapist refuses to accept neurotic expressions as responsible or real; he points out that neurotic expressions are irresponsible and asks the patient to discard them, taking instead the responsible position which respects the needs of others. He tries to make the patient accept the reality of social living, in which we can only satisfy our own needs by fulfilling the needs of others. This practical hard-headed approach is, of course, not new at all but is the basic technique of old-fashioned education and is also the meaning implicit in the Golden Rule.

The neurotic person gets so wrapped up in his own inner conflict that he forgets the needs of others; when he forgets to do unto others as he would like others to do unto him, he blocks himself and defeats himself. It is sometimes very useful to remind him of this fact.

Patience is essential in living with a neurotic. So is tact. So is tolerance. And so, most particularly, is a sense of humor. Neurosis is not a laughing matter, and it does not help a neurotic to laugh at him; he takes himself too seriously to begin with, and has lost most of his ability to laugh at himself. But a sense of humor is a balance wheel;

it preserves the sanity. Life with a neurotic may well also induce a sense of sadness, for time is short, human life is valuable, and neurosis detracts from the value of human life.

If you cannot live with a neurotic peacefully but are forced by circumstances to live with him anyway, you must face the likely probability that you also are neurotic. In this event, you must hope that the other person can learn to live peacefully with you.

Part Two

OURSELVES

19

Intelligence

The focal point of this study now changes. We have been looking at others, studying adjustment patterns in the faces that we meet. Now we try to turn the camera inward, picturing ourselves.

In certain ways, we know ourselves as nobody else can ever know us, and in certain other ways, we are quite blind. Techniques of deception and evasion, those games of hide-and-seek, are not confined to our relationships with others; we fool ourselves quite often. The very human tendency toward self-deception makes introspection imperfect and biased and also poses difficulties for this book. For example, a given reader may be neurotic, as so many of us are; the blocking tendency of neurosis may make such a reader immune to discussion of a point close to his own dilemma. His immunity will manifest itself in a lack of interest in that portion of the discussion. He rejects a written analysis of the problem because he cannot bring himself to face his own unresolved conflict; to face it, even in the abstract, in print, would cause him emotional disturbance. We do our best to avoid emotional disturbance. Treatment by a psychiatrist or any other sort of psychotherapy is always disturbing and painful to the patient at some point during therapy; the patient accepts it because he is seeking relief of more fundamental pain, as he would permit himself to be subjected to surgery. But the reader of a book does not have to read a given part of the book; even the student, with a compulsory assignment, can skip. And therefore, if this book should touch too close to home, the reader will reject it, which dooms the author to failure in advance if he hopes to make the reader know himself by means of the discussions here.

As a matter of fact, the author of this book had a disconcerting experience of this kind during preparation of the manuscript. One early reader, close to the writing of the book and personally involved in its success or failure, displayed interest in parts of the book concerning distant and rather exotic problems in others, but after reading a part quite close to home rejected that material as being of little interest or relevance. I was dismayed by the reaction and was about to rewrite the material until I recognized the reason for the rejection. In conversation at a later date, the reader brought up the subject, using the same phrases and concepts in conversation which I had written, which led me to believe that the reader in question had not been entirely uninterested in the material. One could avoid this danger by avoiding material possibly disturbing to any given reader, but this would give material of little interest to any reader. The problem could be partially averted by sticking to generalities.

As a matter of fact, we must stick to generalities. Although we are trying to write about the self, obviously we cannot address the book to any given individual reader; a different book would be needed for every reader. We must therefore confine ourselves to common generalities.

This part of the book does not pretend to offer the reader an opportunity to analyze himself. This is almost impossible to do in a book. I say "almost" because I know of one book which consistently performs an astonishingly acute and perceptive job of self-analysis to any reader brave enough to tackle it honestly. The book in question was first published in England under the title *Meet Yourself as You Really Are* and was revised and reprinted in America as *Analyze Yourself*. This is one of the most valuable books in my library. I have used it many times: on myself, on patients, on members of my family, and even for characterization for my novels. Somebody who wants an honest look at himself should look there, not here.

Likewise, this is not a "self-help" book. That sort of book accomplishes its results through "the power of positive thinking" which is another way of saying suggestion. Much, both good and bad, can be accomplished through suggestion. But the positive power of suggestion has a temporary effect; it wears off; to have beneficial long-term results, the suggestion must be reinforced. To obtain lasting effects from an inspirational book, the book must be read repeatedly and frequently. Only classics can stand multiple reading; most self-help books are not written that well; and for this reason most self-help books do not help very much or very long.

The intent of the second part of this book is the same as that of the first. Avoiding id, idiom, and inspiration, we want to take an honest look at common patterns of motivation and behavior, this time as we may encounter them in the self, rather than in the people whom we meet. We will attempt to keep the approach as objective as possible considering the subjective nature of the material, and to keep the discussion logical and calm.

A word in general about introspection and self-analysis. If honest, it does mean some breaking through the protective deceptions which we use to fool ourselves. This intrinsically may be disturbing. If not disturbing, the analysis has been superficial. It is good to understand ourselves through education. There are, however, certain areas in every individual best left undisturbed. If you lift up every rock in the cave, some strange things come crawling out. The reader will decide for himself which rocks to lift and which to leave undisturbed.

We will begin the second part of this book on the same

subject with which we began the first: that of intelligence, because it is perhaps the most "pure" factor to be considered. We presume intelligence to be constant; if so, why study it in ourselves? Should we not accept the fact that God gave us a certain amount of brains, for better or for worse, that we will never be smarter than people born more intelligent than we, but will never be dumber than people born more stupid than we, and accordingly we should do the best we can with what we have? A reasonable point of view, perhaps, but it seems quite possible that most people do not use all the intelligence they have, and we might be able to discover ways to act smarter than we seem to be. Presumably this would be to our advantage.

What is intelligence anyway? We seem to recognize it. On meeting a stranger, we make a first impression within a minute or two. Among the things we estimate is his intelligence. Our first impressions may often change as we get to know a person better, but one of the things least likely to change is our opinion of his intelligence. If we think he is smarter than we are, or dumber, or of average intelligence, or approximately as intelligent as we, we are likely to retain the same impression. Other observers are apt to reach the same assessment of the intelligence of a given individual that we have reached. These things suggest that intelligence is an entity which is constant and which is not difficult to gauge, and therefore there ought to be scientific ways to record and measure it.

The first modern scientific approach to the problem of measuring intelligence occurred in France in 1905. A commission to study methods of teaching retarded children was appointed. There were two members of this commission—Alfred Binet, a psychologist, and Théodore Simon, a psychiatrist—whose names are familiar to us for their work in this connection. Simon and Binet devised a set of questions which were intended to test the following functions: comprehension, suggestibility, attention, imagination, language functions, memory, logic, information, and the ability to solve problems, to detect illogical absurdities, and to discriminate between concepts. The sum total of these functions would appear to be a valid definition of intelligence, although definition and recording of any of the component functions might be difficult.

The Simon-Binet tests were introduced into the United States and given to large numbers of children from pre-school age up through the age of fifteen. For persons older than fifteen, it was felt that the questions did not test intelligence but were instead a measure of the education and experience of the individual and his attitudes toward them. From this conclusion, the postulate was derived that full maturation of intelligence is reached at the age of fifteen. Investigators at Stanford University, working with modifications of the Simon-Binet test questions, evolved the concept of the intelligence quotient.

There is a set of Simon-Binet questions for each year of age up to sixteen. When a child is tested, the highest year in which he answers all questions correctly is noted as is the highest year in which he answers at least one question correctly. These two years are added and divided by two and the resulting figure is taken to represent his mental age. Then his mental age is divided by his chronological age (or by fifteen if he is older than fifteen), the quotient is multiplied by a hundred, and the resulting figure is the so-called intelligence quotient or IQ.

An IQ of 100, in theory, ought to represent average intelligence, but work with the Simon-Binet questions seemed to demonstrate that 100 is too high and that an IQ of 87 approximates the average. From this, it was decided that the original group of children on whom the questions were worked out were of higher than average intelligence. Let us pause here to note another example of unscientific method in biological research, which we have noted on several earlier occasions in this book, the sort of trap into which workers in human behavior seem to fall so readily. The tests were designed for the study of retarded children but were evolved from an experimental population which was not retarded or even average but of higher than average intelligence. This could easily distort the validity of the testing, at least for its original purpose.

Experience with IQ testing on large numbers of children offered the following conclusions. A child with an IQ of 30 and a mental age of five cannot be expected to complete school work beyond kindergarten; an IQ of 45 and a mental age of seven permit completion of the second grade; an IQ of 65 and a mental age of ten are required for fourth grade work; an IQ of 80 to 90 (or approximately average) permits completion of grade school; an IQ between 90 and 110 permits completion of high school, between 110 and 120 for college, and above 120 for graduate or professional study.

This sounds neat, nice, scientific, and mathematical; you test a young child, and from the mathematical IQ figure you can tell how much formal education he is mentally equipped to deal with. IQ figures have often been so used by educators. They are reasonably valid in generalizing about educational programs for masses of children. The IQ is far less valid for any given individual child. We can see why this might be so.

It is generally considered that intelligence is constant and does not increase as a result of education, but yet the Simon-Binet questions are built on progressively increasing difficulty and therefore, except in the very young, are measuring response to education and not intelligence per se. Being based on an original group of higher than average intelligence, there may be distortion for those less intelligent than average. Being based on a maximum of age fifteen, the questions are invalid for persons of average intelligence beyond age fifteen, and for persons of superior intelligence beyond the age of perhaps eight or ten. Finally, the Simon-Binet type of questions are testing almost exclusively ability in language arts; while a good deal of formal education depends on language arts, facility with words is only one aspect of intelligence, not all of it.

Recognition of the invalidity of IQ testing in adults led to other and more inclusive tests. The most widely used, developed by a neurologist at Bellevue Hospital in New York, is called the Wechsler-Bellevue Intelligence Scale. It tests the following: information, vocabulary, word comprehension, similarities, picture arrangement, picture completion, block design, object assembly, arithmetic, digit span, and digit symbols. Thus this so-called Intelligence Scale tests not only language arts ability but visual ability, mechanical aptitude, and mathematical ability, giving a more comprehensive picture of total intelligence. The results have been standardized against a group of adults, thus removing the age barrier of fifteen. However, this test does not measure what may be the most important facet of intelligence—social sense—and it does not separate the effects of education and experience from those of raw intelligence; it does not filter out psychological and emotional factors at the time of testing.

The IQ will give some valuable information about the retarded child, and the Wechsler-Bellevue Intelligence Scale will give valid data for comparison of intelligence in adults, but we must conclude that all such testing gives only rough estimations and that we cannot yet measure intelligence in a precise and scientific fashion as we can measure the speed of light, the force of gravity, or the distance between two points. Within a minute or two of meeting a stranger, we guess his intelligence with an accuracy which holds up quite well for practical purposes. Yet, we test a child for hours at a time and come up with a figure which is not much more accurate. Obviously there are factors in intelligence which continue to elude our definitions and means of measurement.

What is there about intelligence which we intuitively sense but cannot measure or record? There are many such factors, of course, and it is their number and interlocking complexity which defies measurement. We may not be able to define or measure them, but we can discuss some of these factors without losing ourselves in deep water.

First, there is reaction time, speed of information retrieval, the quickness with which the individual responds. Quickness of mind suggests high intelligence, and slowness suggests stupidity. There's a television show called *College Bowl* in which teams of bright college students compete by answering difficult questions. The speed of information retrieval of these smart kids and the amount and complexity of information at their command is often astonishing. At the end of the program, the moderator carefully points out that reaction time is not the sole measure of intelligence or of the education these quick youngsters have received. As a matter of fact, we have probably all known quick clever individuals who dazzle us with their brilliancy but whose brilliant comments, when examined, turn out to be half-right, or ill-considered, or wrong. We also know people who appear to be slow thinkers but whose response when it finally arrives is profound, exact, complete, and wise. To measure intelligence by reaction time alone is obviously not valid, although in general intelligent people are quick thinkers and stupid people slow ones.

Another facet of intelligence we observe is in the nature of the communication we receive. The remarks may be silly, superficial, false, trite, inappropriate, illogical, uninformed, in which case we conclude that the speaker is not so intelligent; or the remarks may be wise, profound, correct, logical, appropriate, informed, or even entirely over our head, in which case we presume the speaker to be more intelligent than we are. Now we are assessing a number of different elements in combination: the amount of information the individual has to be retrieved (which in turn is a reflection of the information to which he has been exposed, his education, and also the amount of information he can readily recall, his memory); the skill with which he communicates his thoughts, which is a reflection of his ability at language arts; his problem-solving ability; sometimes his mathematical ability, the ease with which he can calculate numbers and assess probabilities; the acuteness of his observation of things present and past; to some extent his social ease with us; and, now and then, his mechanical aptitude.

Finally, our assessment of his intelligence is shaded by psychological factors: our mood, his mood, his relative sanity or lack of it, our relative sanity or lack of it, and whether we like him or not. The more we like a person the higher we are inclined to rate his intelligence and vice versa.

Ignoring the psychological variables too subtle and complex for us to measure and define, we might say that intelligence consists of speed of information retrieval, memory, retention of educational and life experiences, language arts ability, mathematical ability, mechanical aptitude, acuteness of perception, and social ease.

Use of such terms as information retrieval makes us think of the computer. The computer is an astonishing recent product of man's intelligence, sometimes thought of as more intelligent than man himself. We tend to fear computers, although people who know most about them seem to fear them least. Instead of fearing the computer, we might study it, for it is like the human brain in many ways and can give us certain clues for better usage of our own intelligence.

The computer consists of individual units, hooked up with a connecting system, controlled with switches and relays, run by electricity, and containing facilities for the input, processing, storage, retrieval, and output of information. The same description applies exactly to the human brain. The computer is not a brain. It can do some things much more rapidly and accurately than the human brain, can perform some "thinking," can make decisions and solve problems, but there are many brain functions it cannot perform, and it is not more "intelligent" than the people building it and using it. With present technology, it is impossible to build a computer containing as many units as the human brain. Despite recent advances in miniaturization and circuitry, it will be a long time before a computer can be constructed anything like as complex as the most primitive primate brain.

There are two general types of computer: the digital computer and the analogue computer. Although they operate differently, they have similar uses and perform similar functions. The analogue computer handles information in the form of a continuously variable curve. The digital computer handles discrete units of data, in other words numbers. The present brief discussion will be confined to the digital computer. The analogue computer is too difficult for me to understand.

As does the human brain, the computer receives information from outside. The input unit of the computer receives its material coded into numerical data it can handle. The brain receives information from the organs of special sense: eyes, ears, nose, tongue, and skin organs of touch, temperature, pain, texture, and position. The computer is no better than the information fed into it; if the data is incomplete or erroneous, the result will be incomplete or erroneous. This is obviously true of human thinking too. Intellectual acuity increases with acuity of the organs of special sense. We all have reserves of perception and observation which we do not use, and we can improve acuity of the special senses with training. When one special sense is disabled, compensation is often achieved by increased acuity of other senses; thus, a blind man learns to use his ears better than the man who can see. Medical students are taught to improve their powers of observation in order to make diagnosis, and as a consequence a physician often notes small deformities and disabilities in passing strangers which escape the untrained eye. Since a considerable amount of information useful in our thinking comes from words on a printed page, improvement of rapidity and comprehension of reading, and such special techniques as speed reading, may often increase practical intelligence.

When appropriate data has been received by the computer, the information is processed. Processing in the computer is of four basic types: control, arithmetic, decision making, and logic. The human brain also processes information in this fashion.

By "control," we mean that the computer tells itself what to do with data received and directs in proper sequence the various operations necessary to produce the desired result. Such "control" is "programed" into the computer in advance by proper wiring and circuitry. The wiring and circuitry of the brain is already there for any thinking process we will ever try and many we will never get around to trying. The use of a proper circuit in the brain for a given thought process is not automatic; it is not born into us; we acquire it through experience and as the result of training and education. Full use of our intelligence requires that we learn from each experience. The process of training and education should be continuous throughout life. We must try new circuitry and new "programs" if we are to use any reasonable proportion of the potential intelligence we possess.

The arithmetical function of the computer is what its name implies: its ability to compute. For mathematical calculation, it is more rapid and accurate than the human brain. This is not because the computer is more complex than the brain. Brain circuitry is much more complicated, and instead of receiving arithmetically coded data from a single source, we receive many different kinds of information simultaneously from many sources. Our complexity tends to confuse and distract us. We cannot exclude all other sources of stimuli to become pure calculators, and we tend to forget some of the figures we are supposed to carry over and utilize. Some persons can handle mental calculation far better than others; perhaps their circuitry is more direct or they are less distracted by other stimuli. There is an interesting form of insanity whose victims are the so-called "idiot savant." Such persons are seriously retarded in all thinking processes except the mathematical but they are able to do mental calculation of great complexity with the speed and accuracy of a computer.

When we calculate, we represent numbers by the Arabic system, which represents all numbers out of the ten symbols: 0, 1, 2, 3, 4, 5, 6, 7, 8, 9. The reason we use the ten-symbol number system is probably a childishly simple one; we happen to have ten fingers and ten toes; a surprising number of intelligent adults actually use the fingers and toes when doing mental calculation. Digital computers can operate on the Arabic system, but for them this is cumbersome, because each component unit must have ten alternative positions or choices. It is much more feasible if each unit has only two choices, corresponding to the on-off alternatives of the electrical switch or relay. Since all numbers can be expressed using only two symbols, such a system, called the binary system, is practical for computer use. The human brain could be taught to calculate in a binary, rather than an Arabic, number system, and this might facilitate mental calculation, since our own brain cells use an off-on electrical circuit. The disadvantage of the binary system for our use is that it renders even simple calculations with pencil and paper so long and cumbersome as to be almost useless.

It is not the ability of the computer to calculate which frightens us; adding machines and other mechanical calculators have long been available; it is the ability of the computer to solve problems and make decisions which we find frightening. In this sense, the computer can "think"; within its own limitations, it can "think" quicker and more accurately than we can.

The computer makes decisions and solves problems by the use of logic. Mathematicians, philosophers, scientists—and males in general—tend to think in logical terms, solving problems and making decisions as the computer does. This is not the only way to think. Many people, and traditionally females, think without logic, using what we call intuition. Intuitive thinking depends on social sense and works with emotional forces rather than intellectual. In certain areas, intuitive thinking is more valuable than logical thinking, which is why females can think better in certain areas than males. The computer has no social sense, can't handle emotional forces, and cannot think intuitively.

Logic, often studied in philosophy, is basically mathematical. It depends on chains of related axiomatic statements. Each such axiom, based on sufficiently complete information, is of such a nature that it can be judged either right or wrong. Two axioms hook up with each other in four fundamental ways: *AND*, which is the additive relation; *OR*, the alternative relation; *NOT*, the antagonistic relation; and the relation of *EITHER BUT NOT BOTH*. Axioms, based on sufficient information to be considered right, hooked together with other such axioms in the various four primary relationships, produce the logical process by which decisions are made and problems solved. The principles of logic were described by Aristotle and we have not managed to improve on his work since. It is apparent that the true-false possibilities of the axioms in logic are of the same nature as the two-symbol binary number system and the on-off nature of the electrical switch. In 1847, a British mathematician and logician named George Boole devised an algebraic system, a "shorthand," for expressing Aristotelian logic in two symbols. This so-called Boolean Algebra caused no great excitement in the last century and was virtually forgotten until 1938 when an American mathematician at MIT decided to apply it to electrical switches and circuits, thus providing the means to put logic into the computer and to make logical thinking compatible with binary calculation. This was the beginning of the modern computer. It is rather interesting to note that the philosophy of an ancient Greek, converted into shorthand by a professor of mathematics at Queen's College, Cork, whose work was overlooked for a hundred years, is basic to the device which in turn is basic in the space explorations which will place man on the surface of the moon.

When information is fed into the computer, some of it is immediately useful but a good deal of it is stored, available for usage at a later appropriate time. Much of the usefulness of the computer consists in the amount of information which can be stored and retrieved. There is a computer in operation containing all the income tax data pertinent to every American taxpayer. No human brain, we might think, could remember and have available for appropriate use when needed such an enormous fund of information. Actually, every human brain contains much more information than that, but it is not of a single unified type. Myriad sensory stimuli flow into the brain at all times; some of this we do not notice and discard as irrelevant or useless; but whatever stimuli, of any kind and at any time, we have "noticed," consciously or subconsciously, we do retain and store away for possible later retrieval and usage. Potentially, at least, we could remember and use anything and everything we have ever noticed or known. Our practical usable memory is only a tiny percentage of our potential memory; the problem is not in the amount of data we can store—we can and do store an incredibly vast amount of material inside the skull—but in our retrieval system. We have small amounts of data in our conscious minds, available for instant use, but most of it we store in the subconscious mind where, often, we cannot retrieve it on command. Practical memory depends, therefore, on accessibility of the subconscious to the conscious mind. It is for this reason that memory is often better when the subconscious is closer and more available: such as just before, during, and just after sleep, in mild and early intoxication, during relaxation, during recreation, when under the influence of the creative arts. At such times, things seem to "pop" into our heads. At such times, also, actual memorization can be more readily accomplished. The computer is able to retrieve usable material from its secondary storage because it is not "distracted"—it utilizes one type of data, under control, programed for a given process. Our brain, under the impact of the continuous flood of so many kinds of sensory input material, tends to get distracted and confused in dealing with material on the conscious level and often cannot find vital storage material when needed, even though it usually is there. Our storage area, the subconscious mind, is where our emotions are bred and reared and play; the emotions tend to have a distracting effect on intellectualization, as if playful and sometimes destructive animals were roaming free among the filing cabinets in the basement. Neurosis, the emotional subconscious unresolved conflicts, has a particularly distracting influence on information retrieval and accordingly neurosis sharply decreases practical memory and interferes with maximum usage of the intelligence.

How can we improve our retrieval system, thereby improving our memory and becoming more intelligent than we seem to be? First, by conscious effort of the will, sheer concentration, the ruthless exclusion of useless or irrelevant conscious sensory material when we are trying to think. This is never easy, especially in a crowded modern world so full of banal irrelevant distractions. Second, we can keep the wires clean and the switches free of rust, meaning the maintenance of maximum physical health through sound physical hygienic measures. A mind in a rested healthy body works much better than the mind in a body which is fatigued or sick. Finally, since the wealth of our stored material is subconscious, we must keep order in the subconscious filing cabinets, resolving unresolved emotional conflicts, keeping neurosis at a minimum. Perhaps the reason that the computer "thinks" better than we do, exerts logic to reach decisions and solve problems more accurately and rapidly than we can, is because the computer has no emotions and is not neurotic. The computer does not have sensitivity, awareness, or imagination; it cannot feel or love; on this plane, it lacks the capacity for intuitive thinking and creativity and is therefore far less intelligent than we. It is not neurotic but we are.

Our thinking process basically is electrical, just as the computer's is, and the electrical processes in our brain are controlled by chemical processes. The chemistry is complex, poorly understood, but almost undoubtedly it is hooked in with the same chemical equilibriums involving serotonin, norepinephrine, and monoamine oxidase which we have mentioned a number of times previously in this book. From this, one might guess that some chemical modality might possibly improve our retrieval system and our memory and make us more intelligent. Recent evidence suggests that this indeed may be the case. There has been recent experimental usage of a drug called magnesium pemoline. In animals, this drug does enhance nucleic acid metabolism in the brain and does make laboratory rats act more intelligently. The same drug given human patients with severe memory defects from senility and psychosis, seems to improve the memory.

There's some fascinating material from the research laboratory suggesting that it may some day be possible to "program" people, to give them certain thinking processes by artificial ingestion or inoculation of a chemical. Apparently, certain of the complicated molecules of the nucleus of the cell can be "tagged" with information; presumably, if such a molecule was introduced into another brain, the information can go along too. Much work has been done on the Planarium, a flatworm. Such a worm can be trained to do certain actions. If the trained worm is chopped up and fed to another worm without training, the untrained worm will acquire ability to do the actions for which the worm it was fed was trained. One can hardly suggest that the brain of an Einstein should be removed at autopsy, chopped up, and fed to the masses, producing quantities of mathematical geniuses. It does seem possible that we may eventually have artificial ways of increasing the intelligence.

We should not be content to wait until genius is available in a pill, however. Each of us has vast resources of memory and intelligence which remain unemployed. We cannot learn to use it all. There are many ways in which we can all learn to use what we have much better than we do.

20

Mood

"I'm not in the mood today."

"I got up on the wrong side of the bed this morning."

"You're in a pretty good mood."

These are very common remarks in conversation. Our enjoyment of life, our pleasure in social relations or lack of pleasure, often seems to depend on the mood we are in and on the moods of the people we encounter. Mood seems to be a very chancy thing, elusive, variable, unpredictable. When all the stars are in proper conjunction, when we are in a good mood and so is everybody we encounter, it is a good day and life is pleasant, but sometimes it seems to take a fortuitous combination of multiple coincidence for everybody to be in a cheerful mood, and it often seems impossible to avoid somebody in a bad mood, which tends to make life's routines unpleasant. Must we be prisoners to our moods which change unpredictably and out of context to the circumstance? What is mood to begin with?

In the broadest sense, mood is the outward manifestation and inner expression of our emotions. Since emotions are many and complex and poorly understood, we can no more describe all possibilities than we could describe the possible variations of cloud patterns in the sky and we can seldom predict cloud patterns more than a few minutes in advance; even the weatherman is notoriously inaccurate.

More specifically, mood can be boiled down into the positive and the negative, and, as in many areas, the bad is easier to describe and define than the good. A bad mood is generally a function of one of the following factors: physical unease, fear, worry, anxiety, sadness, or depression. Pain or any other unpleasant physical symptom has a pervasive quality which tinctures all other areas of the mind and the emotions. So does fear and its chronic cousin, handmaiden of neurosis, anxiety. Worry is a little different; it need not necessarily color mood for more than a few moments at a time; the effect of worry on the mood is a function of the problem-solving and decision-making abilities of the individual and these in turn are functions of his intelligence, maturity, and emotional stability. The worry periods of an individual are critical to his relative successes and efficiencies. The person who does not worry is ignorant, shortsighted, and a fool. The excessive worrier is neurotic. The person during worry is in the act of resolving or not resolving his conflicts and accordingly is in the process of setting up, or not setting up, his neuroses. Sadness is a natural reaction to loss, failure, frustration, and the temporary state of things. Depression, as we have discussed, may be appropriate reaction to sadness, or an inappropriately excessive reaction to sadness, or a reaction inappropriate to the circumstance, and it may be normal, neurotic, or psychotic. The person who is in poor physical health or in poor emotional health is, in fact, a prisoner of his mood, and his mood will be bad; his life experiences will not be happy unless he can find some means to rise above himself.

How about the good mood? When we are in good physical and emotional health and environmental circumstances are favorable, the chances are excellent that we will be in a good mood, feeling happy and enjoying ourselves, for man is a cantankerously optimistic individual, inclined to enjoy life and himself and to feel that all is well despite the voice of logic and experience which ought to tell us that all is not necessarily well. The ability of man to make the best of things and enjoy it may be a part of his divinity.

There are moments of adventure, excitement, pleasure, discovery, satisfaction, good fortune which, unless we are quite sick, will strongly tincture our mood in a positive direction and make us forget our troubles and ourselves. We live for these moments, of course, and fortunately they do occur from time to time. They sometimes seem to make the rest of it worthwhile.

And then there are the moments of inappropriate euphoria which, delightful as they seem to the individual at the time, are dangerous, to himself and others. These come from delirium and the brain has been poisoned: by external drugs or intoxicants, by internal metabolic change from physical disease or psychosis. Can a poisoned brain deliver to itself a message of great well-being and delight? Yes indeed it can, in a number of ways we have previously discussed. This leads man into habits of addiction and delusion and often produces the effect of the disturbed sick brain proclaiming that its sickness and disturbance is the greater state life has to offer us. The ancient concept of a Devil may not be entirely archaic and obsolete. The sick brain pronouncing its euphoria as it hastens its own destruction might seem to be a function of the Devil's hands.

For the person sick in body or in mind, his mood is an important symptom of his disease. Is the well person free of swings in mood? Obviously not; we are all subject to swings of mood in one direction or another. These, for the most part, represent the effects of our internal biological clocks. We have many clock mechanisms working in us, some quite predictable and others entirely beyond our perception and prediction. Perhaps the most obvious and predictable biological clock is the menstrual cycle of the female. Women learn to recognize and predict the premenstrual phase of tension and irritability, the postmenstrual phase of relaxation and well-being. Women learn to plan their schedule of activities according to this obvious and relatively predictable biological clock. The mood according to the menstrual cycle is a physiological mechanism, not a psychological one, and it is not under voluntary conscious control, but yet the psychological influences for functional ability and disability are well-known and strong. Adjusted women who have come to terms with the physical realities of their bodies have very little functional disability associated with the menstrual cycle; ignorant, inhibited, and immature women frequently have a great deal. This suggests that a biological clock, unconscious and involuntary though it may be, need have relatively little functional effect on mood if one is aware of the clock, can predict the timing, and anticipate the effects. There are probably dozens, perhaps hundreds, of biological clocks operative in every individual. Perhaps the person who is least the prisoner of his involuntary moods is one who, subconsciously at least, has studied and noted his own biological clocks.

There's a biological clock which has long been of interest to me because of the place where I live. This is the seasonal or climatic one. I live in a northern New England state where our seasons are very sharp and sharply defined. It is easy for us to tell, to the week and often to the day, when summer changes into autumn, autumn to winter, winter to spring, spring to summer. There is a dramatic and obvious meteorological transition zone between the seasons. Just a few years after I began practicing medicine in the area, I noticed that peptic ulcer, a physical "stress" disease, occurred here in an almost epidemic manner during these transitional zones. Later, when I was a medical examiner, I noticed that the incidence of violence of all kinds—accidents, suicides, homicides, assaults—showed a definite peak during these same specific transitional weeks. Still more recently, I have observed that many patients with emotional disease, both psychosis and neurosis, tend to have crisis periods at these times. In my own case, I have noticed that

I feel vigorous, enthusiastic, and euphoric during the weeks of seasonal transition and I tend to feel flat and depressed in the middle of the summer, winter, fall, or spring. More subconsciously than consciously, I orient my schedule from this point of view. I often plan a trip at the time of seasonal change, and I prefer not to travel in mid-season. In my writing, I try to finish one project and begin another during the transition zone, and I prefer neither to begin nor finish a book in the middle of a season.

It often seems that active people, who produce a steady output of work in one or more fields, are those who have learned to master their moods and not to be enslaved by them. Certainly people who are victimized by mood do not seem to accomplish much. I often encounter people who would like to write but can't seem to find the time; such people, knowing that I am an author as well as physician, often ask me where I find the time. Time is there, for whatever purposes we may care to put it to. People whose output in vocation and avocation is higher than average have three attributes which people who never have enough time are lacking. First, there is motivation. People will always find time to do anything they want to do badly enough. I do not know of any way to instill motivation into people who are lacking it. Second, there is concentration, the ability not to be distracted from the work at hand; as stated in the last chapter, it is difficult not to be distracted by trivia and banality in a crowded world. And third, there is the matter of mood. Some people tell themselves that they will tackle a given creative project "when they are in the mood"; sometimes, they sit down at desk, typewriter, or easel and wait for the mood to strike; if you wait for the proper mood, you will always be waiting. In regard to the specific ambition of writing a book, which a great many intelligent and educated people seem to entertain, the solution may be stated very simply. You write for one or two hours a day. All of us have an extra daily hour or two which we waste in banality and trivia. In an hour or two, most people can easily write a thousand words. Do so every day for two months, and you have a short book; do this every day for four months and you have a book of average size; rewrite the whole thing twice, and you will have a finished book in a year. Thus, it is quite possible for any intelligent educated person to write a book a year, if he wants to. It only takes an hour or two a day, but the secret is: an hour or two *every* day. You can't wait until you get in the mood, for you will never get there. Some days, many days, you will not be in the mood at all, but you do it anyway. The gratifying thing is that, once you get yourself started, you get into the mood by the very act of starting. Often, you use the mood you are in to add flavor and color to the work; if the mood is wrong and the work is poor, you throw it away and try it again tomorrow, and by this process the job is accomplished.

Our Puritan forefathers put strong emphasis on the moral and godly nature of work. It is certainly true that work itself will often improve the mood, will add pleasure and meaning to the passing hours. This is true, however, only if the work is interesting and sufficiently difficult to be challenging. Unhappy are those many people—men at the office or factory, women in the home—whose work is not interesting or challenging; they are merely putting in time until the weekend and earning the necessary buck, and for them, unfortunately, the weekend is less enjoyable and the dollar of less value than to those who take pleasure in the work of the week. Even more unhappy are those who do not have to work and can find nothing interesting, important, challenging to do. For them, mood is likely to be the master. Those who have discovered the therapeutic nature of creative work are not slaves to their moods, but use their moods as servants in the doing of the work.

There are two moods worth special attention if we note them in ourselves, moods which we cannot shake by the act of doing interesting work, moods which prevent us from doing work of value. One of these is chronic worry or anxiety.

As we have previously stressed, anxiety without appropriate cause means neurosis. Neurosis, when suspected in the self, should not be permitted to flourish tolerantly. It destroys the value of the hours. Neurosis can often be self-corrected and, when it can't, the help of others should be sought. The other dangerous destructive mood is depression. True depression, either that which is excessive to an appropriate cause or that without appropriate cause, cannot be self-corrected. It flattens and deadens creative energy. It may lead to suicide. A pathological depression state demands professional attention. No matter how poor one's opinion may be of doctors' wisdom in managing emotional disturbance or of the clarity and sanity of psychiatrists, the fact remains that doctors and psychiatrists can and do correct depression states consistently with psychotherapy, electroshock, and some of the modern drugs, a feat which the patient in a depression state cannot accomplish for himself.

Mood is a chancy thing: elusive, variable, unpredictable. One does not have to be a prisoner of mood, however. A prisoner is never very happy, no matter how benign and friendly the jailer may seem to be.

21

On the Possibilities of Psychosis in Oneself

The psychotic is irrational, inaccessible, out of touch. He is insane. Can he ever know that he is insane? That we ourselves may be or might become psychotic is a real possibility, of course, for psychosis is a major and reasonably common disease. But can we suspect ourselves of being psychotic? Logically, this might seem to be impossible, since disturbance of reason is a major symptom of psychosis, and reason would seem to be necessary in self-evaluation of any reasonable kind.

Logic, however, is not always truth. Experience with numbers of insane persons will quickly convince the observer that psychotic people are often aware of their own insanity. They hide it, of course; all of us attempt to conceal our disabilities; it is my impression, however, that most psychotic persons are aware of their own insanity most of the time and are made acutely uncomfortable and embarrassed and fearful by it. Accordingly I think it is possible for one to suspect psychosis in oneself. It is rather important to do so. We have noted a number of types of psychosis which are amenable to control or cure by proper therapy.

In Chapter 4 we discussed a prominent person, very active and successful in the theatrical world, who had a long history of manic-depressive disease. As we noted, this individual was able to detect in himself warning symptoms of both manic and depressive phases before anybody else could notice them; when he learned to know and live with his disease, he would promptly commit himself into a psychiatric institution early in a crisis in time to prevent the destructive and disruptive effects of his condition.

Let us look at another psychotic individual who apparently suspected that he was insane.

Charles (Case 49)

Charles had an unhappy childhood and home environment, which may have been the root of his troubles. He struck most casual acquaintances as a quick bright cooperative person, but those who knew him better were aware that he had a violent and sometimes uncontrollable temper.

Charles attended college, and his university record was good. On the 29th of March, 1966, he made an appointment with the university staff psychiatrist and had a two-hour interview. He told the psychiatrist that he was very much in love with the young woman whom he had married shortly before, but that he had a problem with his temper. He had beaten his wife several times. He was making an intensive struggle to control his temper but he was afraid that the struggle might be in vain, and that his temper might explode into violence. The psychiatrist described Charles later as a muscular and massive youth who seemed to be oozing with hostility. The psychiatrist made a note of only one direct quotation from the interview, as follows: "I am thinking of going up on the tower with a deer rifle and start shooting people." This remark obviously impressed the psychiatrist, it being the only remark he wrote down. The tower in question rose above the campus, commanding a sweeping prospectus, and disturbed students not infrequently mentioned it, often as a place from which to jump for suicide.

The psychiatrist realized the serious nature of Charles's disturbance. He made an appointment with Charles for another visit, but Charles did not return.

Some four months later, Charles murdered his mother and his wife. Just before committing the murders he wrote the following note: *I don't understand what is compelling me to type this note. I have been having fears and violent impulses. I've had some tremendous headaches. I am prepared to die. After my death, I wish an autopsy on me to see if there's any mental disorder.*

Autopsy was done on him and showed a brain tumor the size of a pecan, highly malignant in nature. Before the autopsy could be performed, however, Charles climbed the university tower in Austin, Texas, taking along three rifles, two pistols, a shotgun, and a large quantity of ammunition. From this vantage point, on the first of August, 1966, he shot and wounded forty-seven people, seventeen of them fatally, before he himself was shot and killed. Charles's full name was Charles J. Whitman.

An interesting point in the Whitman case concerns the brain tumor and its possible effects upon his behavior. The tumor was of the type called glioblastoma multiforme, present in the white matter of the right temporoocciptal lobe; it was highly malignant; it apparently arose from a small vascular deformity which might have been present since birth. A 32-man task force, appointed by Texas Governor John B. Connally to study the case, came to the conclusion that the tumor "conceivably could have contributed to his inability to control his emotions and actions," even though the tumor was not in a place to produce neurological abnormalities. Perhaps the pre-existing congenital vascular lesion caused emotional symptoms before the growth of the malignant tumor.

Another point is the failure of the psychiatrist at the University of Texas to have taken more positive action at the interview in March. A professor of psychiatry at Yale defended his colleague as follows: "Psychiatrists are minor prophets, not major ones. We can't always predict correctly.

Hundreds of people talk about suicide and killing. It rarely happens." It could be rebutted that such talk, heard often, is at least a potential danger sign and should be taken quite seriously by the physician, as, for example, the non-psychiatric physician takes seriously the vomiting of blood. It was honest, and courageous, for the university psychiatrist to release the findings of his interview after the unfortunate conclusion of the case. Some have questioned his right to make such a release, on the grounds that the statements in a psychiatric interview are privileged communications which should be kept confidential. Of course, the literature is full of material from psychiatric interviews. We are bringing up this case specifically to comment on the possibility of suspecting psychosis in the self. Very obviously, Whitman suspected that he was psychotic. It might be fair to say that he suspected his own disease more strongly than did the expert he consulted.

Let's look at another case. This time, since the patient is alive, we will give her an imaginary name and alter the actual circumstances in certain minor respects.

Charlene (Case 50)

Charlene was a quiet girl, reserved, unapproachable. It seems likely that, if she had been subjected to psychiatric evaluation as a child or adolescent, a diagnosis of early schizophrenia or latent schizophrenic tendencies might have been made, although it does not seem likely that anything would have been done, for she was making a reasonable social and environmental adjustment. Her school record was unremarkable. She married young and had three children; presumably she was a good wife and mother.

One evening, her husband returned from work to find her sitting quietly in the corner. In a detached way, without emotion, Charlene told her husband that she had just killed their three children because God had told her to. The husband did not at first believe her, because of the calm matter-of-fact tone of the announcement, but he found the bodies of his three young children in their beds. Charlene had strangled them.

Charlene was arrested. Pre-trial psychiatric evaluation was done, as is customary in these cases. On account of the psychiatric diagnosis of schizophrenia with paranoid tendencies, Charlene was found not guilty by reason of insanity and she was indefinitely committed to a state mental hospital.

The authorities at the state mental hospital are inclined to be very conservative in management of the criminally insane. Few such persons who have committed murder are released. After some years, Charlene was released. Ever since commitment, she had been a model patient, quiet, cooperative, apparently sane and rational. In her case, considerable political pressure plus her apparent sanity persuaded the authorities to reverse the customary policy and release her.

Charlene went home and resumed living with her husband. Still quiet, she was apparently sane. She became pregnant three more times and gave birth to three more children. She was apparently a good wife and mother.

About a year after the birth of her youngest child, her husband returned from work one night to find her sitting quietly in the corner. She informed him calmly that God had told her to kill her children. This time, her husband, with horror, believed her. It was true. Again she had strangled them.

She was again tried, found not guilty by reason of insanity, and committed to the state mental hospital. Although she acts quite sane, it is unlikely that she will ever again be released.

During her first commitment, Charlene had been seen frequently by a minister who was interested in the insane. This minister got to know her very well. It was chiefly through his efforts that Charlene had been released, and she was released in his parole, rather than in that of her husband. In the early weeks after release, the minister had kept in close touch with her until he was convinced that she was acting sane in her home environment. Then as the months and years went by without trouble, the minister had gradually lost touch with her.

A few weeks before her second episode of violence, Charlene

had contacted the minister, telling him that she did not feel well, and that she feared her problems might be returning. He visited her at once. She seemed calm and rational but told him again of her fears. He tried to get her to return to the psychiatrists at the state hospital. She promised that she would if things didn't get better. She made the minister promise not to tell her husband.

The minister kept his promise, though he later regretted it. He debated whether to inform the authorities of the change in Charlene's condition, but he decided against it, although he could have gotten her immediately returned to commitment. He decided that, since Charlene trusted him and confided in him, it would be a betrayal of the trust if he revealed what she had told him, fearing that this might make her worse. Since she seemed so sane and cooperative, and seemed to understand her own condition so well, he presumed that she would take the necessary steps if things did not get better. This, as he later discovered to his profound shock and regret, was a mistake.

Psychotic people often seem to know they are insane. In fact, they often seem to know it better than the experts they consult for help. Even though aware of their disturbance, they are still powerless to control the manifestations of the condition. This should not surprise us. A diabetic may know he will get sick if he eats a lot of candy and may still eat a lot of candy. An alcoholic may know he should not take a drink but will take one just the same.

The psychiatrist who examined Charles Whitman four months before Charles climbed the tower should have recognized a dangerously hostile person, and in fact he did. Charlene's minister, who had experience with mental illness, should have recognized danger in Charlene's confidences, and in fact he did. But neither took the necessary drastic step: commitment of an insane person before the act of violence. Neither, in fact, took an easier and logical step: attempting to persuade the patient with all his power to consent to treatment. It seems likely that Charles Whitman, who knew that he was sick and feared the consequences, might have committed himself for treatment if the psychiatrist had urged it. Charlene's minister did ask her to return to the hospital, but he asked her only once; he should have gone back the following day and asked her again, and she might have consented.

There is a reluctance for an authority, dealing with mental and emotional disturbances, to force treatment on a patient until the patient asks for it, unless the family demands it, or unless violent circumstances make it obviously mandatory. Often, accordingly, the horse is long gone before the barn door is closed.

Part of this reluctance comes from the experience of all persons in counseling professions that guidance counseling and psychotherapy will not succeed unless the patient genuinely wants it to succeed. This is a valid rule of thumb in neurosis and personality disturbance, but not in psychosis where involuntary types of treatment often may succeed. Inability to distinguish between neurosis and personality disturbance on the one hand and psychosis on the other may result in tragedy. Part of the reluctance stems from the heritage of democracy; commitment to a mental institution deprives the individual of his Constitutional liberty and cannot be done without good medical and legal grounds. Attempts to commit a person prematurely or without good grounds may often result in legal repercussions. Part of the reluctance comes from a human tendency on the part of the physician or counselor. Folklore tells us: "If you think you may be crazy, you aren't crazy." Folklore is wrong in this regard, as we have seen. If a patient tells you, sanely, that he thinks he is insane, it is your natural inclination to accept the sane aspect of that patient rather than the insane side. If the patient understands his disturbance so clearly, you think, then he will clearly know when and if he needs to be committed and confined. This is not so. The psychotic may know he is psychotic but he does not necessarily know that he should be confined; he does not want to be confined; confinement, like prison, is not pleasant. Finally, the psychiatrist or counselor cannot advise commitment or psychiatric care every time he encounters a possibly psychotic expression. Asylums are few and crowded; professional therapists are few and busy; facilities are lacking for commitment and treatment of all psychotics, and, in fact, a great many mild psychotics need neither commitment nor treatment. There are a number of psychotics, running around loose, quite safely and harmlessly, in every community.

If you suspect psychosis in yourself, does it do you any good? You may go to a psychiatrist and find that he does not accept your suspicions. We have described an instance where this happened with disastrous results. Why bother anybody else with your suspicions, if he will not believe you?

There is, of course, no guarantee that a psychiatrist, counselor, or physician will be able to help you when you bring your troubles to him. Often, however, he can and does. The act of consulting him increases the chances of cure or symptom relief enormously. Psychosis, as we have noted, not infrequently results from physical disease amenable to cure, and untreated psychosis often produces disaster to the self and others.

In order to suspect psychosis in yourself, you must understand yourself. The Socratic injunction, applicable to education of the sane, is equally applicable to self-understanding by the insane. Know Thyself! The manic-depressive who commits himself at the start of every episode may live a long, constructive, and largely happy life. Charles J. Whitman did not.

22

Obsessions and Compulsions

Carl Jung believed that many of man's emotional reactions are expressed through symbols and that these symbols are part of our cultural heritage from our ancestors. There are certain shapes, forms, figures, and non-representational designs which evoke common moods and emotions; similar symbolic configurations are found in the visual arts from the day of the cave man down to the present. Of a similar heritage are our superstitions. We inherit a common set of superstitions, and we also manage to manufacture certain individual private superstitions of our own.

We each possess a set of cautions and precautions, which we need; without caution and precaution, we would stumble into trouble on every side. But some of these defenses are inappropriate. We think we need them when in fact they may hamper and hinder us. These may become obsession and compulsion which lie close to superstition at the roots of the personality.

Some obsession and compulsion is harmless; existing as part of the uniqueness of the individual, setting him apart from other individuals, it serves no other purpose, good or bad. Some obsession and compulsion may be exaggerated beyond the point of harmlessness, causing difficulty in social relationships; the habits, mannerisms, and eccentricities strike our neighbors as bizarre and make them uncomfortable in our presence. Carried further, obsession-compulsion may express unresolved emotional conflict, in which case it is a neurotic expression, and carried still further, it may so distort our orientation and rationality as to make us frankly psychotic or insane.

It is difficult, perhaps impossible, for us to recognize our own obsessions and compulsions. When recognized, obsession and compulsion can almost never be considered illogical or unreasonable by the particular individual. These things are so close to the basic essence of the self, the "real us," that we can scarcely do without them. If forcibly stripped of an obsession or compulsion, we feel so lost and naked that we may have a serious identity crisis, a panic reaction in which we lose conviction as to who we are and what we are doing.

In others, we recognize the obsessions and compulsions easily, and we can readily determine the degree of abnormality. Social experience tells us to steer away from the prejudices, fixed ideas, notions, delusions, obsessions, and compulsions of the people whom we meet. This is forbidden ground. Any attack or assault upon these sacred ideas will be taken as an assault on the identity of the individual and will be defended by him with all his force and power as a matter of life and death. For example, we can discuss politics on general terms with most people reasonably whether we belong to the same party or not, but there are certain people with whom we would not dare discuss politics at all. We think of them as rabid, as if they were infected with a deadly virus. Even though more than two decades have elapsed since the death of the 32nd President of the United States, there are certain people who still cannot even hear the name of Franklin Delano Roosevelt and retain their equanimity. Mention of Lyndon Johnson to some people, or Barry Goldwater to others will make them almost physically sick. Many people have a favorite prejudice to which they respond like a bull to a waving red flag. They may be entirely sane, rational, and reasonable outside their prejudicial areas, but within the area they turn deaf and dumb and blind and furious and have no rationality at all. Such prejudices will usually lie in one or more of the following subjects: politics, race, sex, and religion. These areas are close to the basic root of identity and personality.

Since obsession and compulsion are so fundamental, and so ferociously defended, is there any likelihood that they could ever be changed? Occasionally, yes, but this is very occasional and very difficult.

When I see a patient in the office with an obvious prejudice, obsession, or compulsion sticking out all over him, I will avoid the trouble area if I can. I do not bring up the subject. If the patient brings the subject up to me, I try to ignore his dissertation, provided it is not related to the symptom or disease I am trying to treat him for. I would not discuss politics with a Roosevelt-hater, even though I am a registered Republican myself; I would not discuss the Negro problem with a red-necked Tennessee hillbilly, even though I passed most of a happy boyhood in the Tennessee hills; and there are very few Negroes with whom I would discuss race relations today even though I was strongly sympathetic with civil rights long before it became a national issue. This is not necessarily because I am a coward or afraid to speak up for my own beliefs. In the office, if I get into the patient's obsessive-compulsive area, I cannot get out, and I have become powerless to help the patient in any way. If the patient's obsession-compulsion happens to be related to his disease or symptom, then I either have to tackle it in order to help him, or admit my inability to help him and send him away.

Minor obsession-compulsion, the silly harmless little prejudices, probably should be left alone. We all discover this in social experience. We learn to avoid discussion of the silly prejudices of those with whom we live and work. Socially, when we encounter a person with what we consider to be a major dangerous prejudice, we do our best to avoid that person altogether; he makes life entirely too unpleasant for us; we would not work with him or live with him. We sense that nothing will change him and that he will never be happy except in the company of other nuts as rabid as himself on that subject. It is a middle area that gives us trouble: prejudice not exactly harmless or silly but not sufficiently dangerous to warrant severing major relationships. We sense that these people could grow out of their prejudice but that it would take a major personality upheaval for them to do so; and we wonder whether it is worth our while to roll up our sleeves and start trying to heave the earth.

In ourselves, likewise, it is the middle area of obsession-compulsion which should concern us, if we are wise enough to see it and brave enough to tackle it. The silly little prejudices we may ignore. If we have a major obsession or compulsion, it is likely that we cannot change it and must live with the distorted social relations it will cause. But we may have a prejudice giving us trouble which we might be able to change to our advantage. How can such a thing be done?

Probably we cannot do it alone. Probably we could do it with specialized help of two kinds: formal psychoanalysis and hypnosis.

In this book, we have referred to formal psychoanalysis a number of times in a derogatory fashion. In my opinion, formal dynamic analysis is a vastly overrated psychotherapeutic technique. I think that analysis does not work in psychosis at all. Although analysis may often be helpful in neurosis and personality disturbance, I think that these conditions may receive equal or greater help with shorter simpler less expensive treatment techniques. There is one area where I think analysis may be the therapy of choice, and this is the present subject of discussion: minor or moderate obsession-compulsion. However, there aren't very many trained psychoanalysts; most of them are busy and cannot accept new patients; and analysis is so expensive in terms of time and money that very few people can afford it.

In my opinion, hypnosis can also be of help in minor or moderate obsession-compulsion. It is much easier and much less expensive than analysis, but probably there are even fewer hypnotists capable of treating this condition than trained analysts. Hypnosis is fairly widely used by both psychiatric and non-psychiatric physicians, but usually for certain types of pain relief and treatment of hypochrondria, not for obsession-compulsion. Hypnosis carries a generally shady name, being associated in the popular mind with magic, quackery, and science-fiction. Hypnosis is not black magic; it is only a technique which short-circuits the conscious mind and brings the subconscious mind to the surface. It is easy to hypnotize suggestible persons; it is difficult or impossible to hypnotize non-suggestible people; very suggestible people go around unconsciously hypnotizing themselves a good deal of the time. Self-hypnosis can be quite valuable in positive ways. The Dale Carnegie course and similar courses which teach confidence and salesmanship are basically courses in self-hypnosis and, in suggestible people, they work very well. It is, in general, suggestible people who are inclined to develop obsession-compulsion in the first place and therefore, if the obsession-compulsion is not too deep-seated, it can be changed or erased by hypnotic suggestion. Fooling around with the subconscious of a suggestible person can be rather dangerous, unless you have a very clear idea of his history and background and personality; to get such a clear idea requires weeks and months and years of study of that individual; since few hypnotists have the time or the training to explore the subconscious mind, there are few of them competent to use the technique safely for therapy of obsession-compulsion.

Turning from obsession-compulsion, let us think of the allied problem of the rigid personality. As we have said before, rigidity of personality seems to be a typical American problem, stemming from our Puritan heritage. No matter what our race or religion, we are under the influence of Puritanism. We are unconsciously haunted by the pleasure-as-sin principle and we struggle against it. In the reaction against rigidity, we may indulge excessively and inappropriately, which may bother us in the conscience, and we may also deprive ourselves of what we know to be reasonable pleasures out of inhibition and repression. Is there any way we can overcome such personality rigidity, becoming less inhibited and repressed without becoming altogether immoderate and indulgent? Could we find healthy pleasure with clear consciences?

This is a particular problem which has always bothered me, since I inherited a considerable Puritan legacy. Given my heritage, I will never solve it completely. But I have come across a couple of quotations which have often been helpful to me in this connection. I offer them in the hope that others may find them helpful.

One of these quotations is from Ecclesiastes, that short book of the Bible which is subtitled *The Preacher.* I have often thought that this scripture might have been subtitled *The Novelist,* for it is the source for the titles of dozens of published novels and is full of the sort of paradox which novelists love. This particular quotation is verses 18–20, Chapter 5, and it goes as follows:

> Behold that which I have seen: it is good and comely for one to eat and to drink, and to enjoy the good of all his labour that he taketh under the sun all the days of his life, which God giveth him: for it is his portion. Every man also to whom God hath given riches and wealth, and hath given him power to eat thereof, and to take his portion, and to rejoice in his labour; this is the gift of God. For he shall not much remember the days of his life; because God answereth him in the joy of his heart.

Especially pertinent to me is the last sentence of that quotation. When one is busy and active and creative, enjoying one's work and equally enjoying the rewards which have been honestly earned by the work, one does not remember the passing days. Looking back in memory, we recall with vivid and disagreeable clarity every detail of certain bad times we have been through; but we can't recall the details and moments of the happy days; we only remember the happiness of the days. In view of our discussion of intelligence, we ought to be able to retrieve from the storage system details of happy as well as unhappy days; and if we can't, it may be that the happiness lies deeper in storage, near the roots. Perhaps this is as it should be. Perhaps, in health, we should not remember the detail of the pleasure. To recall each pleasure in detail may mean that we have made an unhealthy obsession or compulsion out of it. We should recall the joy the pleasure may have given us, rather than the individual pleasure in itself.

The other quotation offered here is very similar. It is a favorite of my wife. I cannot trace the source of it, I know only that it was written by some anonymous Civil War poet, presumably Confederate. I have seen two versions, but I prefer the shorter of the two, which goes as follows:

I asked God for strength that I might achieve,
I was made weak that I might learn humbly to obey.
I asked for power that I might have the praise of men,
I was given weakness that I might feel the need of God.
I asked for all things that I might enjoy life.
I was given life that I might enjoy all things.

The emphasis here is on *all* things: in balance, without prejudice, without immoderation. This is the key to flexibility. Flexibility is not to be confused with weakness. Rigid structures break under stress; flexible structures may bend but they return to their original shape.

23

Addictions

To recall each pleasure in detail may mean that we have made an obsession or compulsion out of it: or an addiction. An addiction is a habit which has mastered the man.

And what is a habit? We mean something done habitually, usually daily. We must eat and sleep, urinate and defecate, and breathe in order to live; ordinarily we do not consider these physiological functions as habits. Actually, one may make a bad habit out of any of them. We have spoken of food addictions. As psychosomatic disease and partly expression of neurosis, some people urinate very frequently and others have functional diarrhea; narcolepsy is a functional condition of excessive sleep; overbreathing or hyperventilation often occurs in hysterical people. But when we speak of a habit, we imply something that the individual does by choice as part of his daily routine, presumably for pleasure or perhaps out of psychological necessity. There are good habits, but we don't often mention them; we are inclined to think of the habit as bad.

Why bad? Is the person who smokes cigarettes or the one who has two martinis before his dinner every night immoral or sinful or evil on account of this habit? Although a few rigid ascetic people do ascribe sin or immorality to the individual with a habit, the majority does not reach such a moral judgment, and we usually do not condemn a person with a habit unless the habit appears to be excessive, in which case we consider him addicted. However, we do feel implications of harmfulness in the habit itself, even though it may be one of our own habits, and in thinking of our own indulgences we do so with at least a slight trace of guilt. Part of this appears to be the Puritan pleasure-as-sin principle which we cannot entirely shake. We do not phrase it so. We fall back on the excuse that the habit is potentially harmful to our health. We enjoy it so much, presumably, that we are willing to take this risk.

As a matter of fact, part of our pleasure may lie in the risk-taking. Part of the enjoyment of a habit may lie in transgression against taboo. This is what induces young persons to begin bad habits against the advice of parents and teachers.

Is there a confident and secure individual who can say, without reservation, "I am perfectly sure that smoking will never harm my health in any way," or, "Alcohol has never been, and will never be, in any way dangerous to me"? If we heard somebody make such a remark we would consider him a fool. Everybody knows that cigarettes may be harmful to the health; the package says so. The evils of drink, surely, have been well pointed out.

But, people smoke and people drink, although they know these habits are potentially harmful. Why? Would life be incomplete and empty without smoke or drink? Obviously there are individuals living fully satisfactory lives without smoke and drink. The average smoker or drinker would be likely to say, in self-defense, "Well, damn it, I enjoy it, and the habit doesn't seem to have hurt me yet, and until I know that it is hurting me, I am going to continue to enjoy myself. I'm not hurting anybody but myself."

This declaration says several things. The defendant is trying to clear himself of the Puritan moral condemnation,

"Pleasure for its own sake is not necessarily a sin," even if he does not entirely believe it. The very fact that he has to defend himself implies that he recognizes a certain validity in the charge. Also he is saying, "I am aware of the risk, but after weighing the probabilities I have decided to take the risk in order to enjoy the pleasure, for life itself is a risk operation." And finally, our spokesman is stating that very human fallacy by which we all deceive ourselves: "What may be dangerous for others is not dangerous to me; although I concede bad things may happen to anybody else, I deny the possibility that bad things can happen to me."

For purpose of the present discussion, we will skip the Puritan condemnation, having emphasized it quite heavily in other places in this book, and we will also skip the fallacy of self-deception. Let us consider the problem of risk-taking.

In my part of the country, at a certain time of the year, small chipmunks race across the roads just in front of automobiles. A few of them fail to make it and are crushed beneath the wheels, but most survive to try it again, and they try it repeatedly. They do not seem to cross empty roads. They wait until a car is coming, and they seem to wait until the very last moment before making the dash. One doubts that there is a really valid reason why a small chipmunk must get from one side of the road to the other at that particularly dangerous moment. One is sure that the crossing is made for the pleasure and thrill of sheer excitement, and that successful risk-taking adds completeness to the exciting life of the small chipmunk. Humans, similarly, get enjoyment and excitement out of driving fast cars, on the race track and off it; out of parachute jumping and scuba diving and skiing and climbing dangerous cliffs and swimming the English Channel and going over Niagara Falls in a barrel. Part of the pleasure may lie in sensory satisfactions from the act itself, and part of it may lie in praise, publicity, and sometimes financial rewards for bravery, but part of the pleasure at least is gratification of the death-defying urge. In a sense, having attempted something dangerous and gotten away with it, one has reinforced a feeling of invulnerability and perhaps immortality. The death-defying urge appears to be a frequent human motivation.

It may seem like a long stretch to compare the climbing of Mount Everest with the smoking of a cigarette from a labeled package, but the element of purposeful risk-taking does appear to be a part of the motivation for pursuing a potentially dangerous habit. It might be noted that, in recent years, when publicity about the dangers of the cigarette habit has been enormous, the number of cigarette smokers has increased as never before. This is not just coincidence, and it does not imply that the population, like lemmings, is rushing suicidally over cliffs. Four decades ago, during Prohibition, the incidence of individual drinking and the incidence of clinical alcoholism was greater than it has been since alcohol became legal again. If a reformer was genuinely interested in stopping some dangerous national habit, and if that reformer was a student of psychological motivation, he or she might be aware that the customary approach has a paradoxical reverse effect. Actually, if you wanted to stop young people from drinking or smoking, the best way to do it might be to advocate the use of tobacco and alcohol on the grounds that these substances make the user moral, godly, and virtuous. This suggestion may sound cynical from the moral point of view, but psychologically it is valid. This does not mean the psychologist is saying that the younger generation is intrinsically immoral; it does take into consideration the valid principle of the pleasures of transgression against taboo. Incidentally, thinking along these lines, we make sexual promiscuity taboo; what would happen if society advocated promiscuity? Since transgression urges do exist and cannot always be sublimated or suppressed, it is probably better to channel them into relatively harmless areas. The violence of football and the watusi is better for the young than gang warfare. It is probably better for collegians to throw a beer party than to commit mass rape; it is probably better for a businessman to have a martini at lunch and at supper than to murder his boss or his wife. It is probably better for a chipmunk to run across a road in front of an automobile than to eat his own young.

Psychologically speaking, a habit is apt to give the most satisfaction when it violates a mild taboo without causing serious distortion of social relationships or major infraction of the law; when the habit is relatively high in sensual gratification; and when the habit is relatively low in actual risk to physical health. As we have previously noted, the reason that tobacco and alcohol have always been among man's favorite indulgences is not because these substances are so dangerous but because they are so safe. Although some smokers and some drinkers have seriously disabled themselves and died from direct or indirect effects of the habit, most smokers and most drinkers do not become disabled or die from the habit but enjoy it happily for many decades and die of something else.

It would be nice if we could identify in advance the particular smoker or drinker whose habit places him in real danger. A good deal of the time, we can't. In some instances, of course, we can: the patient with emphysema shouldn't smoke and the chronic alcoholic shouldn't drink. The average emphysema patient, preferring free breathing to the symptom of suffocation, quickly and easily gives up smoking, even though he has been a heavy smoker for years; if he does not give up smoking, he is obviously addicted and his major problem is a psychological disturbance. Rather obviously, the trouble with a chronic alcoholic is a psychological disturbance rather than the liquor that he drinks.

What advice should be given to the person not truly addicted who has bad habits? To what extent should that person be urged to give the habit up? Or, more close to home, at what point should the individual make himself stop smoking, stop drinking, stop eating sweets, reduce the coffee and tea consumption, discontinue the tranquilizer or barbiturate? Since these problems are individual, answers must be individualized, and must be given by the health counselor who knows the individual best: in other words, his family physician. There is of course one generality which can be made: have no bad habits and you will never have bad effects from any habit. On the other hand, Sir Winston Churchill enjoyed his Havana cigars, his heavy meals of meat and sweets, and he took more out of alcohol than alcohol took from him; if you had advised him to become ascetic, I do not think he would have taken your advice; if you maintain that Churchill's habits stopped him from achieving full potential, I do not think history would believe you; if you maintain that his habits caused the disagreeable period of senility at the end of his career, a visit to any nursing home will show you similarly deteriorated senile persons who have never smoked or consumed alcoholic beverage. Of course, you do not have Churchill's constitution, and the amount of brandy that seemed to be good for him would almost certainly flatten you. This is the point: the degree of bad habit which a man can safely handle is a function of his constitution and also of his psychological adjustment and personality, varying widely from one individual to another.

Although a habit is a personal affair and the risk-taking element is personal, there are areas in which a habit may distort social relationships with others and at certain times the adjusted person will adjust his habits, not for his own sake but for the sake of others. For example, cigar smoking may be—and is—much safer than cigarettes from the point of view of cancer of the lung; but cigar smoke is offensive to many people; in order to avoid constantly offending his wife, a man might smoke a pipe instead, which is as safe as cigars and much less offensive. Alcohol in social moderation is often very helpful in easing tensions in stressful social or business situations; faced with a more stressful situation than average, an individual might increase the amount of his consumption of alcohol and, in so doing, make himself less capable of handling the stress; the answer here, of course, is less, not more.

Many of us do have habits. Bad habits? That depends. I have seen many middle-aged people give up smoking on account of the cancer scare, and after having stopped put on weight to such extent as to offer a real health hazard from obesity. I think there are some people for whom smoking is healthier than not smoking. I know there are some people for whom light drinking is healthier than total abstinence. I have often seen old men put on the wagon by conscientious rigid wives or daughters, becoming as a result far more difficult, irritable, sleepless, and cantankerous than ever. More than once I have prescribed a tonic whose chief active ingredient was alcohol to ferociously prohibitionistic old ladies with obviously beneficial results. I have seen a compulsive eater go on a compulsive crash diet and die of malnutrition. Fat people do not become old people, but, on the other hand, I do get the impression that fat people are more cheerful and happy than thin people, don't you?

We were given life that we might enjoy all things: with moderation and self-knowledge. It isn't the habit, necessarily, that's bad; nor is the person with the habit necessarily bad; the way in which the person uses the habit may be good or bad for him. We should master our habits. We are in trouble when the habit begins to master us.

24

Transgressions and Taboo

Puritans, meaning all of us to some extent at least, are
caught in the conflict between inhibiting taboo and the
urges toward transgression. The push and pull of this struggle may find expression in our obsessions and compulsions,
and may influence our habits and addictions. As we have
seen, taboo operates in the interests of society, not those
of the individual, and may often work against the individual.
Transgression, which is basically antisocial, can also be considered an expression of individuality.

Can the mature adult free himself from the basic taboo-
transgression conflict? Probably not. As long as man has a
social need, rules and regulations and etiquette are needed
to facilitate social relationships. As long as man has the
need to identify himself as an individual, he will have urges
to transgress against taboo. The psychopath, who lacks taboo
sense, expresses himself freely and piles up a formidable
record of transgression; he may seem to defeat society for
long periods of time; we may envy or admire him because
of the success of his defiance of taboo; eventually society
catches up with him. Sooner or later, the psychopath finds
himself in conflict with the law and he usually goes to jail;

in jail, at least, he is required to conform by force. Although he freely expresses his individuality and is not inhibited or repressed, and although he seeks to help himself freely to the rewards of life, the greatest rewards of society are not available to him. These are granted on the basis of confidence and trust. The psychopath misuses confidence and proves himself unworthy of trust. Hostile people, the aggressive and immature rebels, the "non-psychiatric criminals," also express their individuality too freely, also abuse confidence and trust, are also apt to find themselves in jail.

Most of us are not psychopaths, for we have a social need, but there is a rebel in all of us. When taboo is unnecessarily prejudicial, restrictive, and punitive, rebellion is a positive and laudatory act. Many of our greatest heroes have been rebels in the name of a cause which we admire. This country was founded by rebels and we are inclined to be sympathetic with rebellion, especially rebellion against tyranny or oppression. Even in the most benign and free society, taboo restricts individuality and creativity of expression. The original and creative person, in any line of endeavor, must break taboo if he is to express himself; original creative expression will always shock, offend, and disturb certain segments of society until it is generally accepted; when accepted, it becomes incorporated into taboo and in turn exerts restrictive and inhibitive effect upon original creative work of other kinds. The act of self-expression in the face of social criticism and disapproval requires what we have called creative courage, and, as we have noted, every person must have some creative courage if he is to show his individuality.

Society supports taboo and punishes transgression, but paradoxically society does not admire full and spineless conformity. The totally conforming person is recognized as drab and dull, a bore, a repressed rigid inhibited individual who has surrendered his individuality to the establishment. Society has an unconcealed admiration for the transgressor: we admire the bravado of the burglar, the gall of the confidence man, even at times the lust of the rapist, the freedom of the prostitute, and the violence of the murderer, although we also know these things are dangerous. There is always a great hue and cry before the murderer has been discovered but after his arrest and during his trial there is a large segment of sympathy on his behalf. We sense that we have hostility within us which we must conceal, but we admire those less restrained and inhibited than we; they seem to do what we might like to do if we had the courage. We resent the social establishment which inhibits and represses us, which crushes and flattens our individuality.

The most staid and proper individual may have a momentary impulse to act like that monk from Siberia, whose life grew drearier and drearier, till he broke from his cell with a hell of a yell and eloped with the Mother Superior. Sometimes, even at the risk of danger, disapproval, jail, and death, we would like to express ourselves with violence and unrestrained hostility to add a touch of color and excitement to our lives. We will express ourselves with violence and hostility if we can find a cause which strikes us as right and righteous and suitable.

On the other hand, the psychopath is sometimes puzzled when society reacts against him violently. Although he has no social sense or need, he can see the rewards of social trust and confidence granted others and he sometimes wonders why they are unavailable to him. The most aggressive and hostile antisocial rebel does desire to be accepted, trusted, admired, and praised by people that he meets.

We all seem to be pushed and pulled by the two opposing forces; few of us can find the absolute point of balance between transgression and taboo. We tend to fluctuate, sometimes more inhibited and sometimes more hostile. The more mature we are, the more we understand this fluctuation and the forces behind it, but coming to terms with it continues to provide difficulty. In our more conventional and restrained moments, we feel bored, frustrated, and restless. In rebellious moods, we are uneasy in the conscience and unduly sensitive to criticism. These symptoms are neurotic expressions which result from lack of resolution of the taboo-transgression conflict.

This particular source of neurotic expression is not easy for the individual to identify in himself. It is a subject which is resistant to examination. It is somewhat improper and unconventional to admit that hostile aggressive antisocial forces exist in every individual. Taboo insists that taboo be accepted without question or reservation even when the taboo is illogical, irrational, or prohibitive. "Goodness" axiomatically is presumed to be "good" and even to question "goodness" is presumed to be "bad." Virtue permits no argument and is supposed to be its own reward. Perhaps the transgressor will really go to Hell. Whenever the transgressor is caught and punished, our conventional proper side feels a thrill of pleasure and may even contribute with sadistic satisfaction to the punishment. Cotton Mather delighted in preaching at condemned criminals and pirates; the same mob which shouted praise and worship at a prince in power will turn on the prince savagely with rocks and eggs and fire when he has fallen from the seat of power. We get a thrill of pleasure when the U. S. Cavalry rides onto the scene in the nick of time and begins to slaughter the Indians in just as savage and bloodthirsty a fashion as the Indians were previously slaughtering the pioneers. We approve when James Bond is sadistic to Goldfinger, because Bond is a "good guy." In this case, we are turning transgression urges into a force supporting taboo. Perhaps this is how we must utilize hostility for peace of mind.

Certain psychiatrists have decried the prevalence of sadism and violence in the entertainment diet of the young: in comic books and on the television screen. Such psychiatrists maintain that the violent diet increases transgression and violence on the streets. In point of fact, it may very well be the other way around. Violence in the realm of fantasy may express and discharge hostility, preventing violence in the streets. These psychiatrists subscribe, whether they know it or not, to the assumption that man is by nature good, and that evil does not exist within him until transplanted from the outside by evil influences. A corollary to this assumption must be that evil is more attractive than good, for, if man were by nature good and evil was less attractive, he would resist the evil influence. This theory obviously is shared by certain religious individuals and moralists. It may be reassuring to the moralist to believe that he himself is by nature good and has no evil in him if he can resist the attractions of outside evil influences. Such a moralist, however, is in danger of being a hypocrite. The observer can see hints of violence and hostility in him which he denies in himself. The impartial observer can hardly escape the conclusion that elements of violence and hostility exist in every man and that human history is full of violence and sadism practiced in the name of righteous causes. Religion, ethics, and morality have not yet in any significant degree reduced the incidence of human violence. It might be a more rational and logical approach to admit that transgression is not implanted on an innocent individual by an outside evil force but exists in all of us as a basic part of personality; if this admission can be made, then channels for the harmless discharge of hostility can be studied and explored. When transgression forces in the individual are not admitted, they rage unchecked.

There are dangers in total dedication to taboo and conformity. There is a passive danger: the "good person," never daring to be anything else but "good," guiding his every action to avoid social disapproval, so represses and inhibits himself that he has no individuality. The active danger is that of hypocrisy. The hypocrite whose transgression urge is strong becomes the zealot, and some of the most atrocious crimes of man against man are committed by the zealot in the name of righteousness. The concept of the "witch-hunter" is by no means obsolete.

Although surrender to conformity has passive and active dangers, it is obviously not healthy to give free rein to transgression. As is so many areas of biology, health represents a changing but reasonable balance in the middle between the poles of opposing forces. Emotional health lies somewhere between full inhibition and full expression.

The taboo—that "right and proper thing to do" which was taught us by parents and teachers and which is enforced by the police and which is expected of us by strangers whom we meet—asks to be accepted in its own name without question, reservation, or doubt, but such blind acceptance is dangerous. The wise man questions taboo whenever he encounters it, never accepting anything as axiomatically and automatically "good." From the wisdom of his experience and judgment, he will conform to that taboo which is necessary to fulfill his social needs, even when he recognizes that the taboo is silly or irrational or inhibitory. When he recognizes a taboo unduly restrictive to him, which would deprive him of the expression of his individuality, he takes his creative courage in his hands and breaks it, no matter what the cost. The cost may be only criticism and social disapproval, but it may be much higher than that. It may mean imprisonment, torture, or death. Most of the great causes of humanity have demanded martyrs, and men are called upon with some frequency to die for their beliefs.

We fear the hostility and aggression in ourselves, which is why we wish to deny these elements, but, although the thought may be frightening, hostility and aggression are necessary for life. If you see a tiny animal under a microscope, you find out whether it is alive by poking it; it is alive if it shows signs of fight or flight, and if it shows neither fight nor flight it is dead. Similarly, coming across the body of a snake, we would poke it with a stick to see if it were alive or dead. The living human runs away from forces too great for him and, when cornered so that he cannot run away, he fights. Man has always thought that war would be abolished when the race became sufficiently mature; he has always thought that individuals, when sufficiently mature, can learn to live in peace with neighbors. This, we hope and pray, may eventually be the case; if it is not the case, man as a race or as individual will not achieve his full potential and may, in fact, destroy himself. Man seems to think that this can be achieved by abolishing hostility and aggression within himself. Sociologically, this hasn't worked yet, to put it mildly. Biologically and psychologically, this is unsound. Animals show what is called territorial aggression, the need to defend the home area against invasion and intrusion. In animal ecology, when natural territorial boundaries are changed by man, the result may be disastrous. For example, when an African game reserve is fenced off so that elephants cannot roam, the elephant herd will thrive and increase for a time, but as they increase they so devour the available food supply that the forest and plain is devastated; no more food grows; the entire herd is in danger of starvation. Man has territorial aggression, both physically and psychologically, and shows definite tendencies toward devastating his forest and his plain.

The biologist would say that if man loses his hostility and aggression, he will not survive, for he needs these things to overcome hostile elements in his environment. The psychologist would be inclined to say that man should not attempt to deny transgression urges but should admit that they are basic and study them. The sociologist might say that the road to peace does not lie in the suppression of hostility and aggression but in the channeling of these urges from destructive into constructive purposes.

How can the individual handle his own hostility and aggression? Physical exercise; sports and games and all competitive activity which is regulated by rules and conducted in the spirit of fair play; work; recreation; hobbies and avocations; participation in and enjoyment of the creative arts. These things can be learned and they must be taught.

25

On Drowning a Unicorn

The area of the taboo-transgression conflict most disturbing to the average modern adult, the unresolved conflict most likely to induce anxiety and neurosis, is sex. Or, at least, so our reading and thinking would lead us to believe. Actually, I am sure that the importance of sex in human psychology has been stressed and emphasized far out of its actual relative importance. The revolution started by Freud is still going on. The original basic observation of Freud was so striking and so startling that we still have not fully recovered from our astonishment. So much explanation and exploration has been required that the very study has laid a false and heavy emphasis. Since part of Freud's observation is so obviously valid and correct, we ignore it at our peril. But we cannot fully accept the dominance of sex over psyche; so in fact it seems likely that the observation may not be fully valid or correct. Nevertheless, the author writing on human psychology must dive into the sea of sex, bravely and frankly and, when the water is over his head, blindly too. To avoid the subject, to steer away from the muci-laginous or cloacal facets of the topic, would be regarded as cowardice or prudery or simple ignorance. If you mention such words as "penis" or "vagina" or "orgasm" in print today, you are no longer likely to shock. If you fail to mention these words, you may be regarded as a square.

Accordingly, without putting undue emphasis on a subject already overemphasized, we tackle it for surely it is important. It is not the only element in psychology; eventually it may prove to be one of the less important ones, but not while we are still under the Puritan heritage.

I think there can be small doubt that contemporary moral standards are changing. How much they will change, whether the change will prove healthy or unhealthy, whether we will progress or regress as a result of the change, cannot be determined, I believe, at the present time.

In 1966, a committee of clergymen and laymen was appointed by the British Council of Churches with instructions to prepare "a statement of the Christian case for abstinence from sexual intercourse before marriage and faithfulness within marriage." The report, when submitted in October of 1966, proved to be nothing of the kind. The criterion of morality in sexual intercourse, stated by the committee, was that there should be no sexual exploitation of another person, within marriage or without. The committee refused to endorse the conventional ban against fornication under any circumstances. It took the position that sexual relations between unmarried adults could be an acceptable part of a total encounter and that casual sex can be "trivially pleasant or mildly therapeutic." Furthermore, the committee's position was that adultery "should not be seen as an automatic ground for divorce," that birth control assistance for the unmarried should be endorsed, and that masturbation may be considered as providing a legitimate means for relief of physical tensions.

This is a revolutionary position for an official church group. It could not and would not have been submitted a few years ago. It has been highly praised in certain quarters and loudly damned in others. It certainly cannot be taken to represent the view of the average church or minister today. And yet, it seems likely that this point of view may be very close to that of the average modern intelligent adult.

In an earlier chapter of this book, we stated that the old-fashioned standard of premarital chastity and postmarital fidelity seems to be the best way of obtaining sexual satisfaction in marriage and this, in turn, would seem to be the maximal sexual satisfaction which can be attained. This position was not based on religious or ethical or moral grounds; it was offered as sound psychology. My professional experience in treating many thousands of patients in eighteen years of medical practice has convinced me of the truth of this position and my personal experiences fully endorse it.

Despite this conviction, I find nothing unsound in the report of the committee of the British Council of Churches; in fact, I think that this brave and honest statement concurs in every way with my own personal opinion, and I think that such a position could be a healthy one for any intelligent adult. It is certainly true that casual sex can be trivially pleasant or mildly therapeutic, although it can also be dangerous and does not constitute maximal sensory gratification. From the point of view of a religion whose Founder urged forgiveness of sin, adultery should not automatically produce divorce. Although we have said that sex with love can thrive most readily within the environment of marriage, it is the love which is fundamental and not the marriage. Certainly love can exist outside of marriage, and sex can certainly be an acceptable part of such a love, on psychological if not always necessarily on social levels. Birth control assistance for the unmarried would seem to me to serve the welfare of society much better than either abortion or illegitimacy, although sound education of the young in the psychology of sex would serve both community and individual even better. Dr. Albert Ellis, whom we have mentioned several times, believes that under certain circumstances masturbation may be the preferable recommended outlet for relief of sexual tension; if the statement is not taken as a sweep-

ing generality and if the appropriate circumstances are rather
carefully defined, I agree with him. Regarding masturbation,
the committee of the British Council of Churches added that
it is never more than an "impoverished substitute for the real
thing," which again I think to be a valid statement. Fundamentally, one individual should not exploit another, within
marriage or out, sexually or non-sexually: this, it seems to me,
is the crux of morality in human relationships.

We have coined the symbol of the drowning unicorn;
we do not intend this symbol to refer to acts of loveless
sex. The act of sex without love may not represent the
maximum of human experience but it does not need to be
damned; any healthy unicorn would survive it. When orgasm
itself is considered the epitome of life, out of context with
emotional ramifications and divorced from love or other interpersonal communication, this is what drowns the unicorn.
When orgasm is proclaimed to be a biological necessity which
must be satisfied, such a proclamation is biologically and
psychologically unsound. The isolated moment of orgasm
cannot be more than release of physical tension; the biological mechanism of sex is intrinsically a tension state with
dissatisfaction; the satisfactions that can be obtained in sexual relationships lie in the emotional implications above and
beyond any physical act. Suppressing love is what we mean
by drowning unicorns.

Earlier, we mentioned the concept of "polymorphous perversity" as if to condemn it. The point we were trying to
establish was this: since it has been demonstrated that man
and woman have inherent capacity for almost any sort
of sexual expression and since it has been demonstrated that
many men and women have experienced variety in sexual
outlet, it has therefore been proclaimed as true that variety
in sexual outlet is healthy and that any kind of sexual outlet
is as "normal" and "healthy" as any other—and this is what
we would condemn. It is perfectly true that the potentiality
for attraction to various outlets other than the male-female
heterosexual one may exist in all of us from time to time

and in this sense polymorphous perversity appears to be a valid entity. The existence of polymorphous perversity in the individual does not per se render him abnormal or disturbed. I feel certain that, normally, there is a natural progression from the immature toward the mature in sexual development. There may very well be an early Oedipal attraction toward the parent of opposite sex; then there may be a stage of onanistic self-attraction; then perhaps homosexual attraction; then superficial and loveless heterosexual attraction toward many potential partners; then heterosexual loving attraction toward many; and finally heterosexual loving relationship with a single partner. In order to reach maturity, one must probably pass through each of these stages successively at least in a latent way; at any given stage, there may be overt actual expression, though often there is not. A given individual, having matured through various stages, may regress backward in an immature direction. A given individual may stop at a certain stage short of maturity and remain there. Immaturity is not a crime. But it is a mistake, in my opinion, to proclaim any or all of the immature stages as equally "normal," "healthy," satisfactory, or desirable as maturity. The loving heterosexual relationship with the single partner remains the peak of sexual maturity: not easy to achieve and not easy to maintain but well worth the work and often the suffering required to achieve and maintain it.

In naming homosexuality as an immature expression, this does not imply that the mature male is 100 percent masculine or the mature woman 100 percent female. Physically speaking, the male has rudimentary breasts; the female, in the clitoris, has a rudimentary penis. Psychologically, men have female elements and women have elements of the male.

Carl Jung defined a pair of terms: the "animus," which is the male psychological force, and the "anima," the female psychological force. A given individual, whether biologically male or female, possesses both. The anima, or "woman within," gives integration to the personality and conveys vital messages about the self to oneself, in Jung's concept. One's mother was the original model: source of nourishment, identity, security, warmth, comfort, and life. We have spoken of transgression as an expression of individuality. If the woman within us is an integrating force which confirms our identity and individuality, the anima may also be a force toward transgression. Ladies may resent this implication, but, ever since Eve met the snake, as long as bitches whelp and witches ride, the association of transgression with the female has been present in the mind of man. This rather disturbing association of one's mother with one's desires to transgress against taboo can cause psychological difficulty; this is part of our problem in reconciling the sexual and maternal role of woman; identity problems may arise out of this dilemma and so may fixed immature sexual expressions.

The animus or "man within" gives us drive, the point and the purpose, the creative energy which moves us to accomplish things (as distinguished from the generative capacity to give birth to things). The man within also lays down the rules and regulations, the etiquette and the customs and the law: in other words, the taboo. He controls the science; he also controls the religion. It may seem paradoxical to think of the male force as law-abiding and censorious, for the male is biologically promiscuous and socially rebellious. However, although it is men who rape women or break the law or go to jail, it is also the man who is judge, policeman, jailer, and executioner; it is men who go to war for holy causes. We've always been inclined to suspect that men are basically more restrained, controlled, inhibited, repressed and conservative than women. A man must think before he acts, and he needs the support of a law or a fact to justify his action. The woman acts freely, by instinct and intuition, guided by free emotions unhampered by logic. When there is a disturbance of the animus, rigidity of personality, often with obsession and compulsion, is set up.

To attain mature heterosexual adjustment, the anima of the husband, his "woman within," must have contact, communication, and empathy with his wife; the animus of the wife, her "man within," must have sympathy for and empathy with her husband. I am inclined to think that the animus-anima relationship in sex is more fundamental than orgasm.

The animus, the male element responsible for taboo, is inclined to be sadistic. It might be suggested therefore that a woman in love must have a trace of sadism in her makeup. This suggestion may sound unpleasant or unpalatable. There is considerable evidence to suggest, however, that the wholly passive and dependent, completely "feminine," type of woman lacks the capacity to love. The passive and ultra-feminine woman is often a considerable transgressor, and her transgressions are often expressed through promiscuous sex, but this type of woman is frequently unable to achieve orgasm. The Masters-Johnson study was begun on a group of prostitutes, but they were not found to be good experimental material. The sadistic trait and the proper trait often go hand in hand. It would follow that, in order to achieve the expression of love, a woman must also be proper. In fact, this often seems to be the case. The promiscuous woman may seem to be looking for love, but all she finds is sex.

The anima, Eternal Woman within us, is inclined to be masochistic. For a man to be in love, he must respond to his anima, which means he must have a strain of masochism in his nature, the capacity to accept pain and suffering in the name of love. The anima having a transgressing element, he must also be able to express his individuality and must exert creative courage in the face of taboo, in order to be in love.

When a woman flirts or provokes or teases, or does anything womanly to encourage the interest and desire of a man, she is starting a chain of circumstances which, if followed to the natural conclusion, will result in the birth of a baby. By evoking and encouraging desire of the male, she is offering consent in advance. This consent, implicitly, is a consent to the disagreeable and painful phenomenon of labor.

When a man begins a love relationship, he is also consenting to a future responsibility: to support and protect the woman and the children who may follow. This is usually expensive. It may often be quite painful.

When a woman flirts but has a conscious reservation that she will not let the chain of circumstances result in pregnancy, she is cheating. The offer is not complete. It is very likely that the offer will not give the man the satisfactions it may seem to promise, because it is false and incomplete. Here is a psychological reason why the promiscuous woman, often, is not a good bed partner after all, even on the purely casual terms of mattress gymnastics.

In starting a love relationship, when a man has a conscious reservation that he will not support and protect the woman and that he will abandon any casual children who may appear, he is making a false promise. The woman, being intuitive, can usually sense this reservation. With such intuitive knowledge, although she may give her body, she will not give the precious gift: herself. This is why casual sex often does not satisfy the man.

We can't prove the existence of animus and anima. We can't measure them or record them or photograph them under laboratory lights. The animus and anima are only theoretical and imaginative concepts, not biological facts, and they are only intended to be symbolic of certain psychological verities. Some of Carl Jung's theoretical concepts have had recent verification in the biochemical laboratories, and some day the same may be said for the animus and anima. The animus and anima may turn out to be no more valid than many of the highly imaginative myths and mythologies of post-Freudian thinkers. However, if you study men and women as they spar, embrace, struggle, and grapple with each other, and if you try to analyze behavior in terms of animus and anima, many quirks and eccentricities of human sexual behavior suddenly make sense. Consideration of animus and anima within the individual may give him or her certain clues as to his or her own motivations. Such clues may bring no success in the pursuit of perpetual orgasm, but they may be helpful in exploring the devious paths of love.

A great deal of our fundamental motivation in any social relationship may be a search for impossible love, often in impossible ways. Just because the goal may be impossible, however, does not imply that we should abandon the search. The quest for the impossible dream may be, as many poets have insisted, the greatest life motivation. The wise and sound advice of the psychologist and counselor may not be so practical and wise after all: know thyself, we keep repeating, face reality and truth. We need self-knowledge, a realistic approach, and a struggle for the truth, but in addition we need our dreams. We cannot live creatively without certain illusions and dreams. So here is a final definition of the metaphor we have been using: to abandon all dreams and illusions, to give up the search for impossible love, is also to drown the unicorn.

26

Marriage

Marriage is a tricky game. Approximately one marriage out of every four ends in a divorce; there must be at least that many more where the marriage is maintained as an empty shell enclosing two thoroughly miserable partners who are remaining together only for financial or religious reasons or "for the sake of the children." This leaves us with the presumption that only the minority of marriages succeed. What is the matter with this venerable institution? Has it fulfilled its usefulness? In light of changing moral standards, has it become obsolete and will we soon consider doing away with it?

It has been said that marriage fails because too much is expected of it. Anything short of absolute perfection is apt to be regarded as failure, and absolute perfection in human affairs is rarely attained. It has also been said that modern marriage is the most complex and difficult relationship two persons could enter. Again this may be because so much is expected of it.

In other times and places, marriage by arrangement was the usual procedure. Two families would get together and make a business deal for mutual social and economic advantage, often when the two prospective partners were children.

Such a deal would be regarded with horror today, but perhaps it has one outstanding advantage: it guarantees that the partners are of similar and compatible backgrounds. As nearly as one can gather, marriage by arrangement often worked very well. It did not take into consideration the factor of personal choice or love, and it often meant the marriage of strangers. And yet, one wonders, does not marriage always involve two strangers? Can you know a person until you have lived with them intimately for many years? In the marriage by arrangement, early sexual relationship was probably an awkward and uncomfortable business. But in any sexual encounters, the early experiences are awkward and uncomfortable; too much is expected. When two persons of opposite sex cohabit, and get along with each other well in non-sexual ways, sex relations between them often become more satisfactory to both parties as the years go by. When two persons marry on account of passion, the reverse is apt to be the case. When the two partners are of similar and compatible backgrounds, mutual respect and love easily can grow. Opposites attract, they say. Persons of dissimilar backgrounds are often strongly attracted to each other through the excitement and mystery of difference; as mystery becomes commonplace, excitement seems to vanish, and the partners may be left with little or nothing in common. It is a valid generality that marriages between persons of similar backgrounds are more likely to succeed.

Also at certain other times and places, it was customary to regard passion and marriage as two distinct and different relationships. A man could retain a conventional respectable marriage with all the advantages of family and security and home and indulge his passion by supporting one or more mistresses on the side; the wife too might entertain a lover from time to time without causing scandal or divorce. As nearly as one can gather, this arrangement also often seemed to work. The success of such arrangements might be offered as evidence for the healthiness of variety in sex. It should be noted, however, that such an arrangement will work only if society accepts it and if both partners expect it. If the extra-marital relations must be conducted in secrecy and stealth, the extra strain will usually impair all the relationships concerned. Furthermore, if each partner is led to expect fidelity from the other, infidelity will be regarded as an infraction of confidence and contract.

A curious variant of intersexual relationship was seen in medieval chivalry. Here, marriage on the one hand and extra-marital relations on the other was approved by society and expected by both partners, but sex was confined to the marriage. The extramarital relation was non-sexual and non-physical, a platonic devotion expressed through a complex and artificial set of rules and regulations. The fact that this arrangement too seemed to work could be offered as evidence that sex should be confined to marriage and that a platonic sexless devotion outside of marriage may be a satisfactory relationship.

Another variant appears to be occurring here and there in contemporary society. This is the phenomenon of wife-swapping, sometimes called the velvet underground. The prevalence of this custom is impossible to estimate, and surely it is rare in most areas of society, but in certain social circles it may be rather common. This may be simple interchange of bed partners between two married couples for brief periods of occasional nights or weekends by mutual consent of all four people concerned. According to statements made by persons who have engaged in such relationships, the experience is satisfactory to all concerned and may, in fact, increase satisfaction when the married partners return to the common bed. I don't think such statements can be accepted at face value, however; it is my impression that a marriage where both partners desired wife-swapping is intrinsically an unstable marriage with a short life expectancy. Perhaps more typical of the velvet underground is the sex party, the simultaneous multiple contacts, the modern equivalent of the orgy. This also must be rare, but the evidence appears to indicate that it may be more common than generally supposed; it is probably more common among intelligent, educated, prosperous people in higher social circles than among middle and lower classes. It is stated that a sex experience with multiple partners is exciting, which may very well be true. However, it should be noted that most of our information concerning the velvet underground comes from the writings of psychiatrists and analysts. The sex party quickly degenerates into various expressions of deviation, and most of the partygoers quickly land on the couches of psychiatrists. The participants are unstable immature persons, even though they may be intelligent, educated, and wealthy; and if such a party becomes more common it is evidence of increasing sexual maladjustment, not increasing sexual sophistication.

Still another variant of marriage has been seriously suggested recently by a number of advocates: a so-called Two-Step marriage. In such an arrangement, the first step could be entered into easily and casually and could be dissolved instantaneously at the desire of either partner without financial obligations or legal repercussions; the second step, a true marriage, presumably would follow if the first step was satisfactory. This arrangement is, of course, not now legal, and probably never will be. It conforms to the immature male desire: a variety of partners without responsibilities. I do not think the Two-Step marriage would in any way lead to more stable marriages, which is the intention of those who advocate it. One cannot help but think of the person, especially the female, whose first step of marriage had been dissolved several times; her chances of ever attaining a satisfactory second-step true marriage would rapidly and progressively decrease.

We're really not concerned with possible alternatives to conventional marriage, for the venerable institution is probably here to stay. It is here to stay, and has endured so long, for one obvious reason: it does offer the maximum in human interrelations. How can we achieve the maximum more consistently? How can we make it work? What we are trying to make work is a marriage containing three elements together:

personal compatibility, romantic love, and sexual passion. It is the feat of getting all three such elements in together which makes modern marriage the tricky game.

The arranged marriage is out of fashion and the matchmaker is out of business. It is expected that persons will marry out of personal choice and preference, for "love." A parent who tried to teach his child what to look for in a marriage partner would be regarded as a meddler. The parent is no longer given the right to exercise approval or veto of the intended merger. When two young persons marry for love in the face of parental disapproval, the sympathy of society is entirely on the side of the lovers, not the parents. A conscientious parent would not dare even to render an opinion about the prospective in-law. Not long ago, the prospective groom asked his prospective father-in-law for the hand of the bride. Such a confrontation would prove embarrassing to both parties today. The parents of the bride may not even know the groom; they may consider themselves lucky to be invited to the wedding, although they are still usually expected to foot the bill.

Persons get urges and desires for marriage when they are quite young. They often marry young. Half the women in America have married before their nineteenth birthday, although we consider persons less than twenty-one legally immature and do not permit them to vote or hold political office or, except in one state, to buy alcoholic beverages. Is marriage something requiring less maturity than voting or drinking? Perhaps it is no wonder that marriage so often fails. The young person is taught many facts about science and mathematics and languages but he is expected to work out the complexities of love and marriage for himself with the sole assistance of an equally young and immature partner. The young person does not ask his parents for advice on marriage; his parents are only old married people; what could they possibly know about marriage? As a matter of fact, the young person seldom asks advice from his young married friends. Professional counselors are available, but they are consulted only when a marriage has begun to fail. Like all the rest of us, with the courage and confidence and occasional panic of youth, he just jumps in and hopes that he can learn to swim when he is already in the water.

With the current emphasis and controversy over sex, in an era of shifting moral standards, it is natural to regard marriage problems and sex problems as identical. It is natural to think that healthy and satisfactory sex relations equals a healthy satisfactory marriage. It might be pointed out that a married couple spends only a microscopic fraction of their married lives in sexual contact; most of marriage concerns non-sexual relationships.

Regarding the problem of sex adjustment in marriage, Dr. R. A. H. Kinch, a gynecologist, made what strikes me as a very valid statement in an article entitled *Sexual Difficulties After Fifty* (Canadian Medical Association Journal, 94: 211, 1966): "The tragedy of marriage is that the man is most desirous of sexual contact in his early years while the responses of the female are still underdeveloped and she is struggling to free herself of acquired inhibitions. Over the years the woman becomes less inhibited and develops an interest in sexual activity just as the male's interest is declining." I think this often is the gist of sexual maladjustment in otherwise satisfactory marriages when both partners marry young. I think this may explain why the marriage between an older man and a young woman very often works; the older man, being both more sexually sophisticated and less sexually demanding, can adjust his needs to the lesser drive of the younger woman. When the woman ages and her demands become greater, by then her elderly mate may have died; then she may be free to marry a man younger than herself, which also works, because periods of greater drive in both male and female coincide.

As a generality, I think it can be fairly stated that sex is the expression of the relative happiness of a marriage and not the cause of it. When man and wife like and love each other, their sex patterns will usually be satisfactory—within reasonable limitations—to both. When a marriage starts to fall apart, the stresses and strains may show first in bed.

What advice might be given to a person contemplating marriage? The soundest suggestion, in my opinion, may sound a little silly on first impression: marry somebody you like. However, an awful lot of marriages involve persons who really do not like each other. It should be apparent that such a marriage has small chances of success. The conventional advice would phrase it: marry somebody you love. Yes, but the recognition and definition of "love" is no easy or obvious thing, despite the ease with which we toss the word around. Love, in its broadest and deepest meaning, probably does not occur until you have lived with the loved one intimately for many years. Love, in other words, grows out of a marriage relationship between two people who really like each other and is not a valid reason for the marriage at the beginning. What is so often called love is passion, physical attraction, which, as we have pointed out, so often develops between persons of unlike temperament and dissimilar background who really do not like each other very well and will not be able to get along with each other comfortably in marriage. If you like a person, and share common interests with him or her, and are of reasonably adjusted personality and possess some talent for social compromise, you need not fear marriage with that person. The chances are good that the sex relation will be reasonably satisfactory and that love will grow out of the relationship. If you do not like your mate, your marriage is in trouble before it begins.

Suppose that you are married and that the marriage is something less than absolute success: What then? Presume that you once thought you loved your partner but know now that you don't; perhaps you do not like he or she very much any more: What then? This book should not presume to be your marriage counselor. We would advise that you consult a marriage counselor or an experienced person in one of the other counseling professions. If the union has at one time been reasonable, if backgrounds and personalities aren't too dissimilar, if the partners have liked and loved each other in the past, and if they share things—especially children—in common, it is probable that the marriage can be saved and also probable that the marriage is worth saving. Under these conditions, it is very likely that the marriage has gone bad because of neurosis in one partner or in both. Treatment of the neurosis is treatment of the marriage. Everything we said in the chapter on living with a neurotic person is applicable to these circumstances.

We do not presume to make extensive comment on the subject of divorce. Divorce is messy and expensive, both financially and psychologically, and the divorce laws of this country are obsolete, messy, unfair, and punishing. The difficulties of obtaining a divorce may often exceed the difficulties of maintaining a bad marriage. The trouble with divorce laws is the concept of a bilaterally contested case between the guilty and the innocent, with punishment exacted on the guilty. In any bilateral relationship, the fault can never be unilateral, and divorce will always be a mess as long as it is a contest between lawyers on opposing sides. Perhaps, some day, there will be unprejudiced psychologists and sociologists working in cooperation with a judge. Until such time, the individual must weigh the pain and expense of divorce against the pain and expense of maintaining the marriage, deciding which choice is less costly for him but knowing that either choice will be costly.

If marriage is a tricky game and failure is so common, if marriage failures cause so much unhappiness, should we consider abandoning the institution and substituting looser and less restrictive contracts? My own opinion here is by now quite obvious; I hope that you have had rewards like mine in which case your opinion will be the same. Certainly, there are many people who shouldn't marry at all. There are more people who are going to marry and will marry wrong. It is admittedly difficult to achieve and maintain a good marriage, and more people seem to fail than succeed, but we should not abandon something just because it is difficult. Certainly one should not expect too much out of marriage, and deem it a failure whenever it is not perfectly successful, for, by such standards, all marriage fails. One does not automatically live happily ever after. One must always work on marriage to make the marriage work.

27

Raising Children

Perhaps the best advice which could be given on the subject of raising children can be stated in three words: "Consult Dr. Spock." For a generation, parents have been doing just that. Dr. Spock's major book, one of the best-selling titles of all times, contains a great deal of what the worried parent needs to know. The book is scientifically sound; it is readable, clear, sensible, and wise, and, perhaps most important, reassuring. The danger of any sort of guidance book is that it may increase anxiety in the worried reader consulting it for guidance, but Dr. Spock manages to avoid this pitfall as nearly as it can be avoided.

Dr. Benjamin Spock must have been an unusually mature, calm, and sensible young doctor. Young doctors are learned, but not notably mature or calm. It may not be generally appreciated that the first edition of Dr. Spock's famous book was written near the beginning of his career; from the style and content, one is apt to assume that this was the product of a wise old man, the distillation of a lifetime of experience. In the fall of 1966, Dr. Spock lectured at the woman's college where one of my daughters was enrolled; she was astonished to learn that he was an actual individual, rather than a committee or an institution, and that he was very much alive, since she had been brought up with his help.

The parent, seeking answers to a specific problem, might do better to consult the family physician or pediatrician than to look up answers in a book. However, doctors are busy, expensive, and often hard to reach. For major illness, the parent will obviously want a doctor, but would prefer not to bother him for the minor incidents and episodes of daily life. The pediatrician in turn prefers not to be bothered over trivia, and Spock has also served him well for more than a generation.

The attitude of the parent toward health problems in the raising of children has changed markedly in this century, parallel to the dramatic change in life expectancy. Infant and child mortality today is very low. The infant who survives the first twenty-four hours of life has an excellent chance of living to be an adult; mortality figures for the first day of life have not greatly changed because these early deaths are largely due to congenital conditions which we cannot prevent or cure, but after the first day the present outlook has improved enormously. It's difficult to realize that, as recently as the last century and in all times previous, the majority of children did not live to be adults. Visit an old cemetery and notice how many tiny graves surround the larger ones. Children used to die like flies, and parents used to expect it. Then, the doctor was called chiefly to provide prognosis, to tell the mother whether or not the child could be expected to survive. The treatment that the doctor could offer was nothing much more than nursing care which, comforting though it may have been, was not very therapeutic. Modern treatment may lack something in comfort, but it cures. The modern parent expects health perfection in the child; faced with imperfection in the child or with acute disease, the parent is inclined to feel anxious and guilty as if some parental shortcoming had caused the illness. The modern parent accordingly needs much more reassurance than did her great-grandmother although having far better chances of seeing all her children become adults. For such reassurance, a book like Dr. Spock's is invaluable. The pediatrician prefers to spend his time and skill in the actual treatment of disease.

Dr. Spock can't claim credit for the improvement in the health of modern children. Actually, although young children look small and frail and defenseless, they are basically tough in all respects but a few. If support is given them in a few specific areas, their intrinsic toughness will permit them to survive. It is support in these few areas which is responsible for the sharp decline in infant and child mortality.

One of these areas is the basic one: nutrition. It is only in this century that we have learned how to feed our children properly, and then only in the prosperous civilized regions of the world. In underprivileged areas, malnutrition and starvation remain major problems. Part of the improvement of nutrition comes from the biological sciences; only in this century has biochemistry been able to provide scientific backing for nutrition. A good deal of the improvement is due agricultural progress and prosperity. What children of past centuries lacked and what underprivileged children today still lack is protein; this is the important type of food responsible for growth and strength and physical resistance. Protein foods are the most difficult and expensive for mankind to obtain and procure. To fill the protein needs of a nation requires a productive agriculture and consumer wealth. Already scientists viewing the population explosion are becoming concerned about meeting the protein needs of the future.

Great credit for improved nutrition is given to the vitamins, more credit than they actually deserve. Vitamins were among the first biochemical discoveries to be applied to the area of health, and a miraculous aura continues to surround them, reflected in their name. Vitamins are essential; without them, deficiency diseases develop which produce disability and death; but the vitamins are needed only in trace quantities. It is necessary to give supplemental vitamins to infants, for milk, either maternal or bovine, is vitamin-deficient. Rickets and scurvy used to be very common infant diseases which contributed considerably to child mortality. The child old enough to eat a general balanced diet and the healthy adult eating a balanced diet do not need vitamin supplements, for the diet contains all the vitamins needed. Excess vitamins do not increase bodily resistance; they do not prevent influenza and the common cold; they do not give vigor or vitality, despite the name. Fortunately, vitamins in excess of need are largely harmless. The chief effect of taking vitamins is to enrich the pharmaceutical industry.

Adequate protein plus vitamin supplements in infancy produce a child who is tough in all respects but one. The child is vulnerable to infection. Resistance to infection is not born into him; it is acquired; through the magic of the body's immune system, the body learns to resist infection but it is not resistant to a given infection until it has acquired and survived it. It was infection which killed off children like flies. We have now learned to protect the child against infectious disease.

The protection is of several types. General sanitation and hygiene and cleanliness markedly reduce many kinds of infection. The two major weapons are the antibiotics and inoculation. The antibiotic drugs are still miraculous; though often misused and potentially dangerous when misused, they have saved and are saving millions of lives. There are few bacterial infections today which cannot be cured by proper use of these drugs. Useful as they are against bacterial infections, the antibiotics are useless against most infections caused by viruses. Protection against viruses is accomplished by immunization techniques, those "shots" which children dread but which even young children soon learn to accept as an occupational hazard of childhood.

With this support against infection plus good nutrition, most children live to become adults. By far the leading cause of death after the first day of life up to adult age is now accidents, something which it seems difficult for us to prevent. After accidents, the leading cause of death in the younger group is cancer; this may be surprising, for malignancy is usually considered an adult condition; we have not learned to prevent cancer and cure is achieved only now and then. After cancer, again perhaps surprisingly, the leading cause of death in older children and adolescents is suicide.

In the last century and earlier, a mother felt natural grief when she lost a child but not guilt; she expected to lose some of her children. The modern mother does not expect to lose any of her children and she really does not expect them to become seriously sick. In the face of illness in the children, she may become so anxious as to seriously endanger her own psychological adjustment. The anxious mother does not make a very good nurse for her sick child. It is perhaps as much due to the anxiety of mothers as to modern therapeutic tools that sick children are so often hospitalized today rather than being treated in the home. The anxiety of mother is often communicated to the child, which only makes him sicker. Neurotic or hypochondriacal mothers very often manage to implant neurosis and hypochondriasis in children, not infrequently for life.

A few children still die and some are disabled, but the large majority go through infancy, childhood, and adolescence with long periods of excellent health broken only by brief periods of acute illness with full recovery. It is safe to say that physical growth and development, physical health and illness, are no longer the primary problems of childhood or the primary concerns of parents. Psychological growth and development, psychological health and illness, are now definitely and clearly more important. Even in the case of the child with serious physical disability, psychological adjustment is extremely important; the psychologically healthy child can adjust to almost any physical disability amazingly well. What disables and limits and cripples children today, and the adults that they become, is psychological disorder and psychiatric disease.

Parents are aware of psychological hazards to their children. The work of Freud has made it crystal clear that the seed of neurosis can be planted in childhood. Rather than neglecting this aspect of the growth and development of children, the parent may often be unduly concerned with it, and excessive preoccupation may make the hazard worse. From the moment an infant appears upon the scene, the life of the mother—her social patterns, her sex patterns, her personality patterns—begin to be influenced by a suspicion that her life patterns may produce neurosis in her child. To a lesser degree but often quite significantly, the life of the father is similarly influenced.

We have heard so much of the evil effects of inhibition, suppression, and repression. The parent is determined that the child shall not be crushed by such unfavorable influences. Freud and the post-Freudian thinkers seemed to suggest that the best guidance for children was a lack of guidance and that discipline of children was potentially harmful to their psyches. In making the case against inhibition, the case for permissiveness seemed to be established. For a time, progressive education was fashionable; progressive education seemed to mean schools without rules, education without discipline. Many families extended complete permissiveness into the home. Permissiveness in school or home does not seem to work very well; the usual result seems to be spoiled brats growing into spoiled neurotic adults.

A middle ground between strict inhibition and complete permissiveness seems to be desirable. It can hardly be doubted that repression can cause harmful effects, but a certain amount of guidance and discipline appear to be necessary in both home and school. Children need these things; most children, in fact, know that they do, and quite a number of them actually call for guidance and discipline in various subtle ways.

To find a safe middle ground between inhibition and permissiveness, the parent often wants some help. In general it is rather obvious that parents who are themselves mature and adjusted will be able to find this happy medium without outside assistance, and it is rather tragic that disturbed immature parents are least likely to recognize the need for outside help. The child guidance counselor knows that the place to begin treatment of the disturbed child is treatment of the disturbed parent. As a generality, child guidance and child psychiatry are very effective when begun early enough; children are more responsive to psychotherapeutic techniques than adults; they are both tougher and more resilient, psychologically, than adults. As a generality, psychotherapy of the disturbed child is almost never started as early as it should have been; the earlier it is started, of course, the quicker and better the results. As a manifestation of basic human nature, the parent will resist admitting the disturbance of the child, knowing this to be an admission of disturbance in the parent, and it is human nature to protect and hide such weaknesses, rather than expose them. Recognition of the child's disturbance becomes obvious in his exterior environment, meaning his school, and the initial steps toward correction are usually brought about through influence of outside authority: teacher, principal, and not infrequently the police. The parent anxious over the emotional adjustment of a child might be wise to examine his or her own psychological adjustments and begin the guidance at the level of the self. Dr. Spock is full of reassurance and help but he cannot be expected to be the universal psychiatrist of parenthood.

Parenthood implicitly involves anxiety, of course. The natural anxieties should be more than rewarded by the normal joys of parenthood. To be a proud parent is obviously one of the greater satisfactions of a life. However, there is also sadness in parenthood. The sadness of the death of a child, the heartbreak of childhood disability, the disappointment of parent at the underachievement, failure, or delinquency of a child are risks implicit in consent to parenthood. There is also a sadness of the parent which is not related to disaster or catastrophe but which occurs with the natural passage of the years.

We live in what we like to call a free country. The intellectual climate is permissive and liberal. Although we know that privileges are still restricted for certain minority and special groups and that any responsibility implies some restriction of individual freedom, we take pride that our heritage includes, along with life and the pursuit of happiness, the precious prerogative of liberty. We want our children to be free. We want them to be more free than we ourselves have been. Therefore, after having guided our children as well as we know how, provided the best education for them within our means, and disciplined them only to that extent we considered good for them, we do our best to set them free. We want them to be individuals, to think and choose and decide for themselves. So, we push them out of the nest, and they fly away. For the most part, they fly away happily, for they want freedom too: in fact, they insist upon it, often demanding more freedom than they are ready to handle or able to enjoy. Some don't fly very far; many keep coming back; a few can never leave; but often the strongest and the best of them do not return except for occasional moments as casual strangers. This is what we wanted, what we bred and raised them for, but it hurts. We remember them. We have worked to help them grow, but in the heart we sometimes wish they didn't have to grow up.

Raising children is an important part of life for those lucky enough to have had the children to raise. When children are young, they may be, and probably should be, the most important part of the parent's life, especially the mother's. To bind the child with a permanent umbilical cord is to cripple him, and we must encourage him to be free, but it is necessary for the parent, and especially the mother, to retain an element of freedom for herself. For many women, the children may become the only important thing in life; for such women, when the children grow and leave, the importance of life is over. Such women have permitted motherhood to nullify their geriatric years.

It is contrary to all taboo to attack the sanctity of motherhood, but if a woman is to maintain balance in her lifetime she must not let her motherhood become a sanctity. Physically, motherhood is not a permanent condition; psychologically, it should not be. Twenty-five years of preparation, twenty-five years of motherhood, and twenty-five years of nullity does not give a seventy-five-year balanced life. There are, even for a mother, other important things than children. When the children grow up and go, the time has come to discover and explore other things for which previously you did not have the time.

28

The Change of Life

The phrase is frequently heard in doctors' offices. The patient complaining of "the change of life" is frequently, although not invariably, female; she is usually in her forties or fifties, though she may be in her thirties or her sixties, and I have heard the complaint from a woman of seventy-five and from a woman of twenty-five.

The syndrome is associated with the menopause, the normal cessation of menstruation in middle life. The typical symptom is that of the "hot flush" or "hot flash," a flushing and blushing sensation, usually beginning on the face and working downward on the body, coming and going very quickly, often accompanied with sweating. The flushing of the face can sometimes be seen by the observer. The symptom is apparently quite distressing and embarrassing to the patient. Associated with this phenomenon are feelings of fatigue and inertia, depression, poor appetite, insomnia, general lack of vigor and well-being.

The menopausal syndrome is an organic imbalance which has long been recognized and known to be caused by decreasing levels of hormone secretion from ovaries losing their function. As the hormone level falls, a condition of so-called vasomotor instability occurs; there is lack of normal control of dilation and contraction of superficial blood vessels, especially on the face, which accounts for the "hot flash." The other symptoms may be related to a similar cause. When ovarian function disappears completely, the body adjusts itself and the symptoms are no longer present, but the time of change is gradual and the symptoms may persist for some years.

It has long been known that menopausal symptoms can be controlled by the giving of female hormones. This treatment has been in successful use for decades. Physicians used to give hormones rather cautiously and only for brief periods, for the growth of certain female malignancies were believed to be encouraged by high hormone levels.

Recently, there has been a burst of enthusiasm for female hormone therapy in the medical profession and especially outside of it, triggered by articles in women's magazines and a couple of best-selling books. The new theory is to give hormones not only for relief of specific menopausal symptoms but to all women in the menopausal age group, and to give it, not just for brief periods of time, but perpetually. The exciting and desirable rationale for this is that such therapy will give eternal and perpetual femininity, retaining youthful beauty and charm, forever postponing old age in women. Since women, and men, have always looked for the fountain of youth, this theory has a great appeal, especially when backed by reliable authority.

The suggestion for perpetual female hormone therapy came from work on "the pill," the new contraceptive oral drug for women. The ingredients of "the pill" are not at all new, being merely combinations of female hormones which have been known for decades and used for decades, not only for therapy of hot flashes but for suppression of lactation in post-partum women and for regulation of menstrual irregularities in young women. The contraceptive possibilities of hormones had long been suspected and expected on theoretical grounds. Use as a contraceptive in normal women had to await a large long-term experimental trial, to demonstrate safety and efficiency, which explains the long lag between theory and practice in this regard. The drug proved to be quite safe, despite scattered cases of phlebitis associated with its use, and very effective as contraceptive. In normal pregnancy, there is a greatly increased hormone level, which among many other things, suppresses further ovulation and prevents possible superfecundation. Artificial administration of hormones as "the pill" works in the same way, being contraceptive because it suppresses ovulation. The woman taking "the pill" creates in herself an artificial state of false pregnancy without embryo. Side effects sometimes seen with "the pill" are those of early pregnancy: morning sickness and breast engorgement, for example. Many women in early pregnancy normally feel very well and somewhat euphoric. A similar euphoria may partly explain the popularity of "the pill" and may also explain the well-being of menopausal women on similar hormones.

The safety of "the pill" as contraceptive led gynecologists to believe that hormones might be safe long-term therapy during and after the menopause. The reason why hormones had not been used that way before was fear of cancer of primary and secondary female sex organs. Experience with "the pill" has not showed any increased incidence of malignancy; in fact, there is some evidence to suggest that long-term female hormone therapy may actually reduce incidence of carcinoma of the breast. This fear having been removed, the path was open to the suggestion for long-term hormone therapy in many or all menopausal and post-menopausal women. Some gynecologists now favor this suggestion with enthusiasm, though most appear to be somewhat more cautious. If the theory is carried to its logical conclusion, we may see the older half of the female population in a perpetual state of drug-induced false pregnancy with accompanying euphoria.

I do no gynecology in my practice and my professional advice is seldom sought in this connection, but I have definite reservations against long-term hormone therapy for older women. I definitely would not recommend it to the average older woman at the present time. It has been suggested to me that I am anti-feminine because of my position in this regard. Actually, I am fond of beautiful women and I think it would be delightful if all females of every age retained their youthfulness of body and spirit, but I am inclined to doubt that this happy state can come about through the long-term usage of a drug. The hormonal system of the body is complex, and the functions of one endocrine gland interlock with the functions of all other endocrine glands in complicated ways we do not thoroughly understand. I therefore think that tinkering with hormones is a risky and tricky proposition. Long-term administration of ovarian hormones might well produce late disturbances in pituitary, thyroid, and adrenal, for example. Although Mother Nature obviously intended women to be pregnant from time to time, I am not sure she intended all women to be falsely pregnant all the time. A long study of "the pill" was required to demonstrate the safety of its use in younger women. I would require an equally long study of hormones in older women before I felt that safety had been demonstrated.

Returning to the menopausal patient with complaints of "the change of life," treatment with female hormones, for short periods at least, has long been accepted and is successful for those symptoms which are caused by declining hormone levels. Many physicians prescribe such hormones in great quantities for this purpose. Although my practice is not gynecological, I encounter the "change of life" complaints with some frequency. My own results of treatment for these complaints are good, quite comparable to those of the gynecologists, and yet I rarely prescribe female hormones. I get equivalent results with a mild sedative such as phenobarbital plus generous support and reassurance. If I had more confidence in the persuasiveness of my personality, I would omit the phenobarbital.

The organic nature of hot flashes and related symptoms

cannot be doubted. However, these symptoms are relatively minor and do not particularly bother most women. Healthy happy well-adjusted women scarcely seem to notice them and do not consult the doctor with this complaint. The women who do seek help for these symptoms are apt to be emotionally maladjusted women. In other words, although an organic cause is present, the severity of the condition is strongly influenced by emotional factors, and the disability appears to be primarily psychological and not physical. Part of the relief given by hormone pills or shots is undoubtedly psychological, the placebo effect, and part of it may well be the euphoria of artificial pregnancy.

Neurosis alone, unaffected by ovarian function—as for example in a young man—can cause every symptom of the menopause, including the hot flash. In women, when these symptoms are not associated with change in the menstrual pattern (the young woman with normal periods and the older woman some years past complete cessation of menstruation), it can be presumed that the picture is entirely neurotic. Even in women at the proper age with changing menstruation patterns I think that the more severe symptoms are neurotically based.

The women speak of "change of life." I think the phrase should be interpreted more literally than is usually implied. I think it is the change in the life of the woman which makes her neurotic and depressed more than the change in her ovarian function. The late forties and early fifties are a trying time of life. The concomitant disappearance of menstruation is only objective evidence of the same depressing fact: that she is growing old. It is obvious to her that her reproductive period, her capacity to be a mother, is over. It is suggested to her that she will soon lose her charm and physical attractiveness to men and, in fact, has already been losing these qualities for quite some time. For the woman whose life is centered around her motherhood, or around her attractiveness to men, the good life is over and nothing but a long empty stretch of living death lies ahead of her. This will, of course, be depressing. For all women, feminine qualities have been at least to some degree important at one time or another, and even the most mannish lesbian must feel depression at the evidence of passing femaleness.

Physical reproductive capacity ceases for the woman at the menopause. Attractiveness to men by no means ceases necessarily at that time of life. A distant ancestor of mine— Benjamin Franklin—wrote with zest and appreciation of the attractiveness and seductiveness of older women, and there is little doubt that he was writing out of personal experience. One thinks of several female movie stars whose physical image remains unblemished by the passing decades. When I was a boy, Marlene Dietrich was a sexy and desirable female; as I write these words at the age of forty-four, she is just as sexy and desirable. Sally Rand waved her fans when I reached puberty; today, at this writing, she is still waving them on the professional stage. There is documentation of a Parisian courtesan who, at the age of eighty-two, was still the most desirable woman of her social set. In less spectacular manifestations, the marital sexual life of the average woman need not cease at the menopause. For many women, sex is more enjoyable after the menopause than before it. I think that this is true for the majority of happily married women; in fact, I think that in the majority of adjusted marriages, sex life stops from lack of desire of the husband, not the wife, and in many marriages, mutually happy sex continues into geriatric years, and without the use of hormones, whether the young will believe it or not.

There is some question as to whether a physiological menopause equivalent occurs in men. From the point of view of reproduction, there is no question that many men remain fertile until the late geriatric years. Many very ancient men appear to have fathered daughters and sons, by a young wife, although the cynic can never entirely exclude the possibility of some younger male lover in the background. Many men retain potency and desire until late geriatric years, though many men do not. It is generally accepted that the therapy of impotency in aging men is psychological and not hormonal.

There definitely is a crisis period in the lives of many middle-aged males, approximately coincidental with the female menopause. In some husbands, it may be a sympathetic reaction to the menopause of the wife. Possibly some hormonal imbalance may be a factor, although I think this relatively unlikely; surely much or all of it is psychological.

The psychological picture of menopause in women is often that of a depression state. In men, the "change of life" symptoms characteristically take the form of a revolt. Women are inclined to have reduced libido and desire for physical sex during a menopausal crisis; men are inclined to have increased sexual urges at a similar time and often, at this period, they roam. Affairs outside of marriage are not at all uncommon for men in middle life; many wish to rid themselves of the aging wife in order to acquire a younger one, and quite a few succeed. The revolt often may be in the form of economic indulgences: gambling or speculative investments. Sometimes the man will take up a new and dangerous physical sport.

For the man, his middle-aged revolt is most often precipitated by factors concerned with his career. A younger man can always spur himself and reassure himself with thoughts and dreams of future rewards and high achievements in his field. The middle-aged man, in his late forties and fifties, can begin to see quite clearly the limits of the future of his career. If his achievements have been sufficient to satisfy ambition and if he has come to terms with his own limitations, his revolt may be quite weak and minor. If his failure in his own eyes is greater, the revolt may be quite major. His reaction is rather similar to that of the hostile and rebellious adolescent. Like the adolescent, his sense of individuality is threatened— on this occasion by narrowing horizons and approaching age —and he reacts in the familiar way, by revolting against taboo (usually his own taboo which he has set up for himself) and indulging in transgression.

Change is a fact of life in all age groups, but the changes

brought about by approaching age in man or woman may be a major hazard. In a youth-conscious era, the transition period of middle age is inclined to be more trying. In general, the adjusted adult encounters little extra difficulty at this time of life. The maladjusted person must often face his own unresolved dilemmas most strongly in middle life, a period dangerous for many.

29

Misdirection

A distinction should be made, I think, between misplacement and misdirection. Misplacement is a feeling of being in the wrong place, or the right place at the wrong time, or under the wrong circumstances. This is such a common human feeling that we might consider it normal.

A sense of misplacement begins to occur young. In primary school, children from better homes may envy tenement kids who are free to roam the streets, and the children from underprivileged families rightly envy those with more material advantages. Later in education, one may see others get the top grades, become captains of athletic teams, or be socially popular, and one thinks that, with better timing, these things might have gone a different way. Throughout life, one has a tendency to envy those who seem to get the breaks because of luck or circumstance or timing. In middle or later life, looking back, one thinks of the various crucial decisions and turning points and wonders what would have happened if one had turned the other way.

A feeling of misplacement, normal though it may be, probably represents a partial failure of self-knowledge, which also means a failure of education in its broadest sense. Over the long run, at least, it is probably not the luck or the circumstances or the timing that brought one to this time and place, but one's own limitations. There are people who keep changing their locations, or their jobs, or their wives all the time, and they seem to have about the same set of luck and circumstances in any place. They may run to escape their problems, but they can never escape themselves. They bring along inner problems anywhere they go. In general, the person will get as far as he is going, no matter what his place or circumstances. There are certain places exceedingly restricting, such as jail or a desert island upon which one may be marooned, but certain individuals have rather full potentials even in such restricted environments.

Misdirection is another matter. This implies, not the feeling of being in the wrong time and place, but the sense of having aimed in the wrong direction. This is considerably influenced by the relative ambition of the individual. Some persons seem to have little or no ambition, being content to drift along with the current, making the best of whatever may present itself; such people often seem to be very well adjusted, happy, and content. They are often well liked, though perhaps not admired, and their lack of material accomplishment by no means diminishes their value and worth as individuals. Those with excessive or inappropriate ambition, especially those who attempt to attain their goals at the expense of everybody they encounter, are often disturbed persons and are sometimes dangerous. Reasonable ambitions and long-term goals, however, are a characteristic of the mature valuable person.

If the ambition or goal one sets for oneself is early attained, it was probably not a valuable goal, not worth working for, and its achievement is likely to bring few or no rewards in terms of satisfactions. It is a very human tendency to feel dissatisfied on reaching a goal and to desire something more. Psychologically speaking, it is better to set an impossible goal. "The difficult we do at once, the impossible takes a little longer." And, although it may indeed prove impossible to attain such an ambition, by the very act of trying to attain it, one achieves amazing by-products by the effort which originally would have seemed out of reach. Working toward long-term impossible goals must bring discontent, but this is the sort of "divine discontent" shown by the great artist, working toward the impossible perfection in his art, never satisfied with what he has done, but in the process producing great art, perhaps even greater for its ambitious imperfections.

Misdirection, heading for the wrong goals, is also an educational failure in self-knowledge, a lack of understanding of one's own limitations, but it is more than that. It implies what is perhaps a more serious educational deficiency: lack of appreciation of one's own talents and strengths. This is a sort of false modesty which can be fully as damaging as false pride.

Yet misdirection is often difficult to avoid, especially in the complex technologies of the modern world. Subdivision of labor has become increasingly specialized. Labor not requiring specialized knowledge and training is not apt to be rewarding in either psychological or material ways; the rewards go to the specialist. Some of the most rewarding specialties are so complex that the required training consumes not only all of childhood and adolescence but a substantial part of early adult life too, and in many specialties the educational process can never stop. There are many specialists who spend more of their lives training in the specialty than practicing it, and some never get around to practicing it at all. Without long years of specialized education, the individual starts off behind and never can catch up; awareness of this fact is reflected in the constant urging of the young not to drop out of school.

Since the specialties are so complex and the training period is so long, one must start the specialization young if one ever hopes to do any work in the specialty before one is too old. And this is dangerous. The individual must choose his specialty before he is old enough or mature enough to know his bent; he has no chance to sample several fields before he must exclusively limit himself to one; he cannot really know if the specialty is suitable until he has spent so many years in training that it is very expensive for him, financially and psychologically, to leave the specialty.

The tendency to early specialization, although perhaps most striking in the physical sciences, is clearly manifested in my own profession of medicine. Twenty years ago, it was customary to expose all medical students to the same curriculum which covered the basic sciences, explored medicine, surgery, obstetrics, gynecology, and pediatrics in depth, and touched on all the other specialties. This was followed by a general rotating internship where the intern rotated through all departments of the teaching hospital. After internship, some men went directly into residency training in the specialty of their choice, but many went into a general practice first, as I did, picking up qualifications in a specialty later after some general experience. Today, specialization often begins in medical school, many schools having an elective period in the senior year; the general rotating internship is less popular, and the straight internship in a specialty more common; today, few young specialists have had any general practice experience, the vast majority moving directly from internship to residency. The young specialist is highly qualified within his specialty, of course, but he is apt to be inexperienced and ignorant in anything outside of his own specialty, which may sharply limit him, both as physician and as man. Rigid specialization tends to compartmentalize the patient, as if the patient's heart or his lungs or his eyes could be detached from him, studied and treated independent of the rest of the body, and then put back on again, like bolting a new fender to a car. This is poor medicine. Man is a unity who cannot be subdivided by specialty.

Specialization begins even earlier in engineering and the sciences. The young scientist must limit himself by his junior year in college, and often his specialization has begun several years earlier than that. There are rather few adolescents who know themselves well enough to be certain of the best choice of specialty but they are compelled to make a choice if they wish to specialize at all. This causes much career misdirection in modern life. The defense for early specialization is the complexity of the specialties, the long training required, the enormous body of technical information which must be absorbed, and of course these statements are quite valid. But along with these truisms other equally valid statements must be accepted: early specialization is going to produce unbalanced specialists and career misplacements rather universally. It also produces certain social disarrangements: the specialist in one field has difficulty communicating with the specialist in another, since they share no common general ground.

The persons most free of the confinement of specialization are the creative artist, who makes his own rules as he expresses himself, the artisan, who makes something in his own way which others find valuable, and the self-employed person, who has devised a unique or individual service of value. Such people are seldom caught in misdirection. They know where they are going; getting there, however, may be less than half the fun and very difficult indeed. The artist, the artisan, and the person with a service must face a period of economic hardship until the art, the handicraft, or the service becomes salable. They must also face the prospect that the art, handicraft, or service may never be commercial, in which case they must choose between starving in the garret in the name of art or prostituting the talent in some more commercial field. The lives of a lot of talented people get badly messed up by this paradox. A lot of would-be novelists are teaching English in schools and colleges and a lot of persons with ambitions to be Picasso are producing commercial art for Madison Avenue. These persons may feel misplaced but they are not misdirected. The English teacher can write his novel during summer vacation, and the commercial artist can express his soul on canvas over the weekend, and these people eat regularly. On the other hand, Greenwich Village and similar Bohemian establishments are inhabited by people who have the necessary creative courage to defy the prostitution of commercialism but who lack sufficient talent; these persons are probably both misdirected and misplaced, and they, often, do not eat.

The choice of art versus commerce is not as limited an area as might be offhand supposed. Art—both enjoyment of and participation in—and the humanities offer the escape to the rigidly confined specialist and offer much of a broadening influence both within and outside of the specialty. Take a good look at the best specialists in any given field. A few of them are confined entirely to the specialty which is their life without any outside interest, but many of the best of them are broad-based men with wide general interests in other fields and often direct participation in one or many areas of the humanities and the creative arts. Wide general interests not only produce a happier and healthier specialist but often have the paradoxical effect of increasing his interest and ability within his special field. From the other side of the coin, the talented individual, who cannot support himself on his artistic talent and feels that he must prostitute the talent in a commercial field to make a living may profit by the misplacement. The disciplines of commerce may give him increased disciplines in art. If the product of his weekend painting or writing is good enough, he may have the opportunity to redirect his career at some later date; if it is not good enough, he is able to discover the fact without the additional hardship of starvation at the same time. Very often the reason why the Bohemian does not succeed is the lack of discipline of his supposed art. Freedom plus talent is not enough for art; discipline is also needed. The psychological reason why the unsuccessful Bohemian is frequently involved in social transgression should be obvious in light of our discussion of transgression as expression of individuality.

What advice might be given to the individual who feels himself misplaced? There is small chance that advice will give him any help. If he is aware that a feeling of misplacement is due to a lack of self-knowledge, he will already be embarked on a voyage of self-discovery which, if successful, will correct his feeling of misplacement. If he is convinced that his misfortunes are due to luck, timing, or circumstance, nothing you can tell him is likely to convince him otherwise.

What could you say to a person who feels himself misdirected? Nothing needed here: the fact that he is aware of misdirection means that he is seeking newer more appropriate directions, and he will probably find them.

The person to whom advice might be of help is that person who is unhappy and incomplete because of misdirection and doesn't know it. What could you say to him? This, I suppose: if you are unhappy and incomplete, it may not be due to the time or the place, the luck or the circumstances; there may be no leaks in the ship; the ship may be headed in the wrong direction. Turn on the binnacle light and look at the compass; look at the charts; turn off the binnacle light and take another bearing on the stars. If the direction is wrong, the solution is simple; turn the steering wheel. It is better to turn the wheel now, while you still have space and time in which to navigate, than to wait until you are stuck fast upon the reef.

30

Retirement and Aging

A patient of mine recently reached the mandatory retirement age after a long and distinguished career in research science. Like most people of his age, he might have been content to enjoy retirement, reading, resting, puttering around the garden, traveling, engaging himself in social and community activities, pursuing hobbies and other interests of which he has a good many. He could have continued doing independent research in his special field and in fact could have continued to use the facilities of the research laboratory at which he had been employed. Instead, at the age of sixty-five, he started on a new career.

He closed his home and moved to Greece, a country which he had visited before only for a couple of weeks. He plans to live there three years, and he has assigned himself two books to write during that period. One is a translation of a guidebook on Greece from German into English. Although a skillful linguist, he has never before attempted professional translation. The other project is a historical novel about an obscure ancient Greek philosopher. Although he has written many scientific articles and several books in his own field, he has never tried his hand at fiction before.

He will find both projects difficult. He may not finish either, and he may not find a publisher if he does finish them. He has no advance contracts. He isn't doing this for money; in fact, he may make no money from the work. He has earned more honors and distinctions than most men and he surely needs no further achievements for his vanity. The world is not crying for another guidebook or historical novel. Yet, I am sure that the adventure will succeed in its primary objective. My patient will find more fun in life and retain his youthfulness of mind and spirit far better in the new career than he would have in retirement.

Before leaving for Greece, my patient consulted his dentist, a busy skillful practitioner nearing the same age. Being self-employed in a profession, the dentist faces no mandatory retirement; he can work as long as his health permits and there is demand for his services. The dentist remarked to my patient that he was afraid of retirement; he had few interests outside of dentistry, and his chief recreations were hunting and fishing. Years of bending over the dental chair had given him bursitis, and he found it difficult to raise a shotgun to his shoulder or to cast with a fly rod. The dentist was afraid that, when he retired, he couldn't find anything to do. My patient suggested to the dentist that he find some hobby of a creative kind not requiring arm movement at the shoulder but calling for manual dexterity: specifically, woodcarving.

I have another patient of similar age. This man began his career as an antique dealer. Antiques were not in very great demand during the depression, and he changed occupations, utilizing great skill in mechanics to start, with a partner, a garage specializing in expert mechanical repair, which was successful. Throughout the years, he retained an interest in antiques, doing some buying and selling and some appraisal work on the side, but the garage consumed most of his working hours. His partner developed ill health a few years ago, and he and my patient sold the garage and "retired." My patient retired back into the antique and appraisal business. Since his retirement, he has been busier and happier and more prosperous than before. He has become the most sought-after appraiser in this part of the state; he is engaged in extensive dealings in antiques; he works long hours, but at this writing he is in excellent health and enjoys every moment of his present life. In a sense, his "retirement" freed him to return to the work closest to his heart. I am sure that his pleasure and success in his "second career" contributes much to his present physical and emotional vitality and vigor.

If a man has a "second career" after retirement, one can say that he is fortunate. Without such, many men do poorly in retirement, often aging rapidly and losing their interest in life. The man with the second career, however, can't be considered lucky; his opportunity is not a matter of luck; usually he will have been preparing for many years prior to retirement, developing an interest in outside activity which becomes greater than interest in the primary occupation. For such a man, retirement from the primary occupation is a very pleasant event.

Today, the average man can look forward to a decade or more after retirement. These may be gloomy and depressing years; they may be lazy trivial years; or they may be exciting and adventurous. It depends on what one does with them. It is never too late to begin preparing for retirement, but also it is never too early to begin. Many men who enjoy rewarding and exciting later years have been preparing for retirement most of their lives.

I have always been an advocate of hobbies, avocations, and outside interests, having a number of them myself. Such interests add a great deal to the richness and depth of the working years which mere sports and recreations do not add. A lot of people look forward to retirement as an opportunity to pursue their hobbies, but, as a preparation for retirement, I think that hobbies alone are not enough. A hobby, pursued alone as primary occupation, often seems to lack sustaining value, and many retired people seem to lose interest in their previous hobbies. A hobby is often just that: enjoyable and useful for leisure time but insufficiently challenging. What retired people need is the second career.

I recall another patient who was forcibly retired from his blue collar occupation rather young by severe physical disability. Following surgery and a long stormy convalescence, he was physically rehabilitated to a partial degree, becoming ambulatory again and physically fit to pursue sedentary and light activities but not qualified for his previous work. He was a man of little formal education and no outside interests. During the long convalescence, I did my best to interest him in a variety of sedentary hobbies. I hoped that this might help him pass the long hours of convalescence and renew his interest in life and perhaps later lead to employment opportunities of a sedentary kind. My efforts were to no avail. He was interested in nothing. The only spark of interest I caught in him was when, while perusing a hobby magazine I loaned him, he saw an ad for a correspondence course in hotel management. This seemed to me an extremely unlikely field for him and I did not encourage him to pursue the matter any further, but he didn't need my encouragement. He clipped the coupon, obtained the literature, and to my surprise, he enrolled in the course. To my further surprise, he completed the course. When his health finally permitted, he moved to another part of the country and found work in a hotel. He started as a desk clerk and before his death a decade later he had moved up in the chain of command to become assistant manager in a large well-known Midwestern hotel. As a purely incidental note, he also married: not once but twice and he married the second wife before he was legally detached from the first one. I am not suggesting that happy retirement plans should include bigamy, but perhaps his marital activities could be taken as evidence to indicate that he had recovered his appetite for living.

The second career may be more satisfactory than the first because of a new approach and attitude. After retirement, money often is not the problem. Those who have insufficient financial resources after retirement and must work again for a living often find life more dreary and depressing and tiring than before. It is implied that people with the second career are no longer working primarily for money; they work, not because they have to, but because they want to, and the pleasure of the work is in the work itself, not in the financial rewards. Freedom from economic pressures is part of the fun. In the first career, people often feel compelled to seek the job with the highest pay, whether or not they like it. Obviously, part of the preparation for a happy second career is financial planning and saving during the first career. The person who reaches retirement with money in hand is now in the position to seek the kind of work he likes. Ironically, the individual may often become more prosperous in his second career than in his first.

There is also often freedom from another pressure: the urge for advancement, for recognition, and achievement. The individual has often satisfied these urges, or come to terms with his own limitations, during his first career. Again, ironically, he may earn more achievement and advancement when these things are no longer a primary objective, doing the kind of work he likes.

Still another pleasure of the second career is the absence of the pressures for time. Being now "retired" and elderly, the individual is free to work short hours, or only when he feels like it. With a clear conscience, he can take the day off when he doesn't feel well or feels like doing something else, and longer leisurely periods of vacation travel are now his right. Paradoxically, he often works longer and harder on his second career: not because he has to but because he wants to. Often, the retired person is working for himself rather than for an employer. As self-employed people have always known, you work longer and harder when the boss is yourself.

The retired person in his second career does have adjustments to make. He is older. Being older, his body has limitations it did not have when he was a younger man. The older person must learn to live with inevitable and often progressive decrepitudes. A young man expects to feel well all the time and is often upset and dismayed when he does not feel well. The older person knows that he will never feel completely well and is delighted by the days when his disabilities bother him less than usual. The younger person expects to push himself past fatigue into exhaustion from time to time, at the call of either duty or pleasure, knowing that he can recuperate in a day or two of rest. The older person knows that it takes him much longer to recuperate than to become fatigued and that after exhaustion he may not fully recuperate at all. In both work and play, he must learn to pace himself.

The younger worker can afford to neglect his physical health, or at least he thinks he can. The older worker must regard his health as his major asset without which he cannot work at all. Actually, the older worker has a hidden health asset which may not be appreciated. By the very fact of having lived to grow old, he has demonstrated the fact that he is tough. The younger worker may not live to grow old. The older worker has already survived some of the hazards which may kill the younger man. He is more resistant to infection than the younger man, for example, although when he does get an infection it is often more serious. The leading cause of death is coronary artery disease. The peak of coronary disease is in middle life, and the older person has outlived this period. The second leading cause of death is cancer, which also has peak incidence in middle life; the cancers of the old, though common, are slow to grow and slow to spread and the patient often survives them. It may sound paradoxical, but the older person whose death is nearer has already survived the most dangerous periods of the two most common killing diseases; he has outlived those born in the same year who have already died of the common causes. He has proven himself tougher than they.

The major health hazard of the elderly person is the process of arteriosclerosis, hardening of the arteries, which is so common that it may be considered a normal aging phenomenon, though a few appear to escape it altogether. Arteriosclerosis may lead directly to death through stroke or kidney failure. It often contributes to disability, gradually and progressively, and there is the particular hazard of senility. Continued gainful work appears to retard the development of arteriosclerosis, although of course this may only imply that those with the least arteriosclerosis are most able to work. I think that exercise is important in keeping arteries open and elastic. Important in the young and middle-aged, exercise is perhaps even more important in the elderly in contributing to vitality and vigor. This does not mean excessive bursts of unaccustomed exertion, which can kill, in both elderly and middle-aged. It means regular daily exercise within the limits of physical tolerance.

Arthritis, not a killer, is a very common physical disabler of age. We don't know how to prevent or cure arthritis, although we usually can relieve the pain from it. Here again, regular reasonable exercise within tolerance does much to prevent disability.

A sleep problem is a frequent concomitant of age. The elderly person requires less sleep than the younger individual but often cannot accept the fact and finds the restless tossing black hours a great physical and psychological handicap. Many elderly persons have a habit of reversing the day/night cycle: lying awake most of the night and sleeping in a chair most of the day, with unhappy results. The best solutions to this problem are those we have mentioned before: work and exercise.

A major killer and crippler of elderly persons is accidents. Accidents are common in the old partly because of loss of acuity of the senses of vision, hearing, and balance; partly because of slower reflexes and reaction time and loss of muscle tone; and partly because of a state of mind. The older person may have an overconfidence or an underappreciation of risk. He may not realize the degree of his progressive physical deterioration or he may refuse to admit it. He may have gotten accustomed to the degree of relative blindness, deafness, brittleness, and slowness which he showed last year, while not yet realizing, or admitting, the greater blindness, deafness, slowness, or brittleness of this year. The older person may still worry about cancer or coronary disease, but he is more apt to die as the direct or indirect result of an accident, as is a child, and the relatively minor accident, trivial to the child, may be very dangerous to him.

We have confined this discussion of retirement and aging to the older worker. We have not discussed the problems of the older person who does not work. Such problems, though grave, do not seem worth discussion because there is little to be gained by discussing them. Most problems of the older person who does not work are insoluble and will be corrected only in death. By work, in this connection, we do not necessarily imply formal employment or self-employment; we mean any activity pursued, physical or intellectual, whether for money or not, provided it is pursued purposefully and creatively with some constructive goal in view. I feel that every older person must do some work as so defined. Without purposeful creative activity, the individual is dead, though he may continue to breathe. One can pursue some such purposeful creative activity in the face of any and every disability, including such total physical disability as life in the iron lung, including advanced senility, even including severe psychosis. The factor most likely to prevent purposeful creative activity is not paralysis, senility, or psychosis, not blindness or deafness, not chronic pain and not rapidly approaching death, but neurosis: the nonfatal and potentially curable crippler which is such a common hazard at any age. True death, though it may represent a tragedy to those who survive, is a natural and normal event for the individual and especially the older individual. Life without work is living death, and this may be too horrible to contemplate.

31

On Coping with Neurosis in Oneself

We have looked at various personality and behavior patterns in others and we have looked at certain aspects of adjustment in ourselves. Everywhere we look we encounter signs pointing in the same direction: at neurosis, the thief of time, the destroyer of creativity, the irritant in social relationship, the major cause of human unhappiness. A given individual may not be clinically neurotic at the moment, but it is likely that he may be at some future time. The individual should realize that he is often under the influence of neurotic impulses. If he does not understand and accept this fact, he does not understand himself. Many people are able to cope with their own neurosis successfully without knowing what they are doing and why. Those who do know what they are doing are in a position to do it better. The place to begin to cope with neurosis in the self is to admit that a potential for neurosis is present in us.

The actual expression of a neurosis which causes damaging consequences is either a mask for concealment or a red herring for diversion. A subconscious emotional conflict exists. One wishes to conceal the conflict from others, for it is a weakness, and we try to hide our weaknesses. We also try to conceal it from ourselves. An unresolved conflict is disturbing, and we do not like to be disturbed. We therefore adopt a position which seems to conceal our dilemma from others or divert their attention away from it, and to conceal it from ourselves and divert our own attention elsewhere. There is a wide range of behavior patterns available for these purposes. The individual subconsciously selects one which seems to best fit his personality. When the selection has been clever, the conflict is concealed, and we cannot find it with our conscious mind. Therefore we cannot approach it directly or solve it directly. We must use an indirect approach.

The outward expressions of neurosis are apparent to other people but not to us. We have chosen them and we do our best to make them a normal part of us. Neurosis does not admit its own abnormality. The inward manifestation of neurosis is anxiety. We hide the cause but we can't hide the anxiety. Accordingly, when we perceive within ourselves inappropriate anxiety, the anxiety without reasonable cause, we should be able to diagnose ourselves as neurotic.

There are certain common means we use to allay the nagging distress of neurotic anxiety. We reassure ourselves with certain axioms. This reassurance is useful for the anxiety of certain superficial minor neurotic impulses. With the more deep-seated neurosis, the reassurances do not work; in fact, they tend to fix the neurosis, making it less accessible, and therefore increase the anxiety. The axioms with which we reassure ourselves sound valid on superficial scrutiny; in fact, however, they are false. In Chapter 17 we listed a dozen such axioms. The list is by no means complete, but it does include some popular favorites. Let us examine the same list, in order to note the fallacies.

(1) A person should be loved by everybody. In heaven, perhaps, but it does not happen here on earth. We are not loved by everybody that we meet; some people do not like us and some, in fact, dislike or hate us. If we accept this fact,

then we will not be disturbed or upset when some of the people whom we meet do not love us after all.

(2) Accomplishment is the measure of value and worth. Accomplishment is significant, but it is not, or it should not be, the measure of the man. Some who have accomplished little are persons of great value, and some who have accomplished much are persons of small value. It is rather important how the accomplishment was achieved: whether for the sake of other people or at the expense of other people. What we are is more important than what we do.

(3) Failure in one area implies failure in every area. This may be comforting for those who would prefer to accept defeat. However, all who succeed must rise from failure, not once, but repeatedly.

(4) People should treat us better than they do, and things should go better than they are going. It isn't so. People will usually treat us according to their own needs, regardless of our needs. Things will go according to circumstances, and the circumstances are not directed for our particular benefit. We should adjust ourselves to people and circumstances as we find them, and not wait hopefully for them to change.

(5) Since an important happening once influenced our lives, it will always influence our life. It may, but it need not, and often should not. Whenever the sun comes up over the horizon in the east, a new and different day begins.

(6) One has no control over the emotions and must give in to them. This is a sign of immaturity and of the person who is a prisoner of his moods. One must learn to exert emotional control to escape from the prison of the self.

(7) One has complete control over the emotions and should never give in to them. Perfect control is unavailable. Attempts at rigid self-discipline produce inhibition, repression, and coldness. Some emotions are too powerful and we must learn to give them freedom and let them run until they weaken to the point where we can exert control.

(8) Worry in advance will prevent pain and difficulty at the time. It never has yet. Planning and preparation in ad-

vance will prevent much pain and difficulty, but planning and preparation are not the same as worry.

(9) Freedom is the right to do exactly as we please. This is not true. Freedom implies responsibility; the greater the freedom, the greater the required responsibility. The irresponsible person who does exactly as he pleases is transgressing; he is expressing himself by exploiting the people that he meets. The transgressor isn't free. Often he goes to jail.

(10) All men, being equal, deserve equal rewards. But all men are not equal. This was not the original concept of democracy but a dangerous perversion of it. The original democratic concept was that all men deserve equal opportunity to pursue their different individual goals with their different individual endowments and capacities. Being different and having different goals, they will earn different rewards.

(11) Men and women, being equal, have equal desires and needs. Men and women are not equal; they are not identical; they are different, which the French Parliament noticed, even though some sexologists have not. Being different, the desires and needs of men are different from the desires and needs of women. *Viva la différence!*

(12) Tomorrow will be better. Perhaps it may be better, but perhaps it may be worse, and most likely it will be very much the same.

If the fallacy of these popular axioms is perceived, we can approach people and circumstances in a healthy way; if we accept the axioms as truth and use them to reassure anxieties, we are fixing our own neuroses. If we find ourselves using such methods of reassurance, we must suspect ourselves of being neurotic.

If one suspects neurosis in the self, can one cure it? If you can find the inner conflict, bring it out of the subconscious into the conscious mind, and resolve it, yes. The resolution, however, can never be easy; if the resolution was easy, we would have resolved it when we first encountered it.

Now that we have buried it, it is difficult to find it. Obviously we can't resolve conflict we can't find.

How do you find conflict in the subconscious mind? You cannot do it directly. However, there are certain occasions when the subconscious mind is accessible to the conscious mind: just before, during, and just after sleep; in early and mild intoxication; during participation in and enjoyment of the creative arts. At such moments, things "pop" into our minds. They "pop" direct from the subconscious. When something "pops" into your mind, don't just watch it with astonishment or surprise but grab it and hold it tight before it disappears. These are among the most important thoughts we ever have. They often contain the clues to our conflicts and the resolutions needed to cure neurosis.

In this connection, a brief digression on the subject of dreams is warranted. Freud and his followers put great emphasis on the importance of dreams. A good deal of psychoanalysis consists of analysis of dreams. The attempt is made by the analyst to understand the patient by interpretation of his dreams, and the interpretations are then offered to the patient as the way to self-understanding. This ambitious attempt, it seems to me, must almost always fail. The analyst is not at hand when the patient wakes up from the dream. By the time the patient reaches the couch of the analyst, hours or days have elapsed; the patient has had time to rehearse the dream, to embroider it, to make a good story out of it. The patient wants to please his analyst and knows that the analyst is interested in dreams. The story the patient offers the analyst is usually nothing more than that: a good story.

Jung and his followers were also interested in dreams. Their interest was in the symbol rather than the substance of the dream. They noted that the content of dreams is not in words but in pictures and that the pictures are not truly representational but symbolic. The symbols which appear in the dreams of every man are often those which artists of all schools and at all times have drawn. From these observations, the Jungians have reached interesting conclusions about our common heritage of emotion.

I think that the usefulness of dreams to the individual is neither Freudian nor Jungian, but I believe that there is a very important use to which the individual can put his dreams. The moment you wake up from a dream, the first clear moment of consciousness, study the dream: take it out of the subconscious and put it into the conscious mind and work on it; see if you can find out what it means. The meaning is never clear. The dream does come up, not in words or in representational pictures, but in symbols. The symbol is almost invariably that of a subconscious conflict.

We know more about dreams now than in the days of Freud and Jung. We have discovered the phenomenon of REM sleep. We know that REM sleep is necessary to discharge physical and psychic tension; without sufficient REM sleep, the individual becomes psychotic. The dream, part of REM sleep, seems to be Nature's way of discharging subconscious emotional conflict; it is, in other words, Nature's own curative device to prevent neurosis. The individual can reinforce this natural defense by using his own dreams as his window into his own subconscious mind. The healthier we are, the better our communications with our own subconscious minds.

Many individuals correct their own neuroses. Most individuals can learn to correct their own neuroses—the subject isn't easy—it takes time, patience, courage, persistence, and intelligence, but it can be done. It is well worth doing. It is one of the most important things any individual can learn. For the neurosis which cannot be self-corrected, there is only one other appropriate solution: consult a good psychiatrist.

32

"You're It!"

"Tag."

A hand slaps you between the shoulder blades and the voice cries, "You're It!"

The sun is going down. It is late afternoon on an autumn day and the shadows grow longer. There's a chill in the air. You lean against the trunk of a big oak tree, and close your eyes, and start counting out loud to a hundred. You may be tempted to peek and open your eyes just a little, but you don't, or at least not much.

"Coming, ready or not!" you cry.

No other children are in sight, although you know that they are not far off. Somebody hiding behind that tree, or the next tree, or around the corner of the house? You think you see a flash of motion over there. You must find them, but cautiously. When you spot somebody, it is not enough to call his name; you must beat him back to home base; or, if you don't, you will be "It" forever. You think you hear small noises; perhaps they are laughing at you, safely hidden behind their trees. You listen, and now you don't hear anything. Perhaps there isn't anybody there at all. Perhaps, while your eyes were closed, they all left and went home. You have a strong and disagreeable sensation that you are alone.

I am recalling here a distant memory of my childhood. Perhaps some readers may not share it. I think, however, many readers will. The game of "hide-and-seek" seems reasonably universal. Children have played it for a long time; I suppose they play it still. My memory of playing hide-and-seek is chiefly that of being "It," and my memory of being "It" is chiefly that of the strong, faintly exciting, and faintly frightening feeling of aloneness.

I am using a metaphor. "Hide-and-seek" was not my own original title for this book. It was suggested by my agent. It just "popped" into his head at the end of a business lunch. It seemed to me to describe aptly, though obliquely, what this book is about. Of course, I'm not writing about a children's game. I'm not writing about a game at all. The combination of a social relationship, a struggle and a contest, the act of hiding and seeking and running, the faintly cruel aspects of the social relationship, and particularly the sense of aloneness seems to describe the mood of many kinds of interrelations. It is especially appropriate for the last short chapter of the book, where I am speaking of aloneness.

Man does have a social need, varying widely from one individual to another, suppressed almost entirely in the recluse, distorted and lost in the schizophrenic, absent only in the subspecies of the psychopath. However, though he must deal with people and surrounds himself with crowds, man is still alone.

He is born alone. Not in fact, of course: the mother must be there; usually there is an obstetrician and attendants on the scene; but the infant is only aware of his aloneness. Wrenched from the warm security of the womb, he cries. His second cry may be a demand for food, but his first cry is one of fear and protest at finding himself outside and alone.

Man dies alone. Rather often in fact. Even in a hospital, it is more frequent that the final breath of life is not witnessed than that there is a physician or nurse at the bed-side during the terminal moment. In other times, it was customary for a man to die surrounded by his loved ones, but even then he recedes from them and from life, back into aloneness.

And during most of the interval between his birth and his death, man is alone. A third of his life, he is asleep, and then he is surely alone, no matter with whom he may share the bed. For much of his waking hours, he is alone. Never, even during his most intimate physical contact with another or during his most concentrated and intense efforts at communication with the crowd, can he be free of being to some extent alone. It is a crowd of strangers. The wife is a stranger, the child is a stranger, the mother is a stranger. And, in fact, a man often seems to be a stranger to himself.

For a successful marriage, it is necessary to like as well as love one's mate. Can one like oneself? One better, if he must be alone with himself so frequently.

You see a lot of people who do not seem to like themselves. You see a lot of disturbed and unhappy people. There are some who seem to be afraid to be alone with themselves: I immediately think of a prominent politician who must com-municate with others at all times, who must always talk and be talked at, who seems to need the constant actual touch of hands of crowds to reassure himself that he is alive and real and valuable. As a matter of fact, such a fear of aloneness seems characteristic of politicians in general, and one can think of many for whom the same description is equally valid.

Can one love oneself? Some seem to. These we do not like. It is, we think, obscene and gross, to be in love with oneself. Can one hate oneself? Most certainly. We see a lot of people who hate themselves and feel the hate so intensely that they must finally destroy the object of the hatred.

But, can one like oneself? I think one must, if one is to have any small luck in this pursuit of relative happiness. Can one learn to like oneself? Yes, I think so, and I think this process is another definition of maturity and of education in the broadest sense.

How does one learn to like oneself? By learning tolerance, I think. Tolerance is the key to smoothness and ease in social relations. Do unto others as you would have others do unto you—the Golden Rule. There is a similar Golden Rule for living with the self: do unto the self as you would like to do unto others. Just give yourself a break. Does that sound childish? But many disturbed and unhappy people never seem to give themselves an even break.

One has a bargain with oneself. Inside, there's another voice and another ear. We sometimes speak of "the better self." Puritans were intensely aware of the voice and the ear of the conscience. Religious persons visualize the eye and the voice of God, who marks the fall of every sparrow. The most unreligious person, the utter nihilist, still has a bargain to keep with himself. Be true to yourself and preserve your own integrity and you do make a small island of meaning in a chaotic world of meaninglessness.

The person who keeps his own bargains, thereby satisfying what I consider to be man's essential religious need, can be at peace. He can accept the loneliness of birth, the aloneness of death, the fear, the pain, and the panic, and all lack of communication with the faces that we meet, in peace, because he is at peace with himself. If he is troubled and disturbed, as many people seem to be, he might do well to examine the nature of his own bargains with himself. In its essence, peace of mind is not a quality to be derived from reading books, even the great spiritual classics; it is not a quality to be obtained from hearing the words of others, whether they be spiritual leaders or therapists. Peace of mind does not come from words. Words disappear like smoke. Peace of mind is an interior problem which can be solved only by the individual alone with himself.

The state of interior aloneness can often be a cold and lonely state, but the condition is not without hope. Hope is a biological actuality. The intrinsic fight-or-flight reaction of living creatures, the adaptability of protoplasm, the ability of man to adjust and compensate and endure through the most adverse and hostile circumstances, is a measure of the worth of being alive and verification of the axiom: where there's life, there's hope. There is always hope as long as there is time, and there is time enough, more than enough for what we really want to do, more than we really know what to do with. Time is not running out on us. Time is running along with us.

Early in the first chapter of this book we quoted from a poet. We will close with another quotation. The poet, this time, is Angelus Silesius.

Friend, let this be enough. If thou woulds't go on reading
Go and thyself become the writing and the meaning.

SUPPLEMENTARY READING LIST

This does not pretend to be a complete bibliography. Titles listed here have been selected because they are particularly interesting to me or important in the thinking which led to the writing of this book. The critical opinions and capsule reviews offered after each title represent only my personal opinion.

1] *Analyze Yourself*. Loewenstein, Leopold; Gerhardi, William; Rosen, Victor. Hawthorn (1955). Alphabetically, this title comes first in my list; coincidentally, it is to me perhaps the most important in the list. An astonishing book. It offers a system of self-analysis which will give the reader most penetrating, vivid, and revealing glimpses into the mystery of his inner self.

2] *Anxiety*. Steiner, Henri; Gebser, Jean. Dell (1962). One of a so-called "Visual Books" series which are more art than text. This gives a very clear visual portrayal of the symptom of anxiety, in case anybody needs one.

3] *Art of Loving, The*. Fromm, Erich. Harper & Row (1956). A classic, short, important. Everybody should read it.

4] *Common Sense Book of Baby and Child Care*. Spock, Benjamin. Duell, Sloan & Pearce (1946). The original "Dr. Spock." There have been several revised editions and several other books on allied topics by the good doctor.

5] *Crime and the Mind*. Bromberg, Walter. Macmillan (second edition 1965). Classic study of criminal psychology. Although intended for the criminologist and psychiatrist, it is well worth the attention of the general reader.

6] *Discovering Ourselves*. Strecker, Edward A.; Appel, Kenneth E. Macmillan (third edition 1958). The "self-help" book by the two men who taught me psychiatry in medical school. One of the best of its kind.

7] *Emotional Maturity.* Saul, Leon J. Lippincott (second edition 1960). Not a "self-help" book but a scholarly serious and valuable study of the development and dynamics of personality.

8] *Events Leading Up to the Comedy.* Nugent, Elliott. Trident (1965). An interesting autobiography of a talented and interesting man with manic-depressive psychosis, who has learned to live with his disease very skillfully.

9] *Games People Play.* Berne, Eric. Grove (1964). The all-time champion best seller of books on psychology. Curiously, it was not intended for the general reader but as an exposition of the author's special school of psychiatry. Its popular success caught author and publisher by surprise. The success is probably due to a catchy title and to the jazzy swinging style employed. The book is clever. It is also, in my own opinion, superficial and artificial, and I do not think it contributes greatly to understanding of the subject.

10] *General Selection from the Works of Sigmund Freud.* Freud, Sigmund. Doubleday (1957). A sampling from the master. I think Freud in the original is interesting and revealing. I think his original work is of far more value than that of most of those who borrow, embroider, and expand on it.

11] *Great Imposter, The.* Crichton, Robert. Random House (1959). Interesting true account of a psychopath who presumably is still at large and operating, written by the author of a recent best-selling and highly entertaining novel.

12] *How to Live with a Neurotic.* Ellis, Albert. Crown (1957). To my mind, by far the most helpful of all "self-help" books. Short, clear, interesting, readable, extremely valuable.

13] *Human Sexual Response.* Masters, William H. and Johnson, Virginia E. Little, Brown (1966). Another best seller not primarily intended for the general public. The general reader is apt to get very little nourishment from it once he becomes accustomed to imagining the methods and techniques by which the study was conducted.

14] *Liquor: The Servant of Man.* Chafetz, Morris E. Little, Brown (1965). A sturdy defense of the advantages and pleasures of drinking, which will reassure those who drink and will not convince those who do not drink. Curiously, it was written by a physician who specializes in the treatment of alcoholism.

15] *Lore of the Unicorn, The.* Shepard, Odell. Houghton Mifflin (1930). They tell the story of a little girl who came home from school one afternoon; her mother asked her what she had learned in school that day; she said that she had learned more about Madagascar than she ever wanted to know. This book will tell you more about the unicorn than you will ever want to know.

16] *Love and Orgasm.* Lowen, Alexander. Macmillan (1965). Strongly influenced by the theories of Wilhelm Reich, one of Freud's original disciples who subsequently became insane. Although I have strong reservations against and suspicions of this general school of thought, I consider Dr. Lowen's book the most sensible of all the modern sexologies, not because of the emphasis on orgasm but because of the emphasis on love.

17] *Man and His Symbols.* Jung, Carl G. Doubleday (1964). Jung was not a popularizer. He was primarily a practicing physician who chose to approach each patient as a unique and different problem. He did not try to fit the patient to the rigid confines of a specific diagnosis; he did not attempt to set up a school of thought of either diagnostic criteria or therapeutic principles, although his original thinking and skillful therapy attracted psychiatrists to him to form a school. Jung was a close personal friend and original disciple of Freud, perhaps the closest. He broke with Freud early, a break which caused considerable psychological trauma to both men. Jung's work branched off in a different direction. To my mind, it is at least as important as that of Freud. For many years, Jung's disciples attempted to persuade him to set down his thinking for posterity in a unified form. He refused. In the final days of his life, however, he was persuaded by a television reporter to edit a summary of his work. Jung wrote the first part; other parts were written by five collaborators; he devoted the last year of his life almost exclusively to the editing of this book. He finished his own section and had approved the sections written by others only a few days before his death. The book is copiously illustrated and is, in fact, as much of an art book as a psychiatry book. It is an immensely valuable contribution.

18] *Marquis de Sade, The.* De Sade and others. Grove (1965). A generous sample of the works of the "divine Marquis," including the complete *Justine,* plus critical comments by several modern essayists. I think almost anything written about de Sade is interesting and valuable but nothing written by de Sade is worth the reading.

19] *Mask of Sanity, The.* Cleckley, Hervey. Mosby (fourth edition 1964). Classic study of the psychopath which, though intended for the specialist, is well worth the attention of the general reader.

20] *Minivac 601 Manual.* Written and published by The Scientific Development Corporation (1961). The "Minivac" is a small digital computer. The title listed refers to the instruction manual which comes with the computer. My rudimentary knowledge of computer science has been derived almost entirely from reading the manual and playing with the computer.

21] *Modern Clinical Psychiatry.* Noyes, Arthur P. and Kolb, Lawrence C. Saunders (fifth edition 1958). A standard text, for the physician, one of the best.

22] *Neurotic Styles.* Shapiro, David. Basic Books (1965). Introducing the valuable concept of personality style as expression of neurosis.

23] *Patients Who Trouble You.* Steiger, William A. and Hansen, A. Victor, Jr. Little, Brown (1964). It may not have occurred to patients that they sometimes bother, disturb, upset, and trouble their doctors as badly as doctors bother, disturb, upset, and trouble them. This book provides a short, readable, and amusing glance at the other side of the fence.

24] *Psychiatry in General Practice.* Thorner, Melvin W. Saunders (1948). The title sounds like a text. The book was intended as a text for doctors. However, it is crammed with case history material, skillfully presented, which reads like a collection of excellent and entertaining short stories. The book is well worth the attention of any general reader. Unfortunately, it is out of print.

25] *Psychology of Sex Relations*. Reik, Theodor. Grove (1961). Dr. Reik, though a Freudian, does not write or really even seem to think like one. He is a shrewd and sympathetic observer of the human scene, a skillful and prolific author. Almost any of his books—and he has written many—could be recommended to the general reader.

26] *Reality Therapy*. Glasser, William. Harper & Row (1965). Dr. Glasser offers his own school of psychiatric thought. I do not agree with some of the basic concepts of this school. The type of therapy which he suggests, however, can often be very useful. One of Molière's characters was astonished to discover that he had been talking prose all his life. In 1965, I discovered that I had been practicing reality therapy for years, without putting a name to it, and without knowing what I was doing. With or without a name, it often works.

27] *Rebel Without a Cause*. Lindner, Robert M. Grune & Stratton (1944). Interesting case history and detailed study of a young psychopath.

28] *Revolt of the Middle-aged Man, The*. Bergler, Edmund. Grosset & Dunlap (second edition 1957). Written for the layman, readable, perceptive, an interesting study of this common phenomenon.

29] *Sex and the Single Man*. Ellis, Albert. Lyle Stuart (1963). The proper and the conventional will not approve or endorse some of the sexual ethics of Dr. Ellis. The value of the book does not rest here. Perceptive and valuable advice on the subject of love is given which might be most useful to the married, as well as the single, man, and to the conservative as well as to the liberal.

30] *Sexual Behavior in the Human Female*. Kinsey, Alfred C.; Pomeroy, Wardell B.; Martin, Clyde E.; Gebhart, Paul H.

Saunders (1953). The second, and more interesting, of the famous so-called *Kinsey Reports*. A historical landmark but not worth the attention of the average general reader.

31] *Sexual Behavior in the Human Male.* Kinsey, Alfred C.; Pomeroy, Wardell B.; Martin, Clyde E.; Gebhart, Paul H. Saunders (1948). The first of the *Kinsey Reports*, which like the companion volume, is a historical landmark but not worth reading.

32] *Sleep.* Luce, Gay Gaer and Segal, Julius. Coward-McCann (1966). A model for skillful scientific popularization: accurate, comprehensive, crammed with detail, but at the same time readable and fascinating.

33] *Story of O.* Réage, Pauline. Grove (1965). Important, obscene, disturbing, and revolting. The gentle reader is strictly warned to stay away from it.

34] *Stress of Life, The.* Selye, Hans. McGraw-Hill (1956). Popularization of the work of the unrecognized genius of present times. Selye deserves the Nobel Prize for Medicine far more than most of the lesser men who have received it. His work is broad-based and far-reaching, having both important practical applications and profound philosophical implications. I think it very likely that future generations will regard Selye's work as equivalent in caliber to that of Einstein, although most people today, both inside and outside of the medical profession, do not seem to be aware of it.

35] *Ways of the Will, The.* Farber, Leslie H. Basic Books (1966). Contains the classic, hilarious, and biting essay "I'm Sorry, Dear" in its fullest and most satisfactory form plus other essays making exciting excursions into new areas of psychiatric thought.

36] *Women.* Lundin, John Phillip. Julian (1963). A modern erotic autobiography, very candid, one of the most pornographic works of all time. As pornography, it is refreshing because it represents exclusively the mature male heterosexual point of view without the slightest hint of deviation or immaturity. Lundin shows emotional love along with vast physical appetite and zest for his various female partners. There is no trace of homosexuality, sadism, masochism, bestiality, or fetishism in his makeup; few pornographers can make this statement. Psychologically, Lundin has reached the next-to-last stage of sexual maturity but has not reached the last. He loves and enjoys each woman in her turn, but he can never stay with one and must always move along. Although he describes each successive adventure with joy and delight, the total tone of the book is one of regret, frustration, and sadness. He senses, although he cannot precisely define, his failure to achieve the final peak. I think this point is important, especially in light of the present shifting moral standards.

37] *You Are Not the Target.* Huxley, Laura. Farrar, Straus & Giroux (1963). We finish this list with an unusual item. Mrs. Huxley and her publisher take this "self-help" book quite seriously, but I can't. I am sure that Mrs. Huxley helps troubled patients personally; any system helps if delivered with sufficient confidence and enthusiasm, and Mrs. Huxley has plenty of this. The book, though it could be recommended as entertainment, cannot be recommended as a guide. For example, she recommends dancing naked in front of a mirror as a means of releasing inhibition. On the other hand, the central concept of this book, stated in the title, is the single most important ingredient for successful coexistence with neurosis in ourselves and others.

C.H.K.

INDEX

Accidents: proneness to, 87–88; of children, 292; of elderly, 319–20

Addiction, 148–67, 257–63; and habit of indulgence, 149–50, 258; to tobacco, 150–53, 258, 261; medical and psychological, 151; obesity, and addictive eaters, 154–55; to coffee, 155–56; to alcohol, 156–61, 260, 261, 262; to sedatives and tranquilizers, 161–62; narcotic, 162–64

Adjustment: and superior intelligence, 10–16; of intelligent woman to female role, 13–15; and retarded intelligence, 18, 22–24; and the rigid personality, 106; in taboo-transgression conflicts, 115; and early home environment, 128–29; to retirement and aging, 317–18

Adolescence: and taboo-transgression conflict, 125–28, 204; suicide in, 293

Adrenaline, 76

Adultery, and grounds for divorce, 272

Affective reactions, poverty of, in psychopath, 96–97

Aggression: and auto driving, 85–86; of psychopath against society, 93; handling of, in ourselves, 269–70

Aging. *See* Geriatric period of life; Retirement; Senility

Alcohol: and alcoholism, 36, 38, 78, 156, 158, 160–61; and sleeping pills, 52; and hallucinatory psychosis, 78; and auto accidents, 84–86;

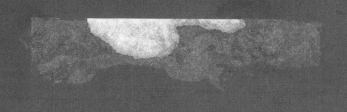